Computer
Numerical Control
Advanced Techniques

Computer
Numerical Control
Advanced Techniques

Mike Lynch

McGraw-Hill, Inc.

New York St. Louis San Francisco Auckland Bogotá
Caracas Lisbon London Madrid Mexico Milan
Montreal New Delhi Paris San Juan São Paulo
Singapore Sydney Tokyo Toronto

Library of Congress Cataloging-in-Publication Data

Lynch, Mike.
    Computer numerical control advanced techniques / by Mike Lynch.
        p.   cm.
    ISBN 0-07-039224-2
    1. Machine-tools—Numerical control.   I. Title.
TJ1189.L95   1992
621.9′023—dc20   92-9222
                                                                CIP

1 2 3 4 5 6 7 8 9 0   DOC/DOC   9 8 7 6 5 4 3 2

ISBN   0-07-039224-2

The sponsoring editor for this book was Robert W. Hauserman, the editing supervisor was Mitsy Kovacs, and the production supervisor was Donald Schmidt. This book was set in Century Schoolbook by McGraw-Hill's Professional Book Group composition unit.

Printed and bound by R. R. Donnelley & Sons Company.

To Cheryl

Contents

Preface

As a computer numerical control (CNC) applications engineer, I witness many successes. Companies everywhere are coming up with techniques that push CNC machines to the limits of their capabilities—and not just their physical capabilities. Some unique feats are possible with CNC equipment that have nothing to do with horsepower or axis travel limits.

Early on in my career, I heard a story that forged my perceptions of what could be done with this amazing equipment. It is relevant to the reason why this book was written. There was a shop I knew of that had several pieces of CNC equipment, including a vertical machining center. This machine had a long running job with a lengthy cycle time. The job required the use of an indexer mounted on the table. The indexer was used to hold and rotate the workpiece to several machining attitudes during the machining cycle.

The indexer was pneumatically activated, but required an operator to press a button for an index to occur. This meant the operator had to stand close by the machine throughout the lengthy cycle in order to press the index push button at the appropriate times. The operator also had to be careful that the correct side of the workpiece was facing the spindle at the completion of each index. If the operator carelessly pressed the button too few or many times, the machine could be damaged and possible injury could occur.

The manager of the shop wanted this job to be run without manual intervention. He wanted the operator to be able to do other things while the machine was running a workpiece. And, since the operator could make mistakes while manually controlling the indexer, he wanted to make the job safer and more accurate.

Therefore, he contacted the machine-tool builder to find out how much it would cost to interface the indexer with the machine tool so that the indexer could be activated automatically, by a programmed command. To the shop manager's displeasure, the machine-tool builder's price to interface the indexer was far more than he was willing to pay.

Frustrated, but not willing to give up, the manager was forced to come up with an alternative. What could be done that would allow safe and automated operation, yet be within the company's means? After pondering the problem for several hours, the answer came. It was simple and easy. And it would cost nothing to implement.

The manager had the operator mount the push button on the top of the indexer, within close reach of the spindle. The program was altered so that, each time an index was required, the tool in the spindle moved over the push button. Then the program actually brought the tool down to press the button! The program then issued a dwell command, making the machine pause long enough to allow the indexer to safely rotate. By the time the dwell period was over, the index would be complete. The program would then continue to machine the balance of the workpiece. Indexing became automatic and more positive. The operator was freed to perform other tasks. And, since there was no chance of too many or too few indexes, the job was safer to run.

Though the indexing done by the shop manager's brainchild could not quite match the efficiency of that done by an indexer interfaced with the machine tool and activated by programmed command, the manager was very happy. A good compromise had been reached since, though cycle time was slightly longer than a totally interfaced system, the cycle was fully automatic.

It is exactly this kind of ingenuity that makes me believe that there is nothing that limits what can be done by this sophisticated equipment. Only your imagination and determination truly limit what can be accomplished. The point is this: while working with CNC, you will be constantly faced with difficult challenges that will push you to the limits of your capabilities. On a daily basis, you must be able to develop new and better methods of accomplishing a wide variety of tasks.

From the time you write, set up, verify, and run your first CNC program, you should constantly strive to find ways to improve every facet of those things you can control in your CNC environment. The better you are at recognizing and implementing potential improvements, the more valuable you will be to your company.

The field of CNC is extremely competitive. At every level of manufacturing, companies are struggling to bring costs down and productivity up in order to underbid competitors. Often the only difference between profit and loss is one small idea or technique that makes one company's CNC machine perform just a little better or faster than a competitor's. The better prepared you can be to meet these challenges, the more potential you will have, and the easier it will be to excel in this field.

Our Objectives

The primary objective of this book will be to show you hundreds of techniques that can be applied to the two most popular styles of CNC machine tools, the CNC machining center and the CNC turning center. Every technique has been proven and is being used by at least one company in manufacturing today. Every technique is aimed at improving your CNC environment in at least one of these ways:

1. Reducing programming time
2. Making programming easier
3. Reducing the program's length
4. Reducing setup time
5. Making setups easier
6. Reducing cycle time
7. Showing a way to accomplish a task which may have been previously considered impossible

Of course, any time savings contributes directly to a savings in costs. All companies using CNC equipment evaluate production costs based on time. By reducing the time for programming, setting up, and producing a workpiece, you will be increasing your company's profits.

While not every technique will apply directly to your particular CNC application at the present time, your eyes will be opened to a world of new possibilities. If the techniques do not apply to your current CNC applications, this book, at the very least, will give you food for thought for your future CNC applications.

We say the first step to applying any new technique is knowing the technique is possible. As you read this book, you will not be able to memorize every detail of each technique. But if you simply remember that the technique is possible, when the need arises, you will have a good method of approaching the problem.

A secondary objective of this text is to make you think in an inquisitive way. As you read the descriptions, keep in mind that almost every technique was developed to solve a problem. No matter how large this book might become, we cannot hope to give you a way of handling every possible problem you will ever come across. But by seeing how related problems have been solved by others, you should receive insight into possible solutions to your particular problem.

CNC Machines Addressed in This Text

While several of the techniques we will give can be applied to a wide variety of CNC machine tools, we will concentrate on the two most popular kinds: CNC machining centers and CNC turning centers. In each category, there are a number of machine-tool types. For example, CNC machinging centers include CNC milling machines, CNC drilling and tapping machines, and CNC drilling centers. CNC turning centers include single-spindle and twin-spindle machines, as well as those of two-axis and four-axis configuration.

Approach to Presentations

Our approach in this book is to make the best use of two presentation styles, reference style and tutorial style. Because of the diversity of subjects presented in this text, the most basic organization for this text is in reference format. However, each presentation assumes the reader has little or no previous understanding of the specific technique being presented. The tutorial style of each presentation will assure that beginner and experienced persons alike will comprehend the subject matter.

This allows the reader to use this text in either of two ways: as a reference book or as a tutorial. If you are trying to solve a particular problem or implement a particular technique, you can look in the table of contents or index to find your subject of interest. During each presentation, you can feel assured that enough background information will be given for you to thoroughly understand the subject matter.

On the other hand, if you are reading the book from beginning to end to discover the variety of techniques, you will find that the presentations follow a logical flow. As in a tutorial text of any kind, we use a building block approach, progressively building on previously presented information.

Specific Examples

Numerous example programs (and portions of programs) are given throughout this text to reinforce the points being made. The specific format for each program happens to be that of the most popular CNC control in the industry. However, CNC controls vary dramatically in their usage. We sincerely believe that if you thoroughly understand the reasoning for a specific technique, and if you understand how it is applied to one specific control, you should be able to adapt the technique to your particular CNC control with relative ease. But you must be prepared for variations.

For this reason, view the example programs given in this text as nothing more than good starting points. In *every* case, when working with a feature or technique that is new to you, you *must* reference your machine-tool builder's and/or control manufacturer's programming and operation manuals to find out how the technique is applied to your machine tool.

Chapter Organization

The subject matter in this text is divided into six basic chapters. Because of the diversity of material presented in each chapter, understanding how it is organized will help you find information and gain an appreciation for how the material is presented.

Chapter 1—Introduction to Advanced Techniques

With so many overlooked features and techniques available on CNC equipment, one has to wonder why it is that CNC people behave as they do. This chapter looks at some of our negative traits as they relate to problem solving, and discusses ways of improving. It also explores methods of heightening awareness to keep on the lookout for possible improvements in your CNC environment.

This chapter also addresses many safety-related issues. Since many of the techniques to be presented by this text will be unfamiliar, the programmer must be very cautious with the implementation of each. Here we review those CNC features that assure safe conditions when you apply new techniques.

Chapter 2—Common Programming Features with Advanced Implications

Many CNC features have multiple applications. This lengthy chapter looks at a wide variety of CNC features, many of which you may use every day, and shows several variations on each feature's usage.

The organization for this chapter is by programming word and is as follows:

/ Optional block skip function

N Sequence numbers

G Preparatory functions in numerical order

M Miscellaneous functions in numerical order

These are followed by other programming words with advanced implications.

By far, the series of preparatory functions (G codes) contains the most information. Notice that this information is organized by numerical value of the G code (G00, G01, G02, etc.). We must point out that CNC control manufacturers vary greatly in how they organize the G code numbers (especially for the more advanced features). Our order of G code presentations follows that of at least three popular CNC control manufacturers. However, as with the specific example programs given throughout this text, you must be prepared for variations. In *all* cases, you must confirm the numeric value and usage for the programming word being discussed in your particular machine's programming manual.

Chapter 3—Techniques with Tool Offsets

In almost every application, tool offsets have an impact on controlling the size of the workpiece. This chapter begins by discussing common techniques using tool offsets to machine workpieces to size.

There are many lesser-known offsetting techniques that can make sizing workpieces much easier. In this chapter, these techniques are presented. In some cases, by using the offsetting techniques we present, it even becomes possible to hold a size on the workpiece that may have been otherwise impossible.

Offsetting techniques for dimensional tool offsets on turning centers, tool length compensation offsets on machining centers, and cutter radius compensation on machining centers are given.

Chapter 4—CNC Techniques for Specific Machining Operations

To this point, all discussions have been organized in order of CNC functions. While machining operations may have been often discussed, the priority was given to CNC functions.

In this chapter, the priority is changed to machining operations. Here we discuss the wide variety of machining operations that can be performed on CNC machining centers and turning centers, showing at least one way each specific operation can be programmed.

If you have good previous machining experience, you may find much of what is presented in this chapter to be review. However, if you are relatively new to the machine shop environment, you will find this chapter to be very helpful. We give many suggestions on how to approach the programming of common machining operations. We also show several ways to make the programming of more difficult machining operations easier to handle.

Chapter 5—Parametric Programming Techniques

Parametric programming (considered an option by some control manufacturers) is a very powerful programming tool that allows general-purpose programs to be created. For the right applications, this feature can actually reduce programming time to almost nothing, and make it possible for the operator to easily create a program to machine the workpiece.

In this chapter, we show the many features of parametric programming, including:

Variable techniques

Arithmetic techniques

Statement labels

Conditional branching

Unconditional branching

Generating alarms

A variety of parametric programming example programs are also given to reinforce your understanding of this very powerful programming tool.

Chapter 6—Minimizing CNC Control Execution Time

There are many ways to format CNC programs that will produce good workpieces. However, the format which a programmer uses within a CNC program has a direct impact on the program's efficiency. In this chapter we look at various techniques that can be used in formatting programs that will keep the cycle time to a minimum.

We also look at those programming features which tend to take a relatively long time to execute and give suggestions as to how to minimize the feature's impact on cycle time.

Author's Note

This collection of ideas and techniques has been accumulated during over 12 years of study while working with CNC users all over the United States and Canada. By no means do we wish to imply that, for any one application, the technique we give is the only (or best) way to handle the situation. In fact, we would be the first to admit that in *every* case, a better way to approach the application is probably possible.

The author encourages suggestions and ideas that would make this text better. If you have comments along these lines, or if you have an idea that would make a good addition to this text, by all means contact the author in writing through McGraw-Hill.

Mike Lynch

1

Introduction
to Advanced Techniques

In this chapter we lay the groundwork for what is to come. Before diving into the main thrust of this book, we want to help you to be in the right frame of mind. It is important that you know when and why to apply advanced techniques as well as how to proceed cautiously while implementing them.

Aggressive Awareness

Have you ever found yourself doing a tedious chore for a long time—maybe even for years—only to find a simpler way existed that would have saved you hours of aggravation? On such a realization, don't you want to kick yourself for not finding the solution sooner?

For years, I dialed phone numbers on my telephone even though it had an automatic dialing feature. I knew it had the feature, but I was just too lazy to look in the manual to find out how to use it. When I finally did, I was surprised to find how simple it was. Instead of pressing 11 buttons to place a call, I now press only one! When I think of all the time I wasted (not to mention the expense of dialing wrong numbers), I feel stupid for not having taken the time to learn the feature earlier.

In similar fashion, the typical computer numerical control (CNC) user has a world of untapped and overlooked resources available. Some, like the automatic dialing feature on my telephone, are common features you know about but have not taken the time to learn how to apply. Others are advanced versions of commonly used features you may not have considered. Yet others are obscure, lesser known features you may have never even heard of, and thus you could never even consider implementing them.

Knowing that a wealth of potential CNC improvements exists, what makes us so set in our ways, unwilling to uncover even the simplest of solutions? What keeps us from picking up the CNC machine-tool builder's manual to learn how to apply new features. What keeps us dialing the 11 numbers instead of one? What does it take to look beyond a way that just works to find a way that works better? It takes nothing more than a willingness to discover the potential improvement, and once discovered, the willingness to take on the challenge.

It is always easier to keep right on doing things the same old familiar way rather than look for ways to improve. Complacent: it is just our nature as humans to be this way. In some cases, we don't know any better; no one has presented us with a better way of handling a particular problem, and we did not even think to try. In this case, if things are working, we are content to leave well enough alone.

In other cases, the urgency of the problem at hand may call for an immediate solution. We simply cannot take the time to look for better alternatives. It is ironic that implementing a timesaving solution can actually *save* a great deal of time in the long run. So often, the short period of time it takes to implement the change will pay dividends in the long haul.

In yet other cases, we are hesitant to seek better methods because we lack help. Most machine-tool and control builder's manuals are, at best, reasonably good reference manuals, but are difficult to learn from. Any reference manual will assume you possess a firm knowledge of the information being presented.

If you work with computers and have ever picked up the disk operating system (DOS) reference manual, you know the kind of manual we mean. Each command in DOS may be well-documented, but how and why it is used is left to the imagination. Also, the terminology assumes you have a computer background. A computer novice will quickly become lost in the jargon.

Beginning CNC programmers avoid programming manuals written in reference style for the same reason computer novices avoid the disk operating system reference manual. They are difficult to learn from. Unfortunately, the CNC programming manual developed by the machine-tool builder or control manufacturer may be the best (if not the only) source of information available to the programmer. (Keep in mind that this text is *not* intended to be a replacement for your CNC machine's programming manual. Here we will show you many techniques aimed at improving your CNC environment. We will even show you numerous example programs. But in *all* cases, we will recommend that you refer to your particular CNC machine's programming manual to confirm your understanding of each technique as it applies to your particular machine.)

Admittedly, there are many reasons why we tend not to develop ways to improve on current methods. However, if our companies are to be competitive, and if we expect improvement in our own careers, we must fight this natural tendency to be satisfied with average or less-than-average results.

To come up with the kind of techniques we show in this book takes little more than ingenuity and determination. It takes a willingness to look consciously at every situation for potential improvement. It takes recognizing when a problem is worth solving. It sometimes takes a willingness to struggle through a problem. It takes being able to read between the lines of your CNC programming manual to extract pertinent implications. It takes a resolve not to take "no" for an answer. And of course, it means taking the time needed to implement the improvement.

There is very little that is impossible with CNC equipment. If you set your mind to it, almost any problem can be solved. In a similar manner, almost any process can be improved. Concerned people working with CNC want to do more than simply make good parts. To stay competitive in today's CNC machining market, companies must do more than just machine parts to size. They must do so in the least possible time while incurring the least possible cost. And an improvement of part quality along the way certainly wouldn't hurt. All of this translates into a need for efficient machining processes, reduced cycle times, optimized cutting conditions, proper tooling application, and efficient programming techniques. Maybe you have heard this saying around the shop: "We do difficult things every day—the impossible just takes a little longer!" It truly applies to CNC machine usage.

While we can talk about improving awareness, ingenuity, and determination, these are qualities that cannot be taught in any textbook. All who work with CNC must see the need to develop these qualities and develop them in their own way.

We can (and will) discuss many specific tools available to the CNC user. In any field of endeavor, it is only when you understand all of the resources available that you can begin to make the most of your abilities. Golfers must know the various clubs at their disposal. They must know their own distance and accuracy capabilities with each club. Only then can they make a wise decision for club selection when it comes time to make a shot. If the club choice is made incorrectly, the golfer will not be able to make the shot.

In like manner, the CNC programmer must possess a firm knowledge of the programming functions available in order to make efficient programs. No matter what level of experience you possess with CNC, you have probably tapped into only a small percentage of your available resources. This book can only show you the many resources that will help improve the usage of your CNC machine. It will be left to you to be willing to apply the techniques we give.

Program Verification versus Program Optimization

It is next to impossible for any CNC programmer, regardless of skill level, to sit down and write a perfect program on the first try. Even for simple workpieces, there are many things that must be considered, and the programmer cannot make perfect choices for everything. And the program itself is only one facet of the programming process.

The workpiece material and rigidity, machining process, workholding setup, tooling, feeds and speeds, and the CNC machine tool itself all contribute to the success of the program, and each must be considered in every key decision. To complicate matters further, if several people are involved in the programming process, it may be difficult to even agree on what a "perfect program" is.

For example, one person may feel that as long as the workpiece is coming out to size, the program is acceptable. Another will not be happy until cycle time is at the bare minimum. Yet another will look for the longest tool life in order to keep tooling costs down. There will be a need to compromise even when the workpiece is being machined in an acceptable manner. Each company will set its own criteria for when a program is acceptable. Here we offer some general guidelines for how these criteria are set. Of course, the first and most important goal of any program is to produce good workpieces.

Assuming the workpiece is coming out to size, the most basic factor used to determine acceptability is workpiece quantity. Almost every important decision relative to the programming environment is based on the quantity of workpieces to be machined. Other factors like accuracy and finish may be involved, but first and foremost is quantity.

Generally speaking, if the number of workpieces to be produced is low (by a company's own standards), just about the only concern will be making good parts. Setup time, loading time, cycle time, and tool life will be of relatively low priority, since the overall time it takes to produce the small lot of workpieces will be relatively short. And just about any process that machines the workpiece to size will be acceptable.

However, as production quantities grow, these factors become much more important. Cycle time becomes of primary concern. For example, say you have come up with an improvement to a program that will reduce cycle time by 10 seconds. For a low production quantity of 25 workpieces, this improvement will save only 250 seconds, or 4 minutes, 10 seconds. The time required to implement even the simplest improvement would take at least this long, meaning the implementation of the improvement could not be justified.

On the other hand, machining 10,000 workpieces is quite another situation indeed. A time savings of 10 seconds per part would result in an overall time savings of 27 hours, 46 minutes, 37 seconds. In this case, it would be well worth the time needed to implement the improvement!

As a concerned CNC programmer, you should always try your best to make every program you are involved with the best it can be. Some companies dictate policies related to making improvements to CNC programs, but in most cases the programmer is left with the decision as to whether a program is acceptable.

Throughout this book, you will be exposed to many special techniques that will dramatically improve the CNC environment. For future programs, by all means, incorporate the techniques we show. However, you must use some common sense when deciding whether the implementation of a suggested technique on a job currently running is worth the effort. When a CNC machine is running workpieces correctly, and if it has been for some time, it may be difficult to justify the implementation of any change, no matter how good the benefit.

There is a certain fear factor that exists in everyone of us that makes us reluctant to change. If faced with reluctance to change on a currently running job, it may be better to leave well enough alone and forego the improvement now. Let the job run out in its normal manner. Implement the improvement for the next time the job, or a similar one, is run. When deciding whether to implement any cycle time-saving technique on currently running jobs, you can use the time calculation technique shown in the example to determine whether the improvement can be justified and make your decision accordingly.

Whenever an improvement is implemented to gain any sort of advantage, there is usually a negative side to making the improvement. In other words, there is usually a tradeoff of one kind or another to consider. Changes of any kind should be made only when the benefits gained by implementing the improvement outweigh the negatives.

This is not only true in CNC but in every facet of life. A bank that offers a credit card with no annual fee may charge a higher interest rate. A grocery store that advertises milk or eggs at a drastically reduced price has probably increased the price of other products to ensure a profit. Sports cars give you excellent performance characteristics but are usually poor on gas mileage. And the list goes on and on. When it comes to advantages having a potential negative side, the CNC environment is no exception.

Just as with other types of compromises, the negatives may not present themselves until after the fact. In many cases you will not be aware that you have created a problem until you implement a change. While in this book we intend to give you a description of possible problems as we discuss each advanced technique, you must be alert for unexpected problems. And safety should be your highest priority.

Safety Considerations

This text will give you countless new and advanced ideas aimed at improving your usage of CNC. As with anything new and/or advanced, you must be extra careful when attempting to utilize unfamiliar CNC techniques. Some techniques will be quite basic, easy to implement, and have a low danger factor. You may feel comfortable with them immediately. Others will require more study, be more difficult to implement, and have a higher danger factor. It may take some time for you to grow comfortable with the more advanced techniques.

In all cases, before implementing any new technique, you must thoroughly study until you are confident with your understanding of the presented material. And even then, you should take every advantage of all CNC safety features when attempting new techniques for the first time. In your previous experience with CNC, surely you have been exposed to the functions we discuss here. So consider this a brief review of the safety features you have at your disposal when working with CNC equipment.

Safety functions

Here are four important functions you should know about when verifying CNC programs. They allow you to stop or slow down the cycle in order to avoid mishaps.

Emergency stop.   This button should be used sparingly. It will cause all moving functions of the machine to be halted. It is most often used when the operator is not directly monitoring the program's motions and suspects a serious problem.

For example, if an operator is working on something else while the CNC cycle is running (measuring a previously machined workpiece, for example), and a terrible sound comes from the machine (possibly caused by tool breakage), the emergency stop button would be the best button to press. All motion would come to an immediate stop.

However, if emergency stop is pressed, the power to the machine tool will be turned off. After pressing the emergency stop button, the operator must follow the procedure to turn the machine back on. For this reason, if the operator is monitoring the cycle, and knows a problem exists, emergency stop is not the best button to press. (See "Feed hold.")

Feed hold.   Like emergency stop, feed hold is a panic button. However, feed hold does not turn off power to the machine. It only stops axis motion. The spindle will continue to run and coolant will still flow, but axis motion will be halted. Using feed hold is an excellent way for the operator to temporarily halt axis motion when a problem is suspected.

For example, as a tool is approaching the workpiece, the operator may be worried about whether the tool will stop before contacting the workpiece. If feed hold is pressed, the motion will stop, giving the operator a chance to check the distance to go in the current move to determine if there are programming mistakes. To get the machine moving again, the cycle start button must be pressed.

Feed-rate override. This multiposition switch acts as a rheostat to allow the operator to control rate of motion when the machine is executing a cutting command (such as G01, G02, or G03). On most CNC machines, feed-rate override is incremented by a percentage of programmed feed rate, usually ranging from 10 to 200 percent. Whenever you are machining a workpiece for the first time and are worried that the cutting conditions (feed and speed) may not be correct, you should turn down feed-rate override to a low setting. As the tool comes into contact with the workpiece and begins machining, you can slowly turn up feed-rate override to increase the motion feed rate. If the programmed feed rate is correct, 100 percent on the feed-rate override switch should be reached at the optimum cutting. Most programmers plan feed-rates so that the feed-rate override switch is set at the 100 percent position under normal operation.

Spindle-speed override. Like feed-rate override, spindle-speed override involves a multiposition switch. But instead of controlling axis motion rate, spindle-speed override allows the programmed spindle speed to be manipulated. If you suspect that the programmed spindle speed is not correct, or if you anticipate problems with vibration (chatter) during machining, you can manipulate the spindle-speed override switch to overcome the problem. Like feed-rate override, the increments for spindle-speed override are in percentage of override, and 100 percent is the desired setting for normal operation.

Conditional switches that help to verify programs

Along with the functions listed above, there are several on/off switches that will help you verify new techniques. We call them *conditional switches* because the machine will behave differently depending on how they are set. On most CNC machines, these functions are simple toggle switches or push buttons. Their functions may vary slightly with the type of machine and the machine-tool builder, but the basic intention of each switch will not.

Machine lock. This conditional switch will allow you to let the control scan the program for mistakes without axis motion. When machine lock is turned on and the program is activated, axis motion will be inhibited. On most CNC machines, the tool changer, coolant, spindle, and other miscellaneous functions will still be allowed to activate, but axis motion will not occur. Machine lock is used to test the program for very basic syntax mistakes. While executing the program under the influence of machine lock, the control will sound an alarm if it finds an error. We recommend using this function as a first step to program verification whenever you apply a technique that requires program changes.

Z-axis feed neglect.   This feature is commonly found on machining centers. Like machine lock, Z-axis feed neglect inhibits axis motion, but only for the Z axis. X and Y will still be allowed to move as they normally would.

This feature allows the operator to see what the program is going to do relative to X-Y motion. Since the Z axis will not move, the operator can rest assured that the tool in the spindle will not approach the workpiece in the Z direction. This allows the operator to concentrate on X-Y motions without concern for interference. We recommend running the machine under the influence of this feature as a second step to verifying techniques that require program changes.

Dry run.   This function is the most important program verification feature. When turned on, it allows the operator to take control of all motion rates the machine makes. Another switch (usually feed-rate override or jog feed-rate) is used to control the motion rate when dry run is turned on. This multiposition switch acts as a rheostat, giving the operator a way to fine-tune the desired rate. When the switch is set at its lowest position, the axes creep along, barely moving. When the switch is increased, the axes begin to move faster.

This function allows the operator to bring a tool into position quickly, yet gives the ability to slow down the approach as the tool gets close to an obstruction. If the operator suspects a problem, the feed hold button can be pressed to halt motion entirely.

Used often during a program's verification, dry run should take control of motion whenever you make program changes. Use dry run to assure that the tool's motion up to the workpiece is correct. Once the tool is in position (with single block on), you can turn off dry run to let cutting occur in the normal manner.

Single block.   When turned on, this function forces axis motion to stop at the end of each command in the program. To continue with the next command, the operator must press the cycle start button. Used for verification purposes, this function gives the operator the ability to go through a program step by step.

Single block is most helpful when the operator suspects that the tool will not stop at a clearance position when approaching the workpiece.

Used in this case with dry run, the operator can turn down the motion to a very low rate, and rest assured that the tool will stop the clearance distance away from the surface to be machined, or, if it does contact the surface, motion will be so slow that no damage will occur.

We recommend using single block with dry run whenever a program change has been made. This will give the operator the ability to verify that motion changes are correct, command by command.

Other safety-related considerations

We cannot stress enough the importance of your understanding safety in regard to implementing any new technique. As long as you feel comfortable with the information presented, you should be able to implement advanced techniques with a minimum of problems. However, the worst thing you can do is assume that a given feature or technique will work a certain way simply because this book said it would. With this approach, you may be tempted to go blindly off in the wrong direction, causing, at best, unpredictable results and, at worst, potentially dangerous situations.

The point is this: stick with our explanation of the advanced technique until you thoroughly understand it. *Do not* attempt the technique until you do understand, and even then, confirm the usage of the technique in your particular CNC control's programming manual. When you finally apply the technique at the machine, use the safety-related features of your CNC machine to assure your safety and *proceed with extreme caution!*

As stated, this book is filled with tips, advanced techniques, and shortcuts that will help you make more efficient usage of your CNC machine. You can expect to save countless hours of programming time, production time, and setup time by applying the techniques we give. However, the success you can expect will be directly proportional to the common sense and caution you exercise when applying these features.

2

Common Programming Features with Advanced Implications

In this chapter we will show some new twists on programming features with which you may have had some experience. It is probable that you have at least heard about many of these features, and quite possible that you have used them in other ways. Much of what we will do in this chapter will simply extend your knowledge of some basic programming tools. We think you will be surprised at the number of features, some of which you may use every day, that have advanced implications.

We start in this manner for two reasons. First, we wish to work from the known to the unknown. By starting with features with which you may have had previous experience, we're sure to keep from losing you with these presentations. Our presentations can become progressively more advanced as the text goes on and discussions will become more difficult to follow.

Second, we want to show how many special techniques have been lurking right under your nose. So many times when you are faced with a seemingly difficult problem to solve, the answer is right in front of you, but you just can't see it. By looking at these relatively obvious techniques, we hope to heighten your awareness for those times in the future when finding the solution to a difficult problem may be as simple as looking for an obvious solution.

The order by which we make presentations in this chapter is as follows:

Using parentheses

Slash code techniques (/)

Sequence number techniques (N words)

Preparatory function techniques (G codes in numerical order)

Miscellaneous function techniques (M codes in numerical order)

Techniques with other programming words (X, Y, Z, H, D, S, T, etc.)

While it may seem as if we are bouncing from one subject to another, we do so because we assume you have (at the very least) some basic experience with the particular feature being discussed. Also, since this is a reference book of special CNC techniques, it is difficult to make one presentation flow to the next in a completely logical order.

While we will give the needed background presentations to assure your understanding of more complicated and lesser known techniques, you will need to draw on your previous CNC experience throughout this chapter. Also, we will try to build on information as the chapter continues, meaning presentations will become progressively more advanced. This should make it easier to read this chapter from beginning to end.

Placing Messages into Your Program within Parentheses

Almost all current CNC controls allow you to document your program with parentheses. The left and right parentheses [()] (also called control in and control out) can be useful in letting everyone know what is going on at any time within your program. When the control reads a left parenthesis [(], it ignores all information it sees until a right parenthesis [)] is found. The information within the parentheses is for program documentation purposes only and has no effect on how the program behaves.

While some older CNC controls do not display the messages given within parentheses on the display screen, most current controls do. This means the operator can monitor the messages as the program is run.

For those controls that do not display messages on the control screen, the messages in parentheses will at least be printed on the hard copy program listing, so the person running the program can follow along with the messages given as the program is run, though this will have to be done from a printed listing, not from the control screen.

Also note that some controls that allow messages in parentheses to be displayed on the display screen do not actually have a way of entering the parenthesis character (left or right) through the keyboard of the CNC control. Probably the keyboard of this kind of control will not even have all letters of the alphabet (as would be needed to input the message itself). With this type of control, if messages must be included within the program, the program must be prepared on some other device (such as a computer), and not typed directly into the control through the keyboard.

You will notice that every command of every example program given in this text will have a message within parentheses at the end to help you understand what is going on within the command. While our use of messages is extreme (documenting *every* command), and we do not recommend that you include them in every command of the programs you write, they have several purposes you should know about.

As stated, most current CNC controls will display these messages on the control screen (in *uppercase* only), therefore the operator can monitor messages as the program is executed. To do so, the operator must set the display screen mode to display the program as the program is run. There are several applications where having this ability will help to avoid confusion and provide much better program documentation for the operator.

Using messages for setup instructions

Some programmers like to include messages at the very beginning of the program to tell the operator how to set up the job. The programmer can be as verbally specific as necessary, letting the operator know exactly what is expected in the setup. Note that most CNC controls limit the number of characters that can be included per message to 80 characters. Also, to keep a message from breaking in the middle of a word at the end of a line, it is necessary to keep each line of the program within parentheses, as this example program shows:

Program:

```
O0001 (Program number)
(PART NUMBER 3504857, OPERATION NUMBER 10)
(TO BE RUN ON VERTICAL MACHINING CENTER)
(OPERATOR: SET THE VISE IN THE MIDDLE OF THE TABLE AND)
(PLACE FIXED STOP ON LEFT SIDE OF FIXED JAW. PLACE)
(WORKPIECE IN SETUP FOR TOUCH OFF. PROGRAM ZERO IS THE)
(LEFT SIDE OF THE PART IN X, THE LOWER SURFACE OF THE)
(PART IN Y, AND THE TOP SURFACE OF THE PART IN Z.)
(SET THE MEASURED PROGRAM ZERO DIMENSIONS IN FIXTURE)
(OFFSET NUMBER ONE.)
(TOOLS REQUIRED:)
(STATION: DESCRIPTION:)
( 1 1" DRILL)
( 2 .500 DRILL)
( 3 6" FACE MILL)
( 4 .427 DRILL)
( 5 1/2-13 TAP)
( 6 1" END MILL)
(OFFSETS: LENGTH VALUES TO BE STORED IN OFFSET NUMBERS)
(CORRESPONDING TO TOOL STATION NUMBERS. RADIUS VALUES)
(TO BE STORED IN OFFSET NUMBERS EQUAL TO 30 PLUS TOOL)
(STATION NUMBERS.)
N005 G54 G90 S400 M03 T02 (Select coordinate system, absolute mode, turn
spindle on CW at 400 RPM)
N010 ...
...M30 (End of program)
```

Notice the lengthy set of instructions following the program number. The programmer can be quite specific (verbally) as to how the job should be set up. Once the job is set up and running, these setup instructions can be deleted from the control's memory since they are no longer needed. This removes unneeded information and makes room in the control's memory for more programs.

Though a set of verbal instructions can be very helpful, many CNC machine setups are quite complicated, and require a drawing for better clarification. For this reason, most programmers prefer to include a separate setup sheet with the program to instruct the operator with regard to how the setup should be made. On this setup sheet, the instructions are written and a drawing of the setup is given.

Messages for tool identification

Many programmers like to identify each tool at the very beginning of its starting information. If the operator is making changes to the program or picking up to run from the beginning of a particular tool, these messages make it easy for the operator to tell one tool's section of program from another. For example, in the command

N050 G54 G90 S300 M03 T02 (1/2 DRILL)

the message in parentheses tells everyone that this is the first command for the ½-inch drill.

Messages to tell the operator what to do

There are times when the operator will be required to perform a manual operation during a CNC cycle. The programmer will stop the machine with a program stop command (M00), at which point the operator is to perform the manual operation. With this kind of application, the programmer *must* make it very clear as to what the operator is expected to do. Here is an example:

...N050 G00 Z.1
N055 G91 X3. Y3.
N060 M00 (MEASURE HOLE AND ADJUST BORING BAR)
N060 G00 X-3. Y-3. M03
N065 G90 ...

In line N060, when the control reads and executes the M00, it will stop the machine. The operator is expected to measure the hole and adjust the boring bar accordingly at this time. To avoid any confusion as to what the operator is expected to do, the message in parentheses spells it out. The operator will simply look at the program page of the display screen to see this message and what is expected will be very clear. On the other hand, without the message, the operator must depend on memory to determine what is to be done.

Other examples of when it is necessary to stop the program for manual intervention include, for machining centers:

1. To clear chips and apply tapping compound for tapping

2. To break clamps loose for a finishing operation

3. To adjust a boring bar

4. To manually back spot face a workpiece surface

and, for turning centers,

1. To reduce chucking pressure for finishing

2. To turn the workpiece around in the chuck for machining on the other end

3. To pull chips out of a hole

Every time you use a program stop command (M00), tell the operator what is expected with a message in parentheses. Especially with programs that require a great deal of manual intervention, this will remove the possibility for mistakes.

Optional Block Skip Techniques

This basic programming feature (also called *block delete*) allows the programmer to prepare a program so that it can behave in one of two different ways, depending on the operator's choice at the time the program is run. Generally speaking, when this feature is used, the programmer is giving the operator a choice between one of two possible conditions, and in effect, making two programs in one. In this section, we will describe the optional block skip feature in detail and show several applications for its use.

Description of optional block skip

Optional block skip is commonly misunderstood. For this reason, before showing applications for this helpful programming feature, we will discuss its basic function.

The programming word used with optional block skip is the slash code (/). The slash code is usually placed at the very beginning of a command, even before the sequence number. An on/off switch on the control panel labeled *optional block skip* (or *block delete*) is used to control what will happen when a slash code is read by the control in the program.

When the control reads a slash code, it looks to the position of the optional block skip switch on the control panel. If the switch is on, the control ignores the command in which the slash code has been included. It would be as if the command was not even in the program at all. If the optional block skip switch is off, the control executes the command in the normal manner.

Before digging in too deeply, you must know how to evaluate what will happen if the optional block skip switch is on or off. Remember that, if the switch is on, commands with the slash code will be skipped. This means that when the switch is on, the program will *not* activate commands with the slash code. This can be somewhat confusing, since in most cases something extra will happen when a switch is turned on. With complicated applications, you may have to think through the situation several times before you are sure as to what will happen when the optional block skip switch is on or off.

Using optional block skip to control coolant.   What follows is a simple example to assure your understanding. Say you have a program which is run for the same workpiece in two different materials. Maybe the same part is required in cast iron and mild steel. For this example, we'll say the speeds and feeds in the program are correct for both materials, but the steel part requires coolant and the cast-iron part must be run without it. Knowing this, the programmer can simply include a slash code as the first character of each coolant command in the program, like this:

/N045 M08

When the cast-iron part (without coolant) is run, the operator must turn the optional block skip switch on. With the switch in this position, the control will *skip* the command that activates the coolant, and coolant will not come on. When the steel part is to be run (requiring coolant), the operator must position the optional block skip switch to the off position. This way the control will *not* skip the coolant command, meaning coolant will come on.

For this example, keep two things in mind. First, using this technique as presented would require that *only* the M08 be included in the command to turn on the coolant. Other CNC functions (axis movement, spindle speed changes, etc.) could not be included in the coolant command since they would be skipped when the optional block skip switch is on.

Second, the slash code would be needed for every time the coolant is turned on in the program. If there are six tools in the program and if the coolant is turned on at the beginning of every tool, this would mean including the slash code at the beginning of the six commands that turn on coolant in the program.

Using optional block skip in the middle of a command.   Some CNC controls allow the slash code to be placed in the middle of a command, making it easier to incorporate the coolant technique just shown. If this is allowed, the control will skip only the portion of the command *after* the slash code if the optional block skip switch is on. Here's an example showing the coolant application just discussed:

N045 G00 X1.5 Y1.5 G43 H01 Z.1 /M08

As you can see, only the M08 is given after the slash code, meaning only the M08 will be affected by the position of the optional block skip switch. The rest of the command will be executed in all cases and will not be affected by the optional block skip switch.

Unfortunately, documentation about this kind of technique can be difficult to find (if it is included at all) in the control builder's manual, meaning you may have to test this technique on your particular control to see if it is allowed.

Conflicting words in one command.   In the coolant example, we said it was all right for the program to use the same feeds and speeds for both materials. In reality, this would seldom be acceptable. That is, the steel part would probably require different speeds and feeds to be used than the cast-iron part. Here is a way to use optional block skip and allow different feeds and speeds in the same program.

Most current CNC controls will execute only the last of two or more conflicting words in a command. For example, if a programmer made a mistake and included two X words in the same command, only the last X would be executed. If, for example, the command

N050 G90 G00 X5. X3.

is read, most current controls would generate no alarm at all. The control would simply move the tool to an X position of 3 in and the first X position of 5 in would be ignored. Of course, the above command is an example of when a mistake has been made. If the above command was for a machining-center program, the programmer probably meant the second X to be a Y. There are times when it can be useful to intentionally include conflicting words in the same command when using the optional block skip function.

If your control behaves in this manner, and if the slash code can be placed in the middle of a command, you can use the slash code to allow for speed and feed differences (among other things) when running two different materials.

For example, say a tool for the cast-iron part was to run at 300 revolutions per minute (RPM) and 5.0 inches per minute (IPM). The steel part requires that the same tool run at 400 RPM and 6.5 IPM. To stay consistent with the coolant example, you want the optional block skip switch in the on condition to run the cast-iron part (skipping coolant). When the switch is off, the operator is running the steel part.

Here is a short program to drill one hole with one tool in both materials that shows how optional block skip can help. See if you can figure out how optional block skip is being used. **Pay particular attention to the commands that have a speed or feed-rate command.**

Program:

```
O0001 (Program number)
N005 G54 G90 M03 S300 / S400 (Select coordinate system, absolute mode, turn
spindle on at desired RPM)
N010 G00 X1. Y1. (Rapid to hole location)
N015 G43 H01 Z.1 (Rapid down to just above part surface)
/ N020 M08 (Turn coolant on if optional block skip switch is off)
N025 G01 Z-1.0 F5. / F6.5 (Drill hole at desired feed rate)
N030 G91 G28 Z0 (Return Z axis to reference point)
N035 G28 X0 Y0 (Return X and Y axes to reference point)
N040 M30 (End of program)
```

When this program is run, if the optional block skip switch is on (cast-iron part), here is what will happen: The S400 word in line N005 will be skipped, meaning the S300 word will be used. In line N020, the M08 coolant command will be skipped, meaning coolant will stay off. And in line N025, the F6.5 feed rate will be skipped, meaning the hold will be drilled at 5.0 IPM.

Here is what will happen if the optional block skip switch is in the off condition (steel part) when the program is run: In line N005, the S400 word will be read (along with the S300). Since the S400 word is the latter of two conflicting S words in the same command, it will be the one used and the spindle will come on at 400 RPM. In line N020, the coolant word (M08) will not be skipped and the coolant will come on. And in line N025, both the F5.0 and F6.5 words will be read, but since the F6.5 is the latter of the two conflicting F words, it will be the feed rate used.

For more complicated programs, requiring more tools, these techniques can simply be repeated for each tool. By repeating this technique, you can make one program machine a workpiece from one of two different materials with relative ease.

Remember that for the above techniques to work, two **important** control considerations must be confirmed. First, the control **must** allow a slash code in the middle of a command and only **skip what** comes after the slash code. Second, the control must allow **conflict**ing words in the same command, and only execute the latter of the **two.**

Again, to find documentation about these kinds of obscure functions in the control manufacturer's manual is, at best, difficult. It is likely that you will not find this kind of documentation, therefore you **must** cautiously test these techniques before actually using them in a program to run production.

Also, if you have more than one CNC machine, it is entirely possible that one machine will allow these techniques while another will not.

Most shops like to maintain as much consistency as possible among their programs for all machines; thus, you may be discouraged from using these techniques if one or more of the machines in the shop do not allow them.

Though you must confirm that these techniques are possible for your particular control, they open the door to some fantastic implications. The feed and speed example is but one of many in which you can customize a program to behave differently, as the operator chooses at the machine when the program is run. As we discuss machining multiple parts with the same program a little later, we will build on the techniques presented here.

Techniques when conflicting commands are not allowed. If the control cannot accept conflicting words, or if the slash code cannot be used in the middle of a command, it is still possible to use the feed and speed technique, but the program must be written in a somewhat unusual manner. Here is a program that will respond exactly the same with regard to the optional block skip function as the one shown above. While it may stray from the way you would normally handle speeds and feeds in a program, it will function just as well as the previous program.

Program:

```
O0002 (Program number)
N002 S300 (Select 300 RPM)
/ N003 S400 (If optional block skip is off, select 400 RPM)
N005 G54 G90 M03 (Select coordinate system, absolute mode, turn spindle on at
desired RPM)
N010 G00 X1. Y1. (Rapid to hole location)
N015 G43 H01 Z.1 (Rapid down to just above part surface)
/ N020 M08 (Turn coolant on if optional block skip switch is off)
N022 F5. (Select 5.0 IPM feed rate)
/ N023 F6.5 (If optional block skip is off, select 6.5 IPM feed rate)
N025 G01 Z-1.0 (Drill hole at desired feed rate)
N030 G91 G28 Z0 (Return Z axis to reference point)
N035 G28 X0 Y0 (Return X and Y axes to reference point)
N040 M30 (End of program)
```

After what you have been exposed to so far, the above program should make sense. Lines N002 and N003 allow optional block skip to be used for the selection of the proper speed when the spindle is turned on in line N005. If the optional block skip switch is on, the control will skip line N003 and the spindle will come on at 300 RPM (for the cast-iron part). If the optional block skip switch is off, the control will read both lines N002 and N003. Since the last read spindle speed prior to the spindle start is 400 RPM, the spindle will start at 400 RPM in line N005. In like manner, lines N022 and N023 allow the selection of the feed rate to be used in line N025.

Using optional block skip to move to the program's starting position

Many CNC machines require that each axis of the machine be positioned to a special starting point for the program. Many programmers elect to use the machine's reference point as this starting position for safety reasons, since an axis-origin light will come on for each axis when the machine is sent to this position. These lights make it very easy for the operator to confirm that each axis is at the proper position before the cycle is activated.

However, from a time-savings viewpoint, a CNC machine's reference point is not always the most efficient position from which to start. For most CNC machines, the reference point is very close to the extreme positive limit for each axis. In some cases this position can be a great distance from the workpiece to be machined.

For this reason, when production quantities are high, many programmers would rather start the machine with each axis closer to the workpiece. They plan the program to start in a way that allows the distance from the tool to the workpiece to be kept closer, minimizing the travel distance between them. This, in effect, shortens the time it will take each tool to reach its first cutting position as well as its retraction time for moving back to the tool change position.

Even when the program is started from a position other than the machine's reference point, in most cases the machine's reference point is used to help determine the starting position. That is, most programmers will base the most efficient starting position on how far from the reference point they wish the program to start.

Generally, when this technique is used, the operator must be much more cautious with the starting point. It will now be the operator's responsibility to position each axis relative to the program's starting position. And, since no control panel lights will come on to assure that the machine is at its proper starting point, the operator must have another way to confirm that the machine is in the proper starting position. If the machine is not in its proper starting point, the results could be disastrous.

For this reason, the programmer must make it as easy as possible for the operator to send each axis of the machine to the program's starting position. One way to do this includes optional block skip techniques. Here's an example.

For a vertical machining center, let's say the distance from the reference point to the workpiece is 15 in in X and 12 in in Y (both minus directions). The programmer wishes to keep the rapid motions from the starting position to the workpiece as short as possible. The programmer decides to start the program with the X axis positioned 15 in to the left (minus) of the reference point, and with the Y axis 12 in (minus) from the reference point in the Y axis.

Before this program can be executed, the X and Y axes (for many

CNC machines) must be positioned to correspond to the planned starting distance from the reference point. One way to accomplish this is
for the operator to position the X and Y axes manually. However, this
method is tedious and error-prone. It is likely that sometime during
the numerous manual positioning movements required during the
running of the job the operator will make a mistake. This is not even
to mention the wasted time taken to make these movements manually.

For this reason, the programmer can incorporate commands under
the influence of optional block skip to return the machine to its reference point and then move to the desired starting point. Here is the beginning of a program that will do this:

```
O0003 (Program number)
/N005 G91 G28 X0 Y0 Z0 (Return to reference point)
/N010 G91 G00 X-15. Y-12. (Incrementally, rapid to starting position)
N015 G92 X _____ Y _____ Z _____ (Assign program zero)
N020 G90 S1000 M03 T02 (Select absolute mode, turn spindle on CW at 1000
RPM, get tool two ready)
N025 G00 X1.5 Y1. (Rapid to first X-Y position)
N030 G43 H01 Z.1 (Rapid down to just above work surface)
N035 M08 (Turn on coolant)
...
```

In lines N005 and N010, the programmer included slash codes to allow the operator to easily send the machine to the starting position for
the program. An operator who wishes to make the machine move to
the starting point will turn off the optional block skip switch and execute the program.

When the program is finished, it will end with the machine positioned at precisely this same starting position. The operator can turn
on the optional block skip switch as soon as the machine actually
starts machining the first workpiece. As long as the optional block
skip switch is on, the machine will skip the wasteful movements back
to the reference point. If the operator is simply loading parts and executing the cycle, there is no need to worry about the machine being
out of position. The machine will end each cycle right back where it
started from, at the starting position.

However, if the operator must stop the program in midcycle for any
reason, or wishes to send the machine to its starting position for the
program for any reason, he or she can simply turn off the optional
block skip switch before executing the program. In this way, the operator can be sure that the machine will go to its proper starting position *before* the program's movements are executed.

As you can see, this technique makes it easy for the operator to send
the machine to its starting position. There is no tedious manual intervention required. The cycle is automatic. However, there is one limitation of using this technique we wish to address: some programmers
would consider this use of optional block skip a waste of the function.

Optional block skip can be used for only one purpose in each program you write. If you wish to incorporate any of the other optional block skip techniques shown in this section (or others of your own design), you can not if you have used the feature for the simple purpose of sending the machine to a special starting position. For this reason, we show another way to send the machine to a special starting position that does not require the use of optional block skip.

Moving the starting position without optional block skip.   This technique requires that the program ending word for your control (usually M30 or M02) return the control to the beginning of the program. For almost all current controls, whenever the program ending word is read, the control shuts down all machine functions and returns the program to the beginning for the time when the operator executes the next cycle. However, some controls do not rewind the memory in this manner if an M02 is used to end the program.

As long as the control rewinds the program with the program-ending word (as almost all do), you can include the series of commands needed to send the machine to its starting position *after* the program-ending word of the program that machines the workpiece. Whenever the operator wishes to send the machine to its starting position for the program, he or she will search to this special series of commands and execute the program from there. We recommend beginning this special series of commands with a remememberable sequence number (like N999). Also, the same sequence number should be used for every program that uses this technique to avoid confusing the operator from one program to the next.

Here is the end of a program for a machining center program requiring a special starting point 15 in in X and 12 in in Y from the machine's reference point (same distances as example above):

```
O0004 (Program number)
N005 G92 X _____ Y _____ Z _____ (Assign program zero)
...N090 M09 (Turn off coolant)
N095 G91 G28 Z0 (Return to tool change position in Z)
N100 G28 X0 Y0 (Return to reference point in X-Y)
N105 M30 (End of program, rewind memory to beginning of program)
N999 G91 G28 X0 Y0 Z0 (Return all axes to reference point)
N1000 G91 G00 X-15. Y-12. (Incrementally, move to starting position)
N1001 M30 (End of special sequence, rewind to beginning)
```

In line N105, the M30 will rewind the memory so that the commands to follow will not be read when the program is being executed in the normal manner. When the operator wishes to send the machine to its starting position, he or she will scan to line N999 and execute the program from there. Of course, this special sequence number N999 cannot appear anywhere else in the program or the wrong line may be searched. When activated, the machine will return to the reference point and then move incrementally to the proper program-starting position. The M30 in line N1001 rewinds the memory to the beginning and stops the program's execution. The next time the operator executes the cycle, the program will be run in the normal manner. When the control gets to line N105, the M30 stops execution and rewinds the program to the beginning, and the subsequent commands beginning with N999 will not be read or executed.

While this technique is not quite as automatic as the one shown with optional block skip (the operator must manually search to the N999 command), it does allow the optional block skip function to be reserved for other, possibly more important, purposes.

Important note about starting positions. The above discussion of the program's starting position assumes that your CNC control demands that the starting position be aligned with the program. If using G92 to assign the program zero point (as our example programs show), this *will be* the case. When G92 is used to assign program zero (possibly G50 on a turning center), the control will assume the machine to be in the correct position when the program zero setting command (G92 or G50) is read. The G92 or G50 simply sets the absolute position displays to correspond to the *current distance* from the program zero point to the starting point.

However, newer CNC controls have a feature called *fixture offsets* (also called *work coordinate system setting*). Fixture offsets are usually commanded by G54 through G59. One advantage of fixture offsets is that the machine's starting position is not nearly as critical as when G92 or G50 is used to assign the program zero point. If you are using fixture offsets to assign your program zero point, the above discussions about the machine's starting position will not apply. With fixture offsets, the machine's axes can be positioned to any location at the start of the program.

Using optional block skip with unexpected rough stock

There are many times when the CNC machining operation is not the first machining operation to be performed on a workpiece. If machining operations must be performed prior to the CNC operation, it is important that those operations be performed consistently. For example, if a part to be run on a CNC turning center is made from round bar stock, the stock is usually cut to length on a cutoff saw of some kind. In this case, it is important that the cutoff saw cut each piece of rough stock to the same length. While the CNC turning center can deal with a small amount of length variance from one part to the next, an overall length much greater than planned can present catastrophic problems for the CNC turning center. This is true of all kinds of CNC machines. The condition of the rough stock to be machined by the CNC machine must be consistent from one workpiece to the next for the CNC machine to perform properly.

Figure 2.1 shows an example of when the rough stock coming to a turning center is *not* consistent. As you can see, the programmer expects only 0.100 in of facing stock on the end of the workpiece. But the cutoff-saw operator made a mistake. Instead of all pieces of rough stock allowing 0.100 in roughing stock, the stock lengths vary. In the worst condition, 0.500 in stock is left on the face of the part to be machined. If machining a workpiece with 0.100 in stock, the program will perform just fine. But if the operator tries to use the same program for the parts with excess stock, the facing tool will try to remove much more stock than it was intended to machine, resulting in damage to the workpiece, the tool, and possibly even the machine. In extreme cases such as this one, the workpiece would probably be thrown from the chuck, possibly causing injury to the operator.

The programmer must constantly be on the lookout for this kind of rough-stock problem. Even when no previous machining operations are performed prior to the CNC operation, the rough stock could still vary enough to cause problems and must be cautiously checked. Castings of all kinds, for example, are notorious for their inconsistency. This variation from one workpiece to the next can raise havoc during machining.

Optional block skip can be used to allow for the undesirable variance of rough stock. The program can be written to behave in one of two ways, depending on the rough-stock situation. A series of extra

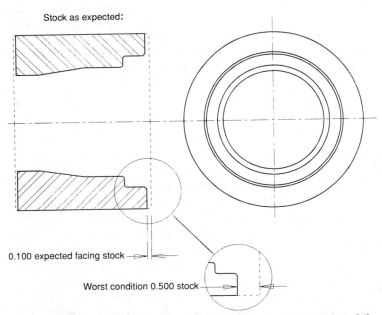

Stock as expected:

0.100 expected facing stock

Worst condition 0.500 stock

Figure 2.1 Some rough workpieces may be cut to length properly, while others are not and have much more stock than planned for.

roughing passes, controlled by slash codes, can be included to machine the undesirable extra stock. Then the normal roughing pass can be programmed without the slash codes. If the workpiece has excess stock, the operator will turn off the optional block skip switch to run the part. The control will execute the extra roughing passes to machine the rough stock. If the part has the proper amount of rough stock (no excess stock), the part will be run with the optional block skip switch on. In this case, the control will skip the extra passes and make only the roughing passes as originally planned.

This brings up a safety-related point. Whenever you are considering the use of optional block skip for *any* application, always ask yourself "What's the worst thing that can happen if the operator has the optional block skip switch in the wrong position?" In this case, if the switch is in the on position when a workpiece with excess stock is machined, the tool would attempt to remove all stock in one pass, causing damage to the tool, workpiece, and possibly the machine. Knowing this, the operator must exercise extra caution while running the job.

Because of this potentially dangerous situation, some shop people will elect not to use optional block skip for this purpose. They will treat the job as two different jobs, separating those parts that have excess stock from those that do not. Then they will create two programs, one for workpieces with excess stock and one for workpieces without, and run the parts separately. One program machines the workpieces with the excess stock, making the needed extra passes. The other program machines the workpieces that have the correct amount of rough stock in the normal manner. This eliminates the risk of the operator positioning the optional block skip switch incorrectly.

Now let's look at an example program that incorporates the optional block skip feature for the purpose of removing unexpected rough stock. Though this is a turning-center example, the same principles will apply to machining-center applications. Figure 2.2 shows two pieces of rough stock. The workpiece on the left is as the rough stock should be, with only 0.100-in stock on the face to be removed. The workpiece on the right shows the worst condition of the batch of rough parts to machine (0.500-in stock on face).

It is this worst condition for which you must plan. That is, as you decide how many rough passes to make, you must know the worst possible condition of the rough stock. Remember, you can give the operator only two choices. Either the rough stock is to the proper length and the optional block skip switch will be turned on, or the part has excess stock and the optional block skip switch will be turned off. If block skip is turned off, the machine must make enough rough passes to allow for the worst-case condition.

Our program will show only the rough facing tool as it rough-faces the part to within 0.005 in of the finished surface.

Here's the program:

Stock as expected: Worst condition:

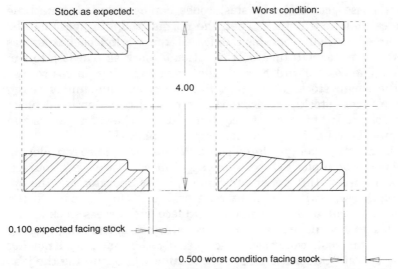

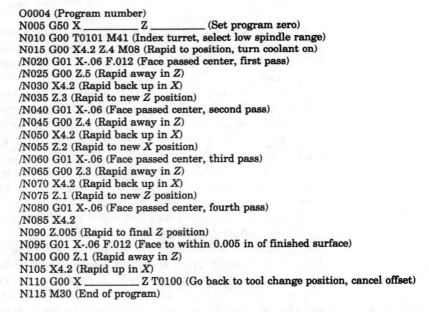

4.00

0.100 expected facing stock

0.500 worst condition facing stock

Figure 2.2 Workpiece for example program showing optional block skip being used for extra roughing passes.

```
O0004 (Program number)
N005 G50 X _____ Z _____ (Set program zero)
N010 G00 T0101 M41 (Index turret, select low spindle range)
N015 G00 X4.2 Z.4 M08 (Rapid to position, turn coolant on)
/N020 G01 X-.06 F.012 (Face passed center, first pass)
/N025 G00 Z.5 (Rapid away in Z)
/N030 X4.2 (Rapid back up in X)
/N035 Z.3 (Rapid to new Z position)
/N040 G01 X-.06 (Face passed center, second pass)
/N045 G00 Z.4 (Rapid away in Z)
/N050 X4.2 (Rapid back up in X)
/N055 Z.2 (Rapid to new X position)
/N060 G01 X-.06 (Face passed center, third pass)
/N065 G00 Z.3 (Rapid away in Z)
/N070 X4.2 (Rapid back up in X)
/N075 Z.1 (Rapid to new Z position)
/N080 G01 X-.06 (Face passed center, fourth pass)
/N085 X4.2
N090 Z.005 (Rapid to final Z position)
N095 G01 X-.06 F.012 (Face to within 0.005 in of finished surface)
N100 G00 Z.1 (Rapid away in Z)
N105 X4.2 (Rapid up in X)
N110 G00 X _____ Z T0100 (Go back to tool change position, cancel offset)
N115 M30 (End of program)
```

Notice that, in line N015, the tool is sent to the first roughing Z position (0.400 in away from the finished face). If the optional block skip switch is off, line N020 will be executed, starting the series of rough facing passes from this point. If the optional block skip switch is on, the next command to be executed will be line N090, which sends the tool over to the 0.005 position in Z. In this case, only one rough facing pass is made.

Though the above example is for a turning center, the same principles can be applied to any form of CNC equipment when there is inconsistency with regard to the amount of rough stock to be removed.

Using optional block skip for trial boring

A very helpful technique incorporating optional block skip techniques is related to boring holes to a critical diameter on a machining center. A boring bar used on a CNC machining center can be very difficult to adjust to a precise size. How the boring bar is adjusted depends on the bar's manufacturer and style. Usually a small set screw is turned to adjust the point position for the cutting edge of the tool. If the set screw is turned in one direction, the diameter machined by the boring bar will increase. If the set screw is turned in the other direction, the diameter machined by the boring bar will decrease. The setting method for boring bars used in this manner ranges from quite crude to very precise, depending on the quality of the boring bar.

For rough boring, the actual hole size after machining is not critical. The only consideration is how much stock will be left for finishing. As long as there is stock left for finishing, the actual rough hole size is not critical, and the adjustment for the rough-boring bar is relatively easy.

On the other hand, finish-boring bars must be set perfectly. The finish-boring bar must machine to the mean value of the hole diameter tolerance. It is not uncommon to have diameter tolerances in the range of ± 0.0001 in for holes machined by boring bars on machining centers. This very small tolerance makes it quite difficult to set the boring bar.

To set the boring bar, most CNC machining center operators will sneak up on the required hole size, intentionally setting the boring bar in a way that assures that the hole will be undersized the first time the boring bar machines. After machining, the hole is measured, and the operator knows how much stock is left in the hole. The boring bar is adjusted accordingly, and the portion of the program for this tool is rerun. Rerunning a tool in a CNC program requires time and caution on the operator's part. After remachining, the hole is checked again, and, if necessary, the boring bar is adjusted further and the section of the program for the boring bar must be run yet again.

This process is tedious and error-prone. Depending on the tolerance of the hole to be machined and the skill of the operator, it is possible that the boring bar will have to be adjusted several times in order to make it machine to the proper size. Only when the boring bar is machining the diameter to the correct size can production be run.

When the cutting edge of the boring bar eventually dulls and the bar must be replaced, the whole process must be repeated. If there are several different critical hole sizes to be machined by the program, several boring bars must be set in this manner, and the above procedure must be repeated for each finish-boring bar. This can be very time-consuming indeed.

For critical boring operations, a concerned programmer can make life much easier for the operator by applying the optional block skip techniques we show here. A series of trial-boring passes can be made under the influence of slash codes to allow the operator to easily adjust the boring bar to the desired size. By trial-boring passes, we mean passes that do not actually go to the final hole depth, but go only deep enough to allow the hole to be measured. Also, at the completion of each trial pass, the program must stop the machine in a convenient position, allowing the operator to measure the current hole size. As many trial passes as needed can be run to assure that the operator will not have to restart the program. Once the boring bar is adjusted correctly, the trial-boring passes can be ignored until the cutting edge dulls and is replaced or sharpened. Then the trial-boring process can easily be repeated.

All of this may sound a little confusing, so here is an example program that will help to clarify. This example program machines a hole at a position of 1 in in X and 1 in in Y and allows three trial-boring passes to be made. To keep it as simple as possible, only the finish-boring bar portion of the program is shown. Figure 2.3 shows the print for this example. The format of this program is for one popular control, but the techniques related to the slash code will remain consistent from one control to the next.

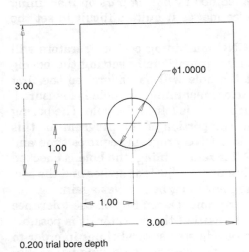

Figure 2.3   Print for trial boring example program.

Program

O0005 (Program number)
(Finish-boring bar)
N005 G54 G90 S800 M03 (Select coordinate system, absolute mode, turn spindle on at 800 RPM)
N010 G00 X1. Y1. (Rapid to hole location in X and Y)
N015 G43 H01 Z.1 (Instate length compensation, rapid to just above work surface)
/N020 G91 G01 Z-.3 F1.5 (If optional block skip is off, feed incrementally just deep enough into hole to measure)
/N025 G00 Z2.3 (Incrementally, rapid out of hole high enough to clear any obstructions)
/N030 X3. Y3. (Incrementally, rapid over to allow measurement)
/N035 M00 (Program stop, operator measures hole here)
/N040 X-3. Y-3. M03 (Incrementally, move back over hole location, restart spindle)
/N045 Z-2. (Move incrementally down to just above surface)
/N050 G91 G01 Z-.3 F1.5 (If optional block skip is off, feed just deep enough into hole to measure)
/N055 G00 Z2.3 (Incrementally, rapid out of hole high enough to clear obstructions)
/N060 X3. Y3. (Incrementally, rapid over to allow measurement)
/N065 M00 (Program stop, operator measures hole here)
/N070 X-3. Y-3. M03 (Incrementally, move back over hole location, restart spindle)
/N075 Z-2. (Move down to just above hole again)
/N070 G91 G01 Z-.3 F1.5 (If optional block skip is off, feed just deep enough into hole to measure)
/N075 G00 Z2.3 (Incrementally, rapid out of hole high enough to clear obstructions)
/N080 X3. Y3. (Incrementally, rapid over to allow measurement)
/N085 M00 (Program stop, operator measures hole here)
/N090 X-3. Y-3. M03 (Move back over hole location, restart spindle)
/N095 Z-2. (Move down to just above hole again)
N100 G90 G00 X1. Y1. M03 (Assure that X-Y position is correct and that spindle is on)
N105 Z.1 (Assure that Z position is correct)
N110 G01 Z-1.05 F1.5 (Bore hole to depth)
N120 G00 Z.1 (Rapid out of hole)
N125 G91 G28 Z0 (Go to reference point in Z)
N130 G28 X0 Y0 (Go to reference point in X and Y)
N135 M30 (End of program)

As you study the above program, this technique should become more clear. While the messages in parentheses help, the procedure does require further explanation. Prior to running this program and whenever a new boring bar insert is used, the operator will intentionally set the boring bar to machine undersize, so that trial boring will be necessary. The optional block skip switch must be placed to the off condition, so the first trial-boring pass commands will be executed.

After the first trial-boring pass, the machine will stop in a convenient position for the hole measurement. In our case, we stopped 3 in to the plus side of the hole in X and Y and 2 in above the workpiece in Z. Of course, you can vary this position to suit your own preference. The operator then measures the hole. This first time, it will not be to size since the boring bar was intentionally set undersize. During the program stop, the boring bar must be adjusted according to the measurement. Then the operator tells the cycle to continue by pressing the cycle start button (with the optional block skip switch still off). Now the second trial-boring pass is made. After the second trial pass, again the machine stops in the convenient position for hole measurement. If the hole is not yet to size, the operator can make another adjustment and another trial pass. By now, the hole should be to size. If not, yet another trial boring pass can be made (three trial passes are allowed in this program). At any time when the hole is measured to size, the operator can simply turn on the optional block skip switch, and the control will ignore the balance of the trial-boring passes and bore the hole to depth.

As stated, the above program allows for three automatic trial-boring passes. The operator can concentrate on setting the boring bar to size without concern for having to restart the program. Restarting is as simple as pressing cycle start. Also, if by mistake the operator sets the boring bar to machine too large, it is possible that the workpiece can still be saved since it will be too large by only 0.200 in in depth.

Using this trial-boring technique makes life much easier for the operator, but, as you have seen, quite a bit harder for the programmer. Let's dissect the program yet further to assure your understanding. Notice that the incremental mode was used exclusively during the trial-boring passes. While it is not necessary, using this incremental technique will ensure consistency for all trial-boring passes. The same set of trial-boring commands can be used for *all* holes that require trial boring if incremental techniques are used. In fact, we will show a little later a subprogramming technique that can be used any time trial boring is necessary. For the subprogram to work in *all* cases, the incremental mode must be used.

You may be wondering why, in lines N100 and N105, the absolute positions in X, Y, and Z were repeated. If all three trial-boring passes were made, or if no trial-boring passes were needed, these two commands would not have been necessary. However, it is possible that, after the first or second trial pass, the hole is to size. In this case, the operator would simply turn on the optional block skip switch to skip the balance of the trial-boring passes and press cycle start. If the absolute position of the hole were not repeated in this case, the boring bar would not be in position to machine the hole (it would be 3 in in X-Y and 2 in in Z away from the hole). Lines N100 and N105 assure that the tool moves to the correct hole location in this case.

Note also that the spindle must be restarted after the M00 commands, or else the spindle will remain in the off condition. This includes line N100, when the actual boring to depth is about to be done. If all three trial-boring passes are not required, the M03 in line N100 assures that the spindle is turned back on. Though our program does not use coolant, this same point applies to coolant. On most machines, the M00 will also turn off coolant. If required during machining, the coolant must also be restarted after the M00 command. Keep in mind that most controls allow only one M code per command, meaning that you would have to add a separate command to turn on the coolant (with M08).

In the actual commands for trial boring (lines N020, N050, and N070), we use a G01 command to accomplish the machining. However, a canned cycle for boring can also be used. In our example, a spiraling drag line will be drawn in the hole during the tool's rapid motion out of the hole because of the tool pressure generated while machining. A G76 or G86 canned cycle for boring command will improve this condition.

Subprogram to make trial boring easier. As you have seen, including trial-boring passes requires quite a number of redundant commands. If you must perform trial boring often, or if you wish to make many trial-boring passes, these commands will become tedious and error-prone. Programming for trial boring can be made much simpler if your control allows subprogramming techniques.

Most CNC controls use an M98 to command that a subprogram be executed. Included in the M98 command is a P word that specifies the program number of the subprogram to be executed. For example, when the control reads the command

    M98 P1000

it jumps from the current program to the program numbered 1000 and continues from there. An M99 is commanded to end the subprogram, returning the control to the original program just after the calling M98 line.

When it comes to trial boring, subprogramming techniques can dramatically shorten your program's length and minimize your programming effort. In fact, once the subprogram needed to do the trial boring has been verified, it can remain in the control's memory and be used for *every* instance when trial boring is necessary! You will *not* have to include the redundant trial-boring commands in each program as in the previous example.

Using subprograms for trial boring also makes it easier to incorporate as many trial boring passes as you want without substantially increasing the program's length. Making a trial boring pass will be as simple as repeating one command. Here is an example. You will find the basic idea to be the same as in the previous example, but the program's length is much shorter.

Main program:

    O0006 (Program number)
    (Finish-boring bar)
    N005 G54 G90 S800 M03 (Select coordinate system, absolute mode, turn spindle on
    at 800 RPM)

N010 G00 X1. Y1. (Rapid to hole location in *X* and *Y*)
N015 G43 H01 Z.1 (Instate length compensation, rapid to just above work surface)
/N020 M98 P1000 (If optional block skip is off, make the first trial-boring pass)
/N025 M98 P1000 (Make the second trial-boring pass)
/N030 M98 P1000 (Make the third trial-boring pass)
/N035 M98 P1000 (Make the fourth trial-boring pass)
N040 G01 Z-1.05 F1.5 (Bore hole to depth)
N045 G00 Z.1 (Rapid out of hole)
N050 G91 G28 Z0 (Go to the machine's *Z* reference point)
N055 G91 G28 X0 Y0 (Go to the machine's *X* and *Y* reference point)
N060 M30 (End of program)

Subprogram:

O1000 (Program number)
N001 G91 G01 Z-.3 F1.5 (If optional block skip is off, feed incrementally just deep enough into hole to measure)
N002 G00 Z2.3 (Incrementally, rapid out of hole high enough to clear any obstructions)
N003 X3. Y3. (Incrementally, rapid over to allow measurement)
N004 M00 (Program stop, operator measures hole here)
N005 X-3. Y-3. M03 (Incrementally, move back over hole location, restart spindle)
N006 Z-2. (Move incrementally down to just above surface)
N007 G90 (Reset absolute mode)
N008 M99 (End of subprogram, return to main program after calling M98)

Note how much simpler it is to make trial-boring passes once the subprogram is written and verified. Only one command per trial-boring pass is needed in the main program, making it very easy to allow for as many trial-boring passes as you want. And, as stated, this same trial-boring subprogram can be used whenever trial boring is necessary.

With the subprogramming example, it is not even necessary to repeat the axis positions after the trial-boring passes (as is required in the longhand example), since the subprogram will return the boring bar to its starting location each time it is executed. The same is true of the spindle start command and coolant. The spindle is restarted in the subprogram (the coolant could be as well). Note that we even included a G90 (absolute mode) command at the completion of the subprogram to assure the absolute mode is instated when the main program continues.

The two discussions for trial boring with optional block skip may take some time to completely understand and visualize. But if you machine with boring bars on a machining center, it will be well worth your time to study until you understand thoroughly. These techniques can save your operator hours of setup time over the life of your CNC machine. But before attempting trial boring with optional block skip, be sure you have a clear understanding of how these techniques work. Even then, proceed with caution as you implement them.

Using optional block skip for multiple parts

For the purpose of organization, it is always best to make one program for each workpiece you machine. This makes it easy to keep track of the programs you use on a regular basis and minimizes the possibility for mistakes. However, there are applications that make it necessary in some shops to combine as many workpieces into as few programs as possible.

Some shops run only a limited number of different workpieces. In high-production manufacturing companies, for example, it is not uncommon for a CNC machine to be dedicated to running only a small number of very similar workpieces in a closely related family of parts. For this kind of application, most companies would like to keep the programs for all the workpieces they machine in the control's memory on a permanent basis. This way the program does not have to be loaded into the control's memory each time a job is run. The operator simply calls up the program currently needed from within the control's memory.

However, every CNC control has a limitation with regard to how many programs can be stored. While some controls allow a great many lengthy programs, many are quite limited in this regard. For this kind of application, it may be necessary to double up on programs needed to machine workpieces in a family.

If you must minimize the number of programs your company uses, you can use the techniques we show here to combine two similar workpieces into one program. However, if you have no memory space constraints, we strongly recommend that you develop a separate program for each workpiece your company makes, even if the differences between the two workpieces is minor. This eliminates the possibility of the operator making the mistake of having the optional block skip switch in the wrong position, causing the wrong workpiece to be machined.

As we began our discussions of optional block skip, we presented a way to machine the same workpiece from two different materials with one program, manipulating the coolant and cutting conditions with optional block skip. In like manner, optional block skip can be used to make your program behave in one of two ways in order to machine two closely similar (but still different) workpieces.

We must point out that, depending on how different the workpieces are, it may not always be possible to write one program to machine two different workpieces. For example, if the two workpieces are almost identical, except that one of the workpieces has one more hole than the other, it will be relatively easy to incorporate optional block skip techniques, as we show. However, if the parts vary dramatically, it may be quite difficult (if not impossible) to combine two workpieces into one program. You may be forced to prepare two separate programs.

The decision as to whether it is possible to use optional block skip for this purpose is easy to make. If one of the workpieces can be made by simply omitting operations from the program of the other, optional block skip can be used to make both parts from one program. However, if the workpieces require different operations with the same tooling, optional block skip cannot be used.

For example, if you have two very similar workpieces, and the only difference is that one has a surface to mill while the other does not, optional block skip can be easily used to make both workpieces from one program. If, however, one of the parts requires the left side to be milled and the other requires a round pocket to be milled, optional block skip will perform with only limited success. If your control allows the slash code to be placed in the middle of a command and if only the latter of two conflicting words in a command is executed, it may be possible to achieve the above situation. However, the complexity of the program would require a great deal of thought on the programmer's part, and would be quite difficult to understand.

Now let's look at a simple example. Figure 2.4 shows two parts labeled *part A* and *part B*. Notice how similar the two parts are. The only difference is that part A requires the machining of a 0.375-in-diameter hole and part B does not.

The example program will center-drill all holes as well as drill them. This will show you how two tools (the center drill and the 0.375-in-diameter drill) incorporate the slash code techniques to make two workpieces from one program. With a little study, you should be able to understand what is happening. Keep in mind that the center drill (T01) is in the spindle when this program is activated.

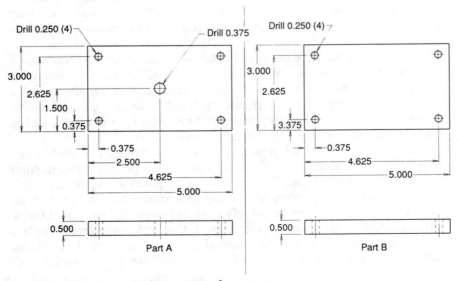

Figure 2.4   Prints for multiple-part example program.

Program:

```
O0007 (Program number)
(Center drill)
N005 G54 G90 S1000 M03 T02 [Select coordinate system, absolute mode, turn
spindle on clockwise (CW) at 1000 RPM, get next tool ready]
N010 G00 X.375 Y.375 (Rapid over first hole)
N015 G43 H01 Z.1 (Rapid down to just above work surface)
N020 G81 R.1 Z-.25 F3. (Center-drill first hole)
N025 Y2.625 (Center-drill second hole)
/N030 X2.5 Y1.5 (If optional block skip is off, center-drill 0.375-in hole)
N035 X4.625 Y2.625 (Center-drill fourth hole)
N040 Y.375 (Center-drill last hole)
N045 G80 (Cancel canned cycle)
N050 G91 G28 Z0 (Return to tool change position)
N055 M01 (Optional stop)
N060 T02 M06 (Change tools to 0.25-in drill)
N065 G54 G90 S1100 M03 T01 /T03 (Select coordinate system, absolute mode, turn
spindle on CW at 1100 RPM, get next tool ready)
N070 G00 X.375 Y.375 (Rapid over first hole location)
N075 G43 H02 Z.1 (Rapid down to just above work surface)
N080 G81 R.1 Z-.65 F2.5 (Drill first hole)
N085 Y2.625 (Drill second hole)
N090 X4.625 (Drill third hole)
N095 Y.375 (Drill last hole)
N100 G80 (Cancel canned cycle)
N105 G91 G28 Z0 (Return to tool change position)
N110 M01 (Optional stop)
/N115 T03 M06 (Place 0.375-in drill in spindle)
/N120 G54 G90 S900 M03 T01 (Select coordinate system, absolute mode, turn
spindle on CW at 900 RPM, get next tool ready)
/N125 G00 X2.5 Y1.5 (Rapid over hole location)
/N135 G43 H03 Z.1 (Rapid down to just above work surface)
/N140 G81 R.1 Z-.65 F4.0 (Drill hole)
/N145 G80 (Cancel cycle)
/N150 G91 G28 Z0 (Return to tool change position)
/N155 M01 (Optional stop)
N160 G91 G28 X0 Y0 (Return to reference point in X-Y)
N165 T01 M06 (Place first tool back in spindle)
N170 M30 (End of program)
```

When this program is run, if the operator wishes to make part A (with the 0.375-in hole), the optional block skip switch must be turned off. In this case, all commands of the program will be executed, and the part will be made, including center-drilling for the 0.375-in hole as well as drilling the 0.375-in hole itself.

If part B is desired, the operator will turn on the optional block skip switch. In this case, line N030 will be skipped, and the 0.375-in hole will *not* be center-drilled. Also, lines N115 through N155 will not be executed, therefore the 0.375-in drill will not be used.

Line N065 requires some explanation. Most machining centers that have automatic tool changers allow the next tool to rotate into the ready position while the current tool is machining the workpiece. This keeps cycle time to a minimum, since no time is wasted getting the tool changer rotated to the next station during a tool change. In line

N005, for example, tool station 2 (T02) is commanded to get tool 2 ready while the center drill machines the workpiece.

Line N065 of this program assumes that your control allows slash codes to be placed in the middle of the program and that your control will execute only the last of two conflicting words (as discussed earlier in this section). If you are making part A (with the 0.375-in hole) and the optional block skip switch is off, *both* T words in this command will be read. But since they are conflicting words, *only* the last T word will be executed (the T03). In this case, T03 would be getting ready while the 0.250-in drill machines the workpiece.

On the other hand, if you are making part B and the optional block skip switch is on, the T03 word will be skipped in the command, and only the T01 will be read and executed. T01 is the correct next tool if the 0.375-in hole is not to be machined.

You may be starting to agree that using optional block skip to machine two different workpieces can be confusing. If using this technique, you will have to think through your application several times to be sure you have it right.

Multiple optional block skip functions

The greatest single limitation of the optional block skip function as we have shown it is that only one application per program is allowed. For example, it is not possible to use optional block skip for the purpose of trial boring and for making extra roughing passes within the same program. Only one of two conditions is possible. Either the optional block skip switch is on or it is off. The control will behave accordingly. What will be correct for one application with the optional block skip switch in a given position may not be correct for the other application.

To allow optional block skip to be used for several purposes within the same program, some CNC control manufacturers allow an option to be purchased which allows the use of more than one optional block skip function in a program. When this option is available, the most common configuration allows nine optional block skip functions. Though this option is not commonly found on CNC machines, it is nice to know about in case the need for this feature arises.

Most CNC control manufacturers that offer this option make it field-installable, so that it can be added to your machine even long after the machine was purchased. If you need this feature and it is not included with your machine, be sure to contact your machine-tool builder to find out if it possible to add multiple optional block skips.

When the machine is equipped with this feature, there will be nine optional block skip switches on the control panel, labeled 1 through 9. In the program, the slash code will include a number that points to which switch is to be used. For example, /1 would be used with optional block skip switch 1, /2 would be used with switch 2, /3 with switch 3, and so on. As you can see, you could use up to nine different applications for optional block skip within one program. However, if you do this, the operator must be well informed of which optional block skip switches are being used and their meaning in the program. As you might suspect, multiple optional block skips in a program compound the complexity of running it and increase the potential for a mistake to be made.

Applications that require more than two or three uses of optional block skip from within one program are few and far between. However, having this feature available for even two or three general-purpose programming applications can sometimes be helpful.

Sequence Number (N Word) Techniques

As you know, sequence numbers allow the programmer to keep commands of each program organized. In most cases, when sequence numbers are used, they are placed in a logical order. This makes searching within the program to a specific command very easy. Most programmers who use sequence numbers like to allow room between lines for extra commands to be added at some future time, if necessary. With one popular method, five numbers between each sequence number are skipped, making the lines of the program follow the order N005, N010, N015, N020, and so on. All examples shown in this book follow this sequence for main programs.

For subprograms, some programmers like to vary the technique with sequence numbers to make it easy to distinguish between main programs and subprograms. For example, they may elect not to skip any numbers between each line, making the sequences N001, N002, N004, N005, and so on.

When an organized technique is used for sequence numbers, if a mistake is found in the program, it is easy to scan to the command including the mistake. It is also easy to add lines in the program without breaking the basic flow of sequence numbers.

Keep in mind that most CNC controls made today do not require sequence numbers and, if they are included in the program, do not require them to be in any particular order. Knowing this, some programmers elect to not include sequence numbers in the program at all. Since sequence numbers do take memory space, many experienced programmers see them as a waste of the control's memory. They are willing to give up the organizational benefits sequence numbers offer in order to gain additional memory space. For beginners, and when there are no memory space constraints, we strongly recommend that sequence numbers be placed in the program and that they be structured in an organized manner.

Using sequence numbers for pickup points

Most CNC machines allow more than one operation per program. For example, a CNC machining center may allow 30 or more tools to be used in one program. Turning centers commonly allow up to 12 tools in one program. There are many times that an operator, while running a CNC machine, must rerun one or more tools in the program. However, it is cumbersome, time-consuming, and possibly even detrimental to the workpiece to run the entire program again from the beginning just to get to the tool to be rerun. If, for example, the sixth tool in the program must be rerun, it would be silly to run from the beginning of the program, waiting for the five prior tools to be run, just to get to the sixth tool.

For this reason, most programmers format their programs in a way that allows the operator to easily pick up in the middle of the program and run from the beginning of any tool. (The formats for *all* multiple tool programs shown in this text follow this logic.) This technique requires that all programming commands needed to start the machine be included at the beginning of each tool, making each tool independent from the rest of the program. In essence, this lets the programmer break the program up into smaller miniprograms, each making up one tool.

To make it as easy as possible for the operator to execute the program from the beginning of any tool, the programmer can start each tool with a special sequence number. This way, the operator can quickly and easily scan to the beginning of a particular tool with a minimum of effort.

For example, if sequence numbers are used in the program only for pickup blocks, you can make the tool station numbers of the machine correspond to pickup sequence numbers. That is, N1 could be the pickup block for tool 1; N2, for tool 2; N3, for tool 3; and so on.

If all commands of the program include sequence numbers, we recommend a slightly different technique to avoid overlapping problems. Simply add the number 1000 to each tool station number to come up with the pickup sequence number. It is unlikely that you will ever run the sequence numbers up to 1000 with any single tool, even if numbers are skipped between each line. This means there will be little chance of overlapping sequence numbers. When this technique is used, N1000 will be the pickup block for tool 1, N2000 for tool 2, N3000 for tool 3, and so on. If the following commands for each tool continue in the same sequence, it will also be very easy to tell which tool is being used at any time throughout the program. Here is an example program that uses this technique. Figure 2.5 shows the print to be used for this program.

Program:

```
O0008 (Program number)
(Center drill)
N1000 G54 G90 S1000 M03 T02 (Select coordinate system, absolute mode, turn
spindle on CW at 1000 RPM, get next tool ready)
```

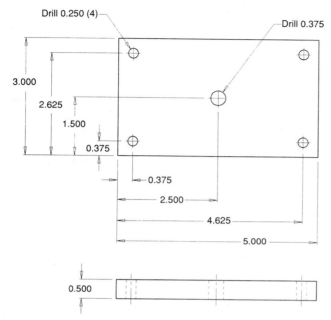

Figure 2.5 Print for pickup technique with sequence-number example program.

```
N1005 G00 X.375 Y.375 (Rapid over first hole)
N1010 G43 H01 Z.1 (Rapid down to just above work surface)
N1015 G81 R.1 Z-.25 F3. (Center-drill first hole)
N1020 Y2.625 (Center-drill second hole)
N1025 X2.5 Y1.5 (Center-drill 0.375-in hole)
N1030 X4.625 Y2.625 (Center-drill fourth hole)
N1035 Y.375 (Center-drill last hole)
N1040 G80 (Cancel canned cycle)
N1045 G91 G28 Z0 (Return to tool change position)
N1050 M01 (Optional stop)
N2000 T02 M06 (Change tools to 0.25-in drill)
N2005 G54 G90 S1100 M03 T03 (Select coordinate system, absolute mode, turn
spindle on CW at 1100 RPM, get next tool ready)
N2010 G00 X.375 Y.375 (Rapid over first hole location)
N2015 G43 H02 Z.1 (Rapid down to just above work surface)
N2020 G81 R.1 Z-.65 F2.5 (Drill first hole)
N2025 Y2.625 (Drill second hole)
N2030 X4.625 (Drill third hole)
N2035 Y.375 (Drill last hole)
N2040 G80 (Cancel canned cycle)
N2045 G91 G28 Z0 (Return to tool change position)
N2050 M01 (Optional stop)
N3000 T03 M06 (Place 0.375-in drill in spindle)
N3005 G54 G90 S900 M03 T01 (Select coordinate system, absolute mode, turn
spindle on CW at 900 RPM, get next tool ready)
N3010 G00 X2.5 Y1.5 (Rapid over hole location)
N3015 G43 H03 Z.1 (Rapid down to just above work surface)
N3020 G81 R.1 Z-.65 F4.0 (Drill hole)
```

N3025 G80 (Cancel cycle)
N3030 G91 G28 Z0 (Return to tool change position)
N3035 M01 (Optional stop)
N3040 G91 G28 X0 Y0 (Return to reference point in *X-Y*)
N3045 T01 M06 (Place first tool back in spindle)
N3050 M30 (End of program)

While this program uses only three tools, you can see how easy the sequence numbers make it to pick up in the middle of the program. If the operator wishes to pick up and run the program from the beginning of tool 3, line N3000 is the pickup block. Also note how easy it becomes to tell which tool any command is related to. If a person viewing the program is looking at line N2030, it will be obvious that the command is part of the tool 2 sequence.

Using sequence numbers as statement labels (branching techniques)

Under normal circumstances, a CNC control will execute a program in sequential order. The first command of the program is read and executed, then the next command, and then the next. And so on, until the entire program has been executed. The control simply follows the instructions given in the program in the same order encountered.

However, almost all current CNC controls allow the programmer to change the order by which the program is executed from within the program itself. The programmer is allowed to cause the control to branch or jump to a specified location within the program.

The level of complexity allowed by CNC controls with regard to branching varies from one manufacturer to the next, as do the actual commands needed to command that the branching takes place. Some controls accommodate elaborate branching, allowing a condition to be stated in order for the control to make a decision. Depending on the result of the decision, the control can be told to branch to one of two different sequence numbers. Controls that have this capability use an IF statement to control this conditional branching. These controls will usually have other computer-programming related features to allow very sophisticated programming techniques like variables, arithmetic, and looping. Grouped together, these sophisticated features are called parametric programming. Parametric programming is discussed at length in Chap. 5.

Other controls are not nearly so sophisticated with regard to branching. They simply allow a statement that tells the control where to branch within the program. Most control manufacturers call this an *unconditional branch*. In all cases, a *sequence number* is used to specify the location at which the control is to continue executing the program. A sequence number used for this purpose is called a *statement label*.

As stated, the actual commands related to branching vary from one control to the next. Some use a GOTO statement that tells the control the sequence number to be used as the statement label for the branch. For example, the command

    N045 GOTO 050

would tell the control to branch to sequence number N050 and continue executing the program from there. Other controls use the word JUMPTO instead of GOTO for unconditional branching.

The most common word used for unconditional branching is M99, although it is normally reserved for subprogramming techniques. When an M99 is used as an unconditional branching command, a P word is included in the M99 command to tell the control the sequence number to which to branch. For example, the command

    N045 M99 P050

tells the control to branch to sequence number N050 and continue from executing the program there.

Since this function varies so dramatically from one CNC control to the next, you must check in your control builder's manual to find which technique (if any) your particular control allows.

Whenever a sequence number is used as a statement label, the programmer must assure that the sequence number appears in the program and that it appears only one time. If the sequence number specified in the branching command does not exist in the program, an alarm will sound. If more than one of the specified sequence numbers exist, the control will usually branch to the first one it happens to come across without generating an alarm, making the program unpredictable.

Using branching techniques to change machining order.   One time when it is helpful to use branching techniques with statement labels is when a mistake has been made in the process used to machine the workpiece. Say, for example, a programmer has written a program to finish-mill a surface before a large-diameter hole is drilled. During the drilling operation, the pressure created by the large drill during machining is forcing the workpiece to move slightly in the setup, causing the previous finish-milling operation to be incorrect. In order to correct the problem, the program must be changed to drill the large hole first and then finish-mill the surface.

One way to correct this problem is to rewrite the entire program to attain the proper machining sequence. In the long run, this is probably the best way to fix the problem for the purpose of keeping the program easy to follow. However, making such dramatic changes in the program will take time. If the job is on the machine, and verified when the problem is discovered, such time-consuming changes will be costly. The machine will sit idle while the programmer makes the necessary changes and loads the corrected program into the control's memory. Having the ability to easily change machining order from within a program can save time during the program's verification, and the machine will be producing parts sooner.

Here is an example to stress these concepts. Figure 2.6 shows the print for a workpiece to be machined. First we present the original program that machines the part with an *incorrect* sequence of operations. In this process, the right side of the workpiece is being milled with a 1-in end mill. Then the 0.250-in holes are center-drilled. Next the 0.250-in holes are drilled. Finally the large 1.500-in-diameter hole is drilled.

Program (Original):

O0009 (Program number)
(1 in end mill)
N005 G54 G90 S400 M03 T02 (Select coordinate system, select absolute mode, turn spindle on CW at 400 RPM, get tool station 2 ready)
N010 G00 X5.5 Y-.6 (Rapid to first milling position)
N015 G43 H01 Z.1 (Rapid down to just above work surface)
N020 G01 Z-.6 F30. (Fast-feed below work surface)
N025 Y3.6 F3.5 (Mill right side of workpiece)
N030 G00 Z.1 (Rapid to above work surface)
N035 G91 G28 Z0 (Rapid to tool change position)
N040 M01 (Optional Stop)
N045 T02 M06 (Change tools to center drill)

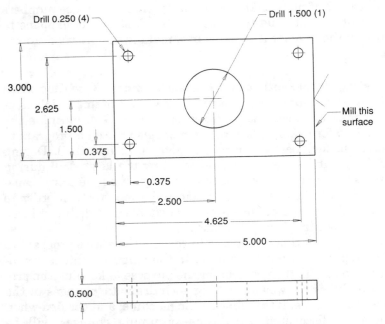

Figure 2.6   Print for machining-order change example program.

N050 G54 G90 S1000 M03 T03 (Select coordinate system, absolute mode, turn spindle on CW at 1000 RPM, get next tool ready)
N055 G00 X.375 Y.375 (Rapid over first hole)
N060 G43 H02 Z.1 (Rapid down to just above work surface)
N065 G81 R.1 Z-.25 F3. (Center-drill first hole)
N070 Y2.625 (Center-drill second hole)
N080 X4.625 (Center-drill third hole)
N085 Y.375 (Center-drill last hole)
N090 G80 (Cancel canned cycle)
N095 G91 G28 Z0 (Return to tool change position)
N100 M01 (Optional stop)
N105 T03 M06 (Change tools to 0.25-in drill)
N110 G54 G90 S1100 M03 T04 (Select coordinate system, absolute mode, turn spindle on CW at 1100 RPM, get next tool ready)
N115 G00 X.375 Y.375 (Rapid over first hole location)
N120 G43 H03 Z.1 (Rapid down to just above work surface)
N125 G81 R.1 Z-.65 F2.5 (Drill first hole)
N130 Y2.625 (Drill second hole)
N135 X4.625 (Drill third hole)
N140 Y.375 (Drill last hole)
N145 G80 (Cancel canned cycle)
N150 G91 G28 Z0 (Return to tool change position)
N155 M01 (Optional stop)
N160 T04 M06 (Place 1.500-in drill in spindle)
N165 G54 G90 S300 M03 T01 (Select coordinate system, absolute mode, turn spindle on CW at 300 RPM, get next tool ready)
N170 G00 X2.5 Y1.5 (Rapid over hole location)
N175 G43 H04 Z.1 (Rapid down to just above work surface)
N180 G81 R.1 Z-.85 F4.0 (Drill hole)
N185 G80 (Cancel cycle)
N190 G91 G28 Z0 (Return to tool change position)
N195 M01 (Optional stop)
N200 T01 M06 (Place first tool back in spindle)
N205 G91 G28 X0 Y0 (Return to reference point in *X-Y*)
N205 T01 M06 (Place first tool back in spindle)
N210 M30 (End of program)

As this program is being verified at the machine, it is discovered that the very powerful operation to drill the 1.500-in hole must be done first. This will assure that, if the workpiece does move during the drilling, at least the subsequent milling, center-drilling, and drilling operations will be in the proper relationship. Here is the modified program that accomplishes the change in machining order. It shows the most common technique used by control manufactures to allow branching with M99.

Program (Modified):

O0009 (Program number)
N003 M99 P165 (Jump to line N165 to 1.500-in drill)
(1 in end mill)
N005 G54 G90 S400 M03 T02 (Select coordinate system, select absolute mode, turn spindle on CW at 400 RPM, get tool station 2 ready)
N010 G00 X5.5 Y-.6 (Rapid to first milling position)
N015 G43 H01 Z.1 (Rapid down to just above work surface)
N020 G01 Z-.6 F30. (Fast feed below work surface)

N025 Y3.6 F3.5 (Mill right side of workpiece)
N030 G00 Z.1 (Rapid to above work surface)
N035 G91 G28 Z0 (Rapid to tool change position)
N040 M01 (Optional stop)
N045 T02 M06 (Change tools to center-drill)
N050 G54 G90 S1000 M03 T03 (Select coordinate system, absolute mode, turn spindle on CW at 1000 RPM, get next tool ready)
N055 G00 X.375 Y.375 (Rapid over first hole)
N060 G43 H02 Z.1 (Rapid down to just above work surface)
N065 G81 R.1 Z-.25 F3. (Center-drill first hole)
N070 Y2.625 (Center-drill second hole)
N080 X4.625 (Center-drill third hole)
N085 Y.375 (Center-drill last hole)
N090 G80 (Cancel canned cycle)
N095 G91 G28 Z0 (Return to tool change position)
N100 M01 (Optional stop)
N105 T03 M06 (Change tools to 0.25-in drill)
N110 G54 G90 S1100 M03 T04 (Select coordinate system, absolute mode, turn spindle on CW at 1100 RPM, get next tool ready)
N115 G00 X.375 Y.375 (Rapid over first hole location)
N120 G43 H03 Z.1 (Rapid down to just above work surface)
N125 G81 R.1 Z-.65 F2.5 (Drill first hole)
N130 Y2.625 (Drill second hole)
N135 X4.625 (Drill third hole)
N140 Y.375 (Drill last hole)
N145 G80 (Cancel canned cycle)
N150 G91 G28 Z0 (Return to tool change position)
N155 M01 (Optional stop)
N160 T04 M06 (Place 1.500-in drill in spindle)
N163 M99 P205 (Jump to N200 and end program)
N165 G54 G90 S300 M03 T01 (Select coordinate system, absolute mode, turn spindle on CW at 300 RPM, get next tool ready)
N170 G00 X2.5 Y1.5 (Rapid over hole location)
N175 G43 H04 Z.1 (Rapid down to just above work surface)
N180 G81 R.1 Z-.65 F4.0 (Drill hole)
N185 G80 (Cancel cycle)
N190 G91 G28 Z0 (Return to tool change position)
N195 M01 (Optional stop)
N200 T01 M06 (Place first tool back in spindle)
N202 M99 P005 (Jump to line N005 and finish-mill)
N205 G91 G28 X0 Y0 (Return to reference point in X-Y)
N210 M30 (End of program)

As you study this modified program, notice that the change was accomplished by adding only three commands (lines N003, N163, and N202). No other changes were necessary to change the machining order. With this modified program, when the operator executes the cycle, the first command in the program (N003) tells the control to branch to line N165. In essence, the control temporarily skips the finish milling, center drilling, and 0.250-in drilling operations, and proceeds directly to the 1.500-in drilling operation, beginning execution from line N165. When the control is finished drilling the 1.500-in-diameter hole and gets to line N202, it is told to go back to line N005 and continue. This causes the control to finish-mill the right side, center-drill, and drill the 0.250-in holes. To avoid remachining the

1.500-in hole, when the control reaches line N163, it is told to jump to N205. From there, the control is allowed to finish the program.

While you may have to study these two programs for a little while to fully understand what is happening, once you do understand, we think you will agree that adding these three branching commands into the program is *much* faster than rewriting the entire program. However, since it is so much more difficult to figure out what is happening in the modified program, we recommend that you eventually go back and change the original program's machining sequence without using branching techniques before the job comes up again. This will avoid confusion in the future for the next time the job must be run. Of course, you can make these changes at your leisure, since there will no longer be the urgency that existed when the machine was down, waiting for the program's machining order to be changed.

Preparatory Function Techniques

As you know, each CNC control has a series of preparatory functions, called *G codes*. The purpose for these G codes is to set the stage for what is to come in the current command or in the balance of the program. There are many G words related to any one CNC machine, and if you have any experience at all with CNC programming, you have probably used many of the various G codes to be discussed in this section.

It is our intention here to show only those G codes that have special or advanced implications. We think you will be impressed with the number of relatively simple G codes (some of which you may use every day) that have advanced implications. All programmers, regardless of skill level, should find many new and helpful techniques in this section.

Circular motion techniques

Clockwise (G02) and counterclockwise (G03) circular motion commands are used to form the radii required along a tool's path. From your previous exposure to CNC programming, you are probably quite familiar with the techniques to form basic circular motions within a program. Truly, they are commonly used with all kinds of CNC equipment.

Within the G02 and G03 commands themselves, the programmer includes the ending coordinate for the motion in each axis along with a designation that lets the control know how to figure out where the center point of the arc is located. For turning-center applications, the end point is specified in both the X and Z axes. For machining-center applications, the end point is usually, but not always, specified in the X and Y axes (sometimes in X-Z or Y-Z).

How the arc center is specified varies from one control to the next.

Some (especially older) controls require a tedious and error-prone directional vector to be specified with I and J. Newer controls allow a much easier-to-use R word. The R word simply tells the control the arc radius to be formed, and the control automatically figures out where the arc center is located.

While it is not our intention to give a primer on circular commands in this text, the above paragraphs should refresh your memory as to how circular commands are used in a program. Here, we intend to expand your knowledge of circular commands with some special applications of how they can be used.

How to determine G02 versus G03.   You may think anyone reading a book on advanced CNC techniques should know that G02 is clockwise circular motion and G03 is counterclockwise circular motion. However, there are those machines on which the G02 and G03 are reversed. Also you may be surprised to learn that the decision to use G02 or G03 follows a special rule you may not have known about.

Which is clockwise?   For almost all CNC machines, G02 represents clockwise circular motion and G03 represents counterclockwise circular motion. However, there is one style of turning center that reverses the directions of G02 and G03. This turning center reverses the X axis with regard to plus and minus.

Most turning-center manufacturers arrange the X axis of the machine so that, as a tool moves in the plus direction in X, the diameter being machined gets bigger. For this most common style of turning center, as a tool faces a workpiece to center, the tool is moving along the X minus direction. For this type of machine G02 is clockwise and G03 is counterclockwise.

However, there is at least one manufacturer of turning centers that reverses the X axis. For this type of machine, as a tool faces a workpiece to center, the tool is moving in the X *plus* direction. For this kind of machine, the directions of G02 and G03 are reversed: G02 is counterclockwise and G03 is clockwise. [Also note that the tool nose radius compensation commands (G41 versus G42) are reversed with this kind of machine.]

Rule governing G02 versus G03.   If you are working with a turning center, or if you are working in the X-Y plane of a machining center, deciding whether to use a G02 or G03 is very simple. It just so happens, in these two cases, that you are allowed to decide which command to use by simply looking at the print from above.

However, there are two times when you must cautiously think through this seemingly simple evaluation. One is related to how you view the print itself. If the print does not follow the basic rules of orthographic projection, or if the attitude from which you must view the print does not match the way it will be held in the machine, it is possible that you will have to look at the print from *below* in order to correctly evaluate G02/G03. If you are not careful, you are likely to make a mistake with your selection.

The other time you must cautiously think through the G02/G03 evaluation is related to machines with more than two axes. For CNC machines that have more than two axes, like machining centers, here is the rule governing how to make the G02/G03 decision:

> Clockwise and counterclockwise (G02/G03) motion must be evaluated by looking at the motion *from the plus side of the perpendicular uninvolved axis.*

With a machining center that has three axes, if you are milling in the *X-Y* plane (as you normally do), this is as simple as viewing (based on the machine's perspective) the workpiece from above. As long as the print orientation matches the way the workpiece will be mounted in the setup of the machine, you can simply evaluate the G02/G03 question by looking at the print from above.

However, if not milling in the *X-Y* plane, you must give this more thought. For example, if the circular motion is to take place in *X-Z*, you must evaluate the G02/G03 from the *plus side* of the *Y* axis. For a vertical machining center, this means you must look at the movement from the column side of the machine (the back side of the machine).

If making circular movements in the *Y-Z* plane, you must view the motion from the *plus side* of the *X* axis. For a vertical machining center, this means looking at the motion from the right side of the machine.

There is another consideration when making circular motions related to plane selection. For the control to make *any* circular motions, the proper plane must be selected (by G code). G17 is used by most control manufacturers to select the *X-Y* plane. On most controls, the G17 is initialized; that is, when the machine is turned on, it will be in this mode. For this reason, if you will be working exclusively in the *X-Y* plane (as you normally will), there is no need to specify the G17 in the program at all.

However, if you will be making circular motions (among other things) in the *X-Z* or *Y-Z* plane, you must include the proper plane selection command *before* making the circular move. With most CNC controls, G18 selects the *X-Z* plane and G19 selects the *Y-Z* plane.

A full discussion of other considerations in plane selection will be given later.

Arc-in and arc-out techniques. For machining centers, circular commands are used almost exclusively with milling operations. Normally an end mill or shell mill machines on the periphery of the cutter and forms a contour on the workpiece. The techniques shown here will help you avoid undesirable witness marks on the workpiece when contour milling is required.

These techniques will apply only when the milling cutter approaches directly to the surface to be machined. Though this condition sometimes exists when machining an outside surface, it almost always applies when machining inside shapes.

By inside shape, we mean a pocket that requires an approach movement directly to the surface to be milled. Figure 2.7 shows three common examples of inside shapes that are milled in this manner with an end mill. On the left is a round inside shape (pocket). In the middle is a rectangular pocket, and on the right is an irregularly shaped pocket.

Whenever machining inside shapes such as these, or when directly approaching the machined surface of an outside shape, you will find that machining is best done if the tool arcs into the surface to be machined. In similar manner, when the inside (or outside) shape is finished, an arc-out motion makes for the best machining. By *arc-in* and *arc-out*, we mean that the milling cutter should be brought to the surface to be milled in such a way that it forms a tangent to it. Figure 2.8 shows examples of arc-in and arc-out motions. Though Fig. 2.8 exaggerates the size of the arc-in and arc-out radius required, it does nicely show the kind of motion being discussed. See how smoothly the tool is allowed to approach to and retract from the surface to be milled.

Arc-in and arc-out motions are necessary for two reasons. The first is easy to visualize and understand. Whenever possible, it is wise to

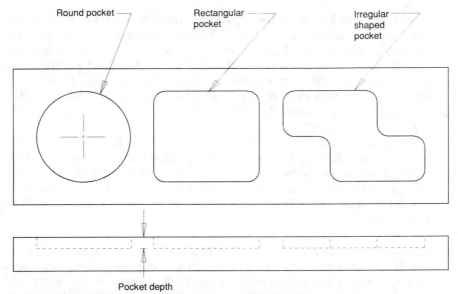

Figure 2.7 Examples of inside shapes milled on a machining center.

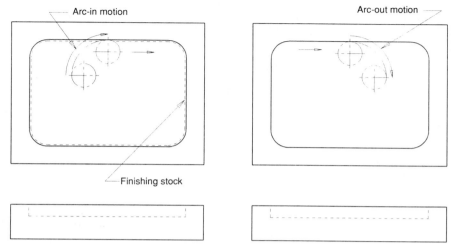

Arc-in motion

Arc-out motion

Finishing stock

Figure 2.8 Examples of arc-in and arc-out motions.

evenly disperse the tool pressure developed during the machining operation. This allows the tool to slowly build to its maximum tool pressure as the full depth of cut is reached. Tool pressure is the amount of force on the tool whenever machining occurs. In milling on the periphery of the cutter, tool pressure has the tendency to push the tool away from the surface being milled.

If arc-in and arc-out motions are used, this tool pressure is increased and decreased slowly, and in a controlled manner. The areas of the part where the approach and retraction are made will be machined in a smooth and acceptable manner. In the arc motions shown in Fig. 2.8, notice once again how smoothly the tool comes into contact with and exits the work surface.

However, if arc-in motions are not used, as demonstrated in Fig. 2.9, the tool will more violently contact the surface to be milled, and almost instantaneously reach full depth of cut. For this reason, the tool will be under the influence of a great deal more pressure when machining begins. The more rough the stock to be machined, the more violent the contact. Without arc-out motions, the tool will move immediately away from the milled surface. There will be much more of a tendency for undesirable witness marks to be left in the approach area. Figure 2.9 also shows the kind of witness mark (though exaggerated) that will be left if arc-in and arc-out motions are not used. Depending on the accuracy required of the workpiece, witness marks may actually cause the workpiece to be scrapped.

The second reason to use arc-in and arc-out techniques whenever milling an inside shape is a little more difficult to visualize. It is applicable only if you are using cutter radius compensation. If you have used this feature to any extent, you know there are several strict rules

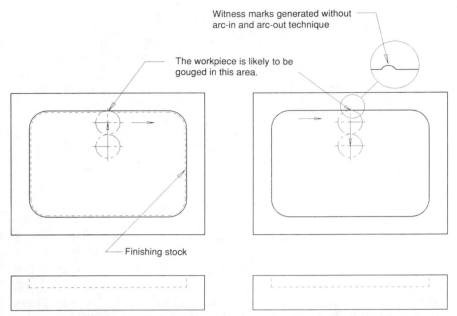

Figure 2.9 Example of what can happen when arc-in and arc-out motions are not used.

that govern its use which cannot be broken. You know that, once instated, cutter radius compensation will keep the milling cutter on the left side or right side (depending on whether G41 or G42 is used) of the series of straight-line and circular-motion commands that follow. With some CNC controls, this can present problems when it comes to the approach and retraction movements necessary to machine a pocket, especially if you do not understand how cutter radius compensation functions for your particular control.

Figure 2.10 shows a series of movements and the actual cutter positions generated by a program that uses cutter radius compensation. In this case, the programmer instated cutter radius compensation on the move to point 2 (with G42). From this point, the control keeps the cutter on the right side of *all* straight-line and circular motions to follow. At the end of this series of motions, when commanding the motion to point 10, the control will be looking ahead to see the next motion. In this case, the next motion (still under the influence of cutter radius compensation) is to point 11. Since the control will keep the tool on the *right* side of this motion line, there will be a small portion of the top surface left unmachined (as demonstrated in Fig. 2.10).

All this means the retraction area of the top milled surface is incorrectly machined. There is still stock that has not been removed from this area. As stated, this problem results from the fact that cutter radius compensation will continue to keep the tool on the right side or

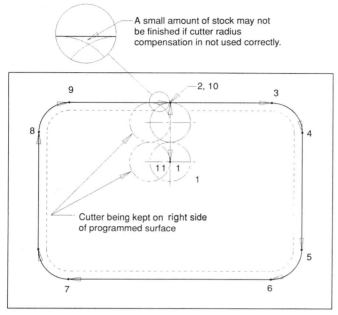

A small amount of stock may not be finished if cutter radius compensation in not used correctly.

Cutter being kept on right side of programmed surface

Figure 2.10 How motions with cutter radius compensation may be incorrect if arc-in and arc-out motions are not used.

left side of the programmed path (in our example, the right side). While most CNC controls have ways to get around this problem (based on how cutter radius compensation is canceled), a typical programmer faced with it will simply overlap the approach area by the amount necessary to clean up the remaining stock. Depending on the accuracy required of the workpiece, this can actually make the problem worse. During the machining of the overlap area, the tool will be under the influence of little or no tool pressure, and will have a tendency to gouge the workpiece.

If arc-in and arc-out motions are used, there will be no incorrect machining in the approach area of the milled surface. This is because cutter radius compensation will be instated and canceled while the cutter is not actually in contact with the work surface. The example program that follows will demonstrate how cutter radius compensation is instated and canceled when arc-in and arc-out techniques are used.

Determining the size of the arc-in and arc-out radius. Most manual programmers will use part coordinates when programming cutter radius compensation. That is, the coordinates going into the program will be positions on the workpiece itself. The offset used with cutter radius compensation will include a value equal to the radius of the milling cutter. If using cutter radius compensation in this manner, the coordinates you will be using in the program will reflect the work surface (*not* tool centerline coordinates). In this case, the approach and retract radius *must* be larger than the radius of the cutter.

On the other hand, most computer-aided-manufacturing (CAM) system programmers elect to base the motions of a program on the specified tool's centerline coordinates. With this method, the offset used with cutter radius compensation is the difference between the planned cutter size and the actual cutter size being used. In this case, the approach and retraction radius can be very small. It is usually set just a little bit larger than the amount of stock to be removed. To keep the actual motions of the arc-in approach and arc-out retraction as simple as possible, we recommend forming a 90° (one-quarter circle) motion during arc-in and arc-out. This will make the calculations necessary to come up with program coordinates quite simple. However, there will be times when this 90° arc motion will be a waste of time if there is no stock being machined. In this case, if you wish to minimize cycle time you will have to calculate points closer to the work surface for the beginning point of the arc-in radius and the end point of the arc-out radius.

Example program showing arc-in and arc-out motions. Figure 2.11 shows the print for the example program. To make it easier to visualize, we include the approach and retraction movements on the print as well as point numbers to be referenced in the program. Though the arc-in and arc-out radius (0.75 in) in this example is much larger than it has to be, it nicely demonstrates the arc-in and arc-out technique. Note that,

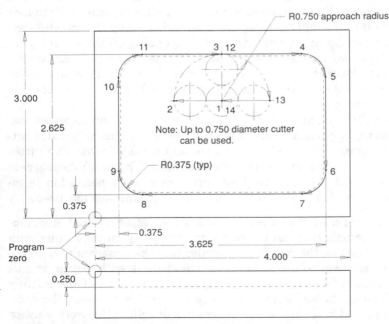

Figure 2.11   Print for arc-in and arc-out example program.

since the radii in all corners is 0.375 in, the largest cutter that can be used is a 0.750-in end mill. This program includes only the finish milling operation.

Program:

```
O0010 (Program number)
N005 G54 G90 S350 M03 (Select coordinate system, absolute mode, turn spindle on
CW at 350 RPM)
N010 G00 X2. Y1.875 (Rapid to point 1)
N015 G43 H01 Z.1 (Rapid down to just above work surface)
N020 G01 Z-.25 F3.5 (Feed down to pocket bottom)
N025 G42 D31 X1.25 (Instate cutter radius compensation, move to point 2)
N030 G02 X2. Y2.625 R.75 (Arc-in to point 3)
N035 G01 X3.25 (Straight move to point 4)
N040 G02 X3.625 Y2.25 R.375 (Circular move to point 5)
N045 G01 Y.75 (Straight move to point 6)
N050 G02 X3.25 Y.375 R.375 (Circular move to point 7)
N055 G01 X.75 (Straight move to point 8)
N060 G02 X.375 Y.75 R.375 (Circular move to point 9)
N065 G01 Y2.25 (Straight move to point 10)
N070 G02 X.75 Y2.625 R.375 (Circular move to point 11)
N075 G01 X2. (Straight move to point 12)
N080 G02 X2.75 Y1.875 R.75 (Arc-out to point 13)
N085 G40 G01 X2. (Cancel cutter radius compensation on straight move to point 14)
N090 G00 Z.1 (Rapid up to above work surface)
N095 G91 G28 Z0 (Return to reference point in Z)
N100 G28 X0 Y0 (Return to reference point in X and Y)
N105 M30 (End of program)
```

Making a full circle in one command.   There are times, especially with machining center applications, when it is helpful to make a circular motion in the form of a total circle. Whenever the surface to be milled is in the form of a circle (either an inside circle or an outside circle), the programmer must drive the milling cutter all the way around the circle in one command.

While most current CNC controls allow a full circle to be formed by one command, some older controls do not allow this function. If your control does not allow a full circle to be programmed in one command, you must break up the circular movement into two or more commands.

Most controls that allow full circles in one command require that the I and J words be used to designate the arc center. That is, depending on your control manufacturer, you will probably not be able to use the R word to designate the radius of the circular movement. Though these techniques vary from one control builder to the next, we will show one very popular way that I and J are used. Here is the definition of I and J for this popular method:

I is the distance and direction *from* the start point of the arc *to* the center of the arc along the X axis.

J is the distance and direction *from* the start point of the arc *to* the center of the arc along the Y axis.

As you can see, I is related to the X axis and J is related to the Y axis. The word *direction* in the previous definitions implies that you *must* include the direction (plus or minus) along with the value. As with all programming words, plus is assumed and need not be included in the word if the value is plus. However, the minus sign must be included if the value is minus.

To evaluate I and J, you can simply draw an arrow on your print *from* the start point of the arc *to* the center of the arc. If the arrow you have drawn is along the X axis, you will need an I in the circular command. If along the Y axis, you will need a J word in the circular command. If the arrow is pointing in the plus direction, the value is plus. If it is pointing in the minus direction, the value is minus. Figure 2.12 shows a tool path that includes circular commands to demonstrate how I and J words are determined. Note that, if available, the R word is much easier to use. We are simply showing how I and J are determined in this example to help with your understanding of how a full circle is commanded in one command.

Once you understand how I and J words work with circular commands, commanding a full circle in one command is quite simple. Since the ending point for the full circle command in X and Y will be the same as the starting point, you need not include an X or Y word in the circular command at all. All that will be required is the G code you wish (G02 or G03) and an I or J word. Since the X and Y values are

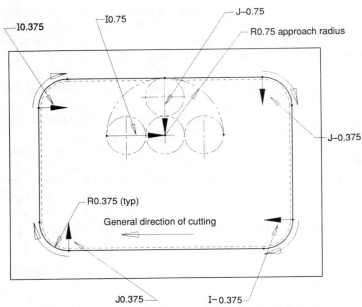

Figure 2.12   How I and J values are evaluated for circular motions.

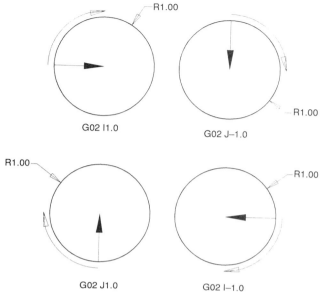

Figure 2.13 Four example commands illustrating how a full-circle motion is related to the arc's starting position.

left out of the command, the control will assume the ending point along each axis to be the same as the starting point.

The direction and value of the I or J word will tell the control how the circle is related to the current X-Y position. Figure 2.13 shows the four possibilities for this relationship with four example commands. While these examples show clockwise motion (G02), the same principles apply to counterclockwise motion (G03).

As Fig. 2.13 shows, all that is required in the G02 or G03 command is the I or J. While the current positions in X and Y can also be repeated, they would not help or hurt the command. Most programmers elect to leave out words that are not required to avoid making mistakes while typing and to minimize the control memory space required to hold the program.

The example program below illustrates a command to make a full circle. Figure 2.14 shows the workpiece.

Program:

```
O0011 (Program number)
N005 G54 G90 S350 M03 (Select coordinate system, absolute mode, turn spindle on
CW at 350 RPM)
N010 G00 X0 Y.50 (Rapid to point 1)
N015 G43 H01 Z.1 (Rapid down to just above work surface)
N020 G01 Z-.25 F30. (Fast feed to work surface)
N025 G42 D31 X-1. F5. (Instate cutter radius compensation, move to point 2)
N030 G02 X0 Y1.5 R1. (Arc in to point 3)
```

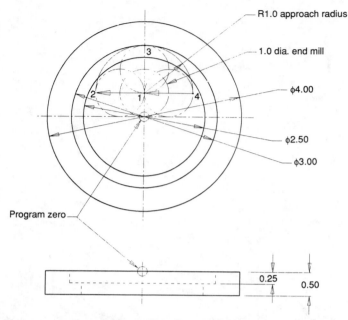

R1.0 approach radius

1.0 dia. end mill

φ4.00

φ2.50

φ3.00

Program zero

0.25

0.50

Figure 2.14   Drawing for full-circle example program.

N035 J-1.5 (Make full circle back to point 3)
N040 X1. Y.5 R1. (Arc out to point 4)
N045 G00 G40 X0 (Cancel cutter radius compensation on move back to point 1)
N050 G91 G28 Z0 (Return to reference point in Z)
N055 G28 X0 Y0 (Return to reference point in X and Y)
N060 M30 (End of program)

In line N035, notice that only the J word was required. The current motion mode at this point is G02 (from the previous command), and since the end point is the same as the start point, no X or Y was needed.

This example also nicely demonstrates (again) how smoothly an arc-in motion will come into contact with the surface to be machined. During the approach to the work surface, the depth of cut in X and Y will gradually increase to the maximum, relieving tool pressure as well as possible.

Spiral milling a circular pocket.   This advanced technique for circular commands can be used on a machining center, when a round pocket must be milled. In the example shown in Fig. 2.14, we circle-milled the round shape with one pass. However, there will be times when it is impossible to use just one pass because of the sheer amount of stock to be removed.

To handle this problem, many programmers will program a series of

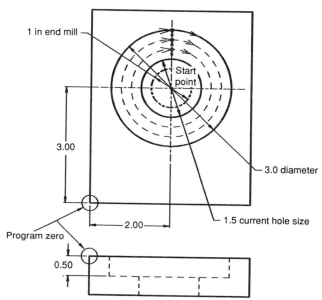

1 in end mill

Start point

3.00

3.0 diameter

1.5 current hole size

2.00

Program zero

0.50

Figure 2.15 Tool path offering limited success for pocketing motions.

motions like that shown in Fig. 2.15. They will simply approach directly to each new machining diameter. However, as the tool is approaching each new pass, the same kind of extreme pressure discussed during arc-in and arc-out will exist. The witness marks on the finish surface generated during the final pass will be undesirable, for the reasons previously given.

Also, using the kind of motions shown in Fig. 2.15 will make it impossible to use cutter radius compensation. Since the control will keep the tool on the left or right side of the programmed path, the movements made during each new approach to a bigger diameter will not be as expected (for the reason demonstrated in Fig. 2.10). The same problems discussed in regard to arc-in and arc-out techniques will present themselves.

Both problems can be overcome with relative ease by machining the round pocket with what will appear to be a series of spiraling motions. Actually, the series of motions will not form a true spiral; it will be a series of arcs, each bigger in diameter than the preceding one.

Figure 2.16 shows the motion. If you look closely, you will see that each half of a movement forms a true circle. Each time the cutter reaches the left side of the circle (points 1, 3, and 5), it begins the next pass to a larger diameter. This series of motions is better than that shown in Fig. 2.15 for two reasons.

First, since the depth of cut is gradually increased on each pass, the tool pressure generated during machining will be more evenly dis-

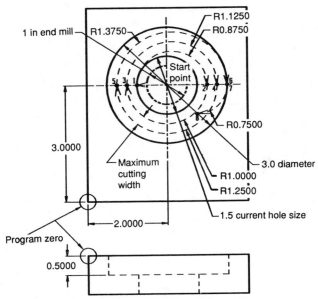

1 in end mill — R1.3750

R1.1250
R0.8750

Start
point

5 3 1   2 4 6
                      7

R0.7500

3.0000

Maximum
cutting
width

3.0 diameter

R1.0000
R1.2500

2.0000

1.5 current hole size

Program zero

0.5000

Figure 2.16   Drawing for spiral milling example.

persed. Second, since all motions form a smooth transition to the tangency point of the next circle, cutter radius compensation can easily be used without fear of unpredictable movements.

At first glance, generating the spiraling motions may seem like a lot of work. However, once you know how most CNC controls handle the R, I, and J words for half-circles, you will find that it really isn't all that difficult to program this series of motions. However, for the first few times you attempt this technique, we strongly recommend that you draw the series of motions you desire to scale (or maybe even 2 or 3 times the scale) on a piece of paper to help you visualize your particular pocketing problem.

How to program half-circles.   For current controls, when programming half-circles, only an axis position different from its starting point need be included in the command. For example, in Fig. 2.16, as each half-circle is commanded, only the X-axis departure needs to be included, since the Y-axis end point is the same as its start point. If you use the R word to specify the arc radius, the control will know to position the arc center precisely halfway from the start point to the end point. If using I and/or J to specify the arc center, the direction (plus or minus) must also be considered. For Fig. 2.16, the arcs beginning at points 1, 3, and 5 will all include an I plus word. Those beginning at points 2, 4, and 6 will include an I minus word.

Example program showing spiral motions.   Figure 2.16 shows the drawing for this example. For clarity, we include the tool motions, motion end-point numbers, and the dimensions relative to the tool path on this print. Of course, when developing your own spiral milling tool motions, you will not have this luxury. This is why we so strongly recommend that you draw the shape to scale (or bigger than full scale) *before* you try to write the program. Notice that the hole has been previously machined to a 1.500-in diameter in the center of this pocket, and we therefore can make rapid motions down to the work surface. Also note that the maximum depth of cut on the side is 0.250 in per pass.

Here is a program that uses the R word for all half-circles:

Program:

```
O0012 (Program number)
N005 G54 G90 S340 M03 (Select coordinate system, absolute mode, turn spindle on
CW at 340 RPM)
N010 G00 X2. Y3. (Rapid to start point)
N015 G43 H01 Z.1 (Rapid down to just above part)
N020 G01 Z-.5 F30. (Fast feed down to work surface)
N025 G42 D31 X1.25 F5. (Feed to point 1)
N030 G02 X3. R.875 (Circular move to point 2)
N035 X1. R1. (Circular move to point 3)
N040 X3.25 R1.125 (Circular move to point 4)
N045 X.75 R1.25 (Circular move to point 5)
N050 X3.5 R1.375 (Circular move to point 6)
N055 I-1.50 (Full circle command to point 7)
N060 X2.75 Y2.25 R.75 (Arc off to point 8)
N065 G00 Z.1 (Rapid to above part)
N070 G40 (Cancel cutter radius compensation)
N075 G91 G28 Z0 (Return to reference position in Z)
N080 G28 X0 Y0 (Return to reference position in X and Y)
N085 M30 (End of program)
```

If you must program all circular commands with I and J words instead of R (as would be the case with older controls), the R word in each half-circle command in the above program must be changed to I. Also, the value for the R word will still be correct for the I, but remember you must consider whether the I value should be plus or minus. All circular movements that begin on the right side of the circle must have a minus value for the I word. All circular movements beginning on the left will include a plus I word.

Dwell techniques

A dwell command tells the control to pause axis motion for a specified period. Other functions of the machine tool (coolant and spindle) continue in their normal manner during a dwell. Depending on the machine and the application, the dwell period can be for a length of time (in seconds) or for a number of spindle revolutions. Most machining centers can accept dwell period in time only, while many turning centers allow both time and number of revolutions to be specified as the dwell period.

The actual word used to specify the dwell period also varies from control to control. The most common word is the P word. (The letter address P is easy to remember if you think of it as pause command.) However, some controls use the letter address X or U to specify dwell period. If you have been working with CNC for any period of time, you have probably been exposed to the dwell command. Here we show you several applications that you may not have considered.

Using a dwell command to relieve tool pressure. This is the most common use for the dwell command. There are many times when the programmer wishes to make axis motion pause after some powerful machining motion to allow time for the pressure of the motion to be relieved. On a turning center, for example, whenever a grooving tool is used to plunge a groove, it is necessary to pause the axis motion to allow time for the grooving tool to machine all the way around the groove. If the grooving tool were to immediately retract from the groove the instant it reached the groove bottom, the bottom surface of the groove on the workpiece would not be perfectly round. The larger the diameter being grooved, the worse this problem would be. Figure 2.17 shows the print for a short example program for a turning center that machines a groove. Included within the grooving operation are dwell commands. The example program below shows commands for the grooving tool only. (SFM represents surface feet per minute.)

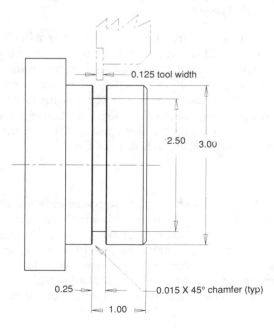

Figure 2.17 Drawing for grooving example program with dwell commands.

Program:

```
O0013 (Program number)
N005 G50 X _____ Z _____ (Set program zero)
N010 G00 T0404 M41 (Index to tool station, select low range)
N015 G96 S400 M03 (Turn spindle on CW at 400 SFM)
N020 G00 X3.2 Z-.9375 M08 (Rapid to groove center position, turn coolant on)
N025 G01 X2.5 F.005 (Plunge center of groove)
N030 G04 P.500 (Dwell for 0.50 second to relieve tool pressure)
N035 G00 X3.2 (Rapid out of groove)
N040 Z-1.015 (Rapid to left side of groove, note chamfer)
N045 G01 X3. (Come flush with groove diameter)
N050 X2.97 Z-1. (Form chamfer)
N055 X2.5 (Plunge left side of groove)
N060 G04 P.500 (Dwell for 0.50 second to relieve tool pressure)
N065 G00 X3.2 (Rapid out of groove)
N070 Z-.860 (Rapid to right side of groove, note chamfer, also note tool width)
N075 G01 X3. (Come flush to groove diameter)
N080 X2.97 Z-.875 (Form chamfer)
N085 X2.5 (Plunge right side of groove)
N090 G04 P.500 (Dwell for 0.50 second to relieve tool pressure)
N095 G00 X3.2 (Rapid out of groove)
N100 G00 X _____ Z _____ T0400 (Rapid to tool change position, cancel offset)
N105 M30 (End of program)
```

In lines N030, N060, and N090, the G04 command is telling the control to pause for 0.5 seconds. In each case, the grooving tool has just plunged the groove and has been under the influence of a great deal of tool pressure (especially on the first plunge). The dwell command (G04) allows this tool pressure to be relieved, besides assuring that the groove bottom diameter is truly round.

Keep in mind that the way the dwell period is specified varies. On some controls, if the P word is used to specify dwell time, it may not allow a decimal point. It may have to be specified in fixed format. For example, a P500 is needed on some controls to specify a 0.5 second dwell. On this particular control, a 1-second dwell is commanded by P1000 without a decimal point. Other controls may use a different word like U or X to specify dwell period.

Though the above turning-center example uses dwell time in seconds, it is possible that the dwell period can be specified by giving a number of revolutions. For example, the dwell commands in the above example program could be modified to

```
N030 G04 P5.
```

to specify a 5-revolution dwell, if the control accepts dwell in number of revolutions. If the control allows dwell to be specified in both time and number of revolutions, a preparatory function (G code) is usually used to inform the control as to which dwell type you wish to use.

Tool pressure during drilling. As a drill is plunging into a hole, the tool pressure generated has the tendency to keep the drill from entering the hole. If a drill is immediately retracted as soon as the hole bottom is reached, the hole will not be to the exact depth programmed. For most drilling applications, however, the hole depth is not critical. Also, most drills have a drill point (118° for standard twist drills) that makes it difficult to measure the precise hole depth. For this reason, most programmers do not attempt to relieve tool pressure when drilling.

Tool pressure during counterboring. The tool pressure generated during counterboring is much the same as in drilling, pushing against the cutting edges of the counterbore tool as it enters a hole. Counterboring is usually done after a hole is drilled. The machining end of a counterbore forms a flat bottom. In counterboring, it is likely that the finished depth of the hole is more critical than in drilling. For this reason, it is necessary to relieve tool pressure once the hole bottom has been reached. Relieving tool pressure will make the machining operation more consistent from one hole to the next. Most programmers include a dwell during the counterboring operation when the counterbore reaches the bottom of the hole. In fact, most controls have a special canned cycle that includes a dwell at hole bottom (usually specified by a G82 command).

Tool pressure during end milling. For the most part, tool pressure during end milling is handled in a different manner. When you are milling on the periphery of the end mill (sometimes called side milling), there is nothing a dwell command can do to help with tool pressure. If the tool pressure that exists in this kind of operation is enough to cause an out-of-tolerance condition, it is normally taken into account by cutter radius compensation.

However, there are times when an end mill is used to plunge into a hole as a counterbore would. In this case, a dwell can be commanded at hole bottom to relieve tool pressure. In this case, the same canned cycle can be used as would be used for counterboring.

During pocket milling operations, many times the end mill is expected to plunge into a solid piece of material and then open up the pocket by side milling. If this is done, the end mill must have center cutting capability and will machine much like a drill while plunging. Once the end mill has reached the bottom of the pocket, it will be under a great deal of tool pressure. It is wise to include a dwell command at this time to relieve tool pressure before beginning side milling motions.

Tool pressure relief versus chatter tendencies. Chatter is an undesirable vibration that occurs during machining if poor cutting conditions exist. It is detrimental to the machining operation, causing (at best) poor finish and (at worst) tool breakage and possible danger to the operator. An experienced machinist will do everything possible to avoid chatter. The conditions which can cause chatter are too numerous to describe here, but, generally speaking, five conditions cause chatter:

1. Speed too fast

2. Feed rate too slow

3. Tool too long (weak tool)

4. Flimsy workpiece (structurally weak workpiece)

5. Weak setup

If machining conditions exist that tend to generate chatter, relieving tool pressure may be the worst thing a programmer can do. In poor setups, tool pressure will actually reduce the possibility for chatter. Pausing at any time while the tool is in contact with the workpiece may cause real problems.

For this reason, you must use the dwell command to relieve tool pressure wisely. If the setup is poor, or tooling is weak, you may not be able to relieve tool pressure without causing unwanted chatter.

Using a dwell command with coolant. Many machining operations require coolant. Of course, coolant aids the machining operation, providing lubricity and cooling action during machining. For most operations, instantaneous coolant flow is not critical to the machining operation. The programmer simply turns the coolant on in the program at the beginning of the tool use. If, for any reason, coolant is not flowing at maximum when machining begins, there is no real problem. Within seconds, the coolant will be flowing properly, providing the necessary lubricity and cooling action.

However, there are certain tools that demand that coolant be flowing at maximum pressure *before* the machining operation can begin. Most carbide insert drills, for example, require that the coolant actually flow through the middle of the drill itself. As the drill enters the hole, the coolant is needed to force the chips out of the hole. Also, extreme heat is generated with this kind of tool and coolant is required to maintain thermal stability. With this kind of tool, if coolant is not flowing at maximum when the drill enters the hole, the drill and workpiece could be damaged.

This coolant flow problem could be considered a machine problem (and one that should be repaired), but it is one that the dwell command can help with. If the programmer includes a dwell command after the carbide drill has approached the hole to be machined, sufficient time can be allowed to assure maximum coolant pressure. Here is a simple one-tool turning center program that includes this technique:

Program:

```
O0014 (Program number)
N005 G50 X_____ Z _____ (Set coordinate system)
(2 in carbide insert drill)
N015 G00 T0101 M41 (Index turret, select low spindle range)
N020 G97 S700 M03 (Turn spindle on at 700 RPM)
```

N025 G00 X0 Z.1 M08 (Rapid to hole position, turn coolant on)
N030 G04 P5.0 (Dwell for 5 seconds to assure maximum coolant flow)
N035 G01 Z-3.5 F.008 (Drill hole)
N040 G00 Z.1 (Rapid out of hole)
N045 X _____ Z _____ T0100 (Return to tool change position, cancel offset)
N050 M30 (End of program)

In line N030, a 5-second dwell is included to allow time to assure maximum coolant pressure. Again, most shops would consider this a waste of cycle time, and would take the steps necessary to fix the coolant system of the machine, making the dwell command unnecessary.

Using a dwell command to allow polishing.   There are times when a subsequent polishing operation is necessary after the CNC operation. In turning-center applications, some companies elect to do the manual polishing operation within the turning-center operation, after the normal automatic machining cycle. With the workpiece still in the chuck, the operator turns on the spindle manually at the desired polishing RPM and manually polishes the necessary surfaces of the workpiece. The operator must be cautious during the polishing operation so as not to come into contact with moving parts, like the chuck. For this safety-related reason, some companies elect not to use this technique.

If the operator must manually start the spindle to do the polishing operation, the machine will be taken out of the automatic mode. It will take time for the operator to start the spindle. When the polishing operation is finished, it will also take time to restart the automatic machining cycle.

The dwell command can help keep the polishing operation more automatic. Before ending the program, the programmer can include a command to run the spindle at the polishing RPM. Then a dwell command can be included that allows the operator enough time to polish the part. The program can be ended in the normal manner. Here is the end of a program that shows the technique:

N240 G00 Z.1 (Rapid out of hole)
N245 X _____ Z _____ T0500 (Return to tool change position, cancel offset)
N250 G97 S300 M03 (Start spindle CW at 300 RPM)
N255 G04 P30. (Dwell for 30 seconds to allow polishing time)
N260 M30 (End of program)

Lines N250 and N255 select the desired speed and allow time for polishing (30 seconds), making the cycle more automatic. However, polishing is not a cut-and-dried operation. That is, it is possible that one part will take longer to polish than another. Add to this the fact that the operator may not be ready to start polishing the workpiece the instant the cycle is finished. Yet another problem related to the above program is safety-related. The operator may think the cycle is finished and open the door before the polishing operation is supposed to begin. These three problems can be overcome with this modified ending to the program. Notice how optional block skip is used to allow the polishing time to be a variable. When the program is run, the optional block switch *must* be turned off. Can you figure out what is going on?

Program:

```
N240 G00 Z.1 (Rapid out of hole)
N245 X _____ Z _____ T0500 (Return to tool change position, cancel offset)
N250 M00 (Program stop, operator now must press cycle start to begin polishing)
N250 G97 S300 M03 (Start spindle CW at 300 RPM)
N255 G04 P5. (Pause for 5 seconds)
/N260 G04 P5. (Pause for 5 more seconds if needed)
/N265 G04 P5. (Pause for 5 more seconds if needed)
/N270 G04 P5. (Pause for 5 more seconds if needed)
/N275 G04 P5. (Pause for 5 more seconds if needed)
/N280 G04 P5. (Pause for 5 more seconds if needed)
/N285 G04 P5. (Pause for 5 more seconds if needed)
/N290 G04 P5. (Pause for 5 more seconds if needed)
N260 M30 (End of program)
```

When line N250 is executed, the machine stops to assure that the operator is by the machine. This also lets the operator confirm that the cycle is truly finished (the in-cycle indicator lamp will go out). The operator will have to activate the cycle again in order to continue with the polishing operation (by pressing the cycle start button).

Line N255 gives 5 seconds of polishing time. It is unlikely that the operator will be finished polishing at this point, so the next command N260 is read (remember, optional block skip is off). Five more seconds is given to polish. If the operator finishes within this time, the optional block skip switch is turned on and the balance of the commands will be ignored. If not, polishing continues. Whenever polishing is finished, the optional block skip switch is turned on and the rest of the dwell commands are skipped. Of course, the operator will immediately turn the optional block skip switch back off to run the next part (or do so at the next program stop).

As you can see, this technique allows the operator as much time as needed to assure polishing can be completed. As many dwell commands as desired can be included, all under the influence of optional block skip. Also, the intervals (5 seconds in our case) can be as short as possible to minimize any wasted time if the operator finishes early.

Note that some machine-tool builders have an interlock switch mounted to the door of the turning center that causes the program to stop if the door is opened. Usually the machine is placed in the feedhold condition if the door is opened during automatic operation. If your machine has this feature, it may not be possible to use manual techniques during automatic operation.

Using a dwell command to force sharp corners. Machinists are taught early in their careers to avoid burrs and sharp corners on workpieces. Sharp edges could cause injury to anyone handling the workpiece as it goes from one operation to the next, so after each machining operation the workpiece is usually deburred.

There are times, however, when design engineers will specify that one edge or another on the workpiece must be sharp. They do not want the edge broken by deburring.

As a CNC machine of any kind makes its motions to machine a workpiece, under normal conditions it will *not* actually stop between commands. Instead, it will flow through the change in motion as smoothly as possible. When a straight motion flows into a tangent radius, this flowing motion is smooth indeed. Even when the change is abrupt, the control makes an attempt at smoothness. For example, as the control flows through one straight-line movement to another intersecting straight-line movement, the control will slightly round the corner, generating a tiny radius between the two movements. Two factors control how much rounding will take place in corners (how big the radius will be). One is the feed rate of the motion; the faster the feed rate, the more rounding. The other factor is the angle being generated between the two movements; the smaller the angle, the more the rounding. Figure 2.18 shows the kind of rounding that will occur between one straight-line motion and another.

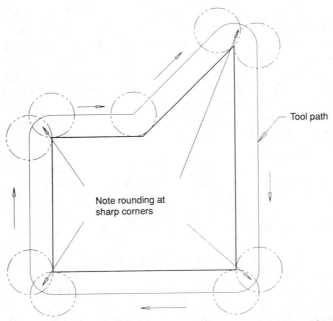

Figure 2.18 Rounded movements between straight-line commands.

Under normal machining, the tiny radius generated between straight-line motion commands will actually help, since sharp edges will be removed. But a programmer who needs to generate a perfectly sharp corner must do something special. One way to handle this problem is to include a short dwell command between the straight-line motion commands. This will cause the tool to actually stop at the completion of one straight-line command before it proceeds to the next. Figure 2.19 shows a drawing we will use for an example of this technique. Cutter radius compensation will be used to allow print dimensions to be used as program coordinates.

Program:

```
O0015 (Program number)
(1-in end mill)
N005 G54 G90 S300 M03 (Select coordinate system, absolute mode, turn spindle on
CW at 300 RPM)
N010 G00 X-.6 Y-.6 (Move below lower left-hand corner)
N015 G43 H01 Z.1 (Rapid down to just above work surface)
N020 G01 Z-.25 F30. (Fast-feed down to work surface)
N025 G42 D32 Y.25 F5.0 (Instate cutter radius compensation, move up to bottom
surface to be milled)
N030 G01 X3.75 (Feed to right-side surface)
N035 G04 P.500 (Dwell for 0.5 second)
N040 G01 Y2.75 (Feed to upper surface)
```

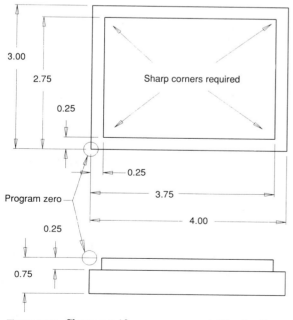

Figure 2.19 Sharp outside corners generated by dwell commands.

N045 G04 P0.5 (Dwell for 0.5 second)
N050 G01 X.25 (Feed to left-side surface)
N055 G04 P.500 (Dwell for 0.5 second)
N060 G01 Y-.1 (Feed past lower surface)
N065 G00 Z.1 (Rapid to above workpiece)
N070 G40 (Cancel cutter radius compensation)
N075 G91 G28 Z0 (Return to reference point in Z)
N080 G28 X0 Y0 (Return to reference point in X-Y)
N085 M30 (End of program)

In line N060, since the tool feeds off the work surface, there is no need for a dwell command at this point.

Pausing after each command with exact stop check.   As you can see, programming a dwell command after every cutting motion can be tedious, especially if the program has many motions. It can also be tedious if it must be done on many parts. For these reasons, many control manufacturers are now supplying a feature that will make the tool physically stop after every motion that does not require the use of the dwell command. Most control manufacturers call this feature *exact stop check* and use three preparatory functions (G codes) to control its use. If the feature is available on your particular control, a G09 is usually the one-shot G code to activate an exact stop check. By *one shot,* we mean that the G code takes effect only in the single-motion command in which it is included; it is *not* modal. A G09 would not help much more than a G04 dwell, since the G04 also must be included in each command.

When the control allows exact stop check, a G61 is usually the modal G code to activate it. Once this command is executed, the control will pause after *every* command until the exact stop check mode is canceled. The command most commonly used to cancel the exact stop check mode is G64.

Understanding the implications of plane selection

These discussions of plane selection apply only to machining centers. Since turning centers have only two axes, they can machine in only one plane (the X-Z plane). This means the programmer has no choice with regard to the plane selection for turning centers.

With a machining center, it is possible to machine in any one of three planes, the X-Y plane, the X-Z plane, or the Y-Z plane. Figure 2.20 shows the relationship of the three planes on a vertical machining center. Figure 2.21 shows the three planes as they relate to a horizontal machining center.

Since the X-Y plane is the plane directly facing the spindle on all machining centers, almost all machining is done in the X-Y plane. For example, if you are machining a hole, coordinates for the hole center are usually in the X-Y plane. If you are milling, the path of the mill-

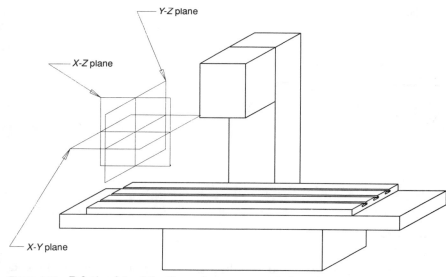

Figure 2.20   Relationship of the three planes on a vertical machining center.

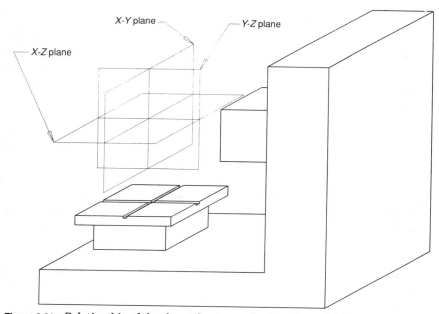

Figure 2.21   Relationship of the three planes on a horizontal machining center.

ing cutter is usually in the *X-Y* plane. Figure 2.22 shows a three-dimensional view of a workpiece as it relates to the *X-Y* plane.

A preparatory function (G code) is used to specify the plane in which you wish to work. On most controls, G17 is used to specify the *X-Y* plane, G18 for the *X-Z* plane, and G19 for the *Y-Z* plane. The G17 (*X-*

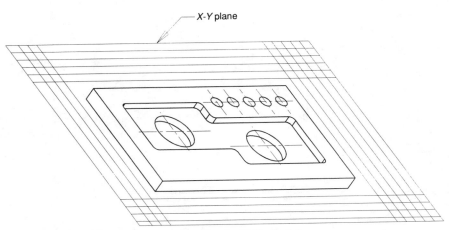

Figure 2.22   Most machining takes place in the *X-Y* plane.

Y plane) is initialized; that is, when the power is turned on, the control automatically selects this G code, setting the *X-Y* plane. This means the programmer does not have to specify a G17 in the program if working exclusively in the *X-Y* plane.

Because so much is done in the *X-Y* plane, you may not have ever considered the possibility of working in another plane. And since the control will automatically select the *X-Y* plane at power up, you may never have even heard of plane selection. There may come a time, however, when you must work in a different plane. Here are some examples with extended discussions.

Plane selection and right-angle heads.   While not yet a common feature, more and more CNC machines are being equipped with a device that allows machining to be done at 90° to the spindle direction (*Z* axis). This device is called a *right-angle head*. The right-angle head can usually be mounted in the spindle in one of two ways, allowing a tool to be facing either the *X-Z* plane or the *Y-Z* plane. Figure 2.23 shows one mounted in the spindle of a vertical machining center with the tool facing the *Y-Z* plane.

Whenever a right-angle head is used, the distance the tool is protruding from the spindle centerline must be taken into account in axis motion commands. If the tool is pointing in the *X* direction (like the tool in Fig. 2.23), this length must be considered with all *X* movements. If the tool is pointing in the *Y* direction, all *Y*-axis motions must reflect this distance in a similar manner. This means the programmer *must* know the distance from the tool tip to spindle centerline *before* the program can be written. Figure 2.23 shows this. Unfortunately, this requires that the tool be preset into the holder to a previously planned length. While this can be cumbersome, and pre-

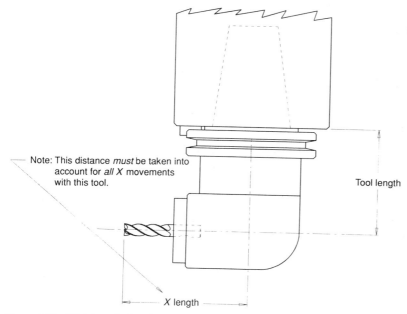

Note: This distance *must* be taken into account for *all X* movements with this tool.

Tool length

X length

Figure 2.23 Right-angle head mounted in spindle of vertical machining center.

setting is considered an obsolete way of setting tools, it must be done on most controls with tools used in right-angle heads.

As with all tools, the tool length is entered into an offset. However, with tools used in the right-angle head, the tool length is the distance from the spindle nose to the *center* of the tool being held. Since the distance from the center of the tool to the nose of the spindle will remain constant from one tool to the next, the offset value will remain the same for all tools used in the right-angle head. Figure 2.23 shows this.

A right-angle head will minimize the number of secondary operations required after the CNC operation. The right-angle head can hold a variety of tools, allowing it to perform a variety of operations. Machining on the sides of a workpiece that would normally require secondary operations can now be performed in the CNC operation. Of course, if multiple operations must be performed on the side of the workpiece, one right-angle head will be required for each tool.

Whenever a right-angle head is used, machining will *not* occur in the X-Y plane. It will now occur in either the X-Z plane or the Y-Z plane, making it necessary to specify the proper G code (G18 for X-Z plane or G19 for Y-Z plane) for certain CNC functions. Note that if only rapid (G00) and straight-line cutting (G01) commands will be given with the right-angle head, there is no need to specify the plane selection command. With rapid and straight-line cutting commands, the control will simply follow your series of motion commands, moving the tool to each programmed position in X, Y, and Z in a point-to-point manner.

However, there are several programming functions that require the use of plane selection when working in the X-Z plane and Y-Z plane. Let's take a look at them.

Circular commands.   Plane selection as it relates to circular commands was discussed earlier in this chapter. Here we give only a quick review.

Any time you give a circular command, you must make the decision as to which command should be used (G02 clockwise or G03 counterclockwise) in the same way the machine will interpret the command. For X-Y circular moves, it's easy. Since you view the movement from the spindle nose position (the plus side of the Z axis), evaluating most X-Y circular movements is as simple as viewing the print from above.

However, for X-Z and Y-Z circular movements, you must view the motion from the *plus side* of the uninvolved perpendicular axis. For vertical machining centers, an X-Z circular motion must be viewed from the back of the machine (from plus Y). A Y-Z circular motion must be viewed from the right side of the machine (from plus X).

Note that the attitude of the right-angle head may confuse you. If the tool itself is pointing in the minus direction (in X or Y), you can view the motion from the tool's side of the workpiece to decide whether to use G02 or G03, making the evaluation slightly easier. However, if the tool in the right-angle head is pointing in the plus direction, you *must still* view the motion from the plus side of the uninvolved axis. In this case, you must evaluate G02/G03 from the bottom side of the tool. If you make a mistake and select the wrong circular command, don't worry too much. You should be able to easily find this kind of mistake during the program's verification.

Cutter radius compensation.   As with circular commands, the CNC control will require that you evaluate cutter radius compensation commands (G41—cutter left and G42—cutter right) from the *plus side* of the uninvolved axis. As long as the right-angle head has the tool pointing in the minus direction (either X minus or Y minus), climb milling will be G41 (cutter left) and conventional milling will be G42 (cutter right), just as it is for machining in the X-Y plane. This assumes a right-hand milling cutter is used (spindle running clockwise). However, if the tool is pointing in the plus direction, this rule for cutter radius compensation must be reversed.

Here is an example program that combines circular motions and cutter radius compensation in the same program for use with a right-angle head. Figure 2.24 shows the part to be machined. To keep this example realistic, we are machining holes in the top surface of this part (no center drilling) as well as milling the right side. Notice that

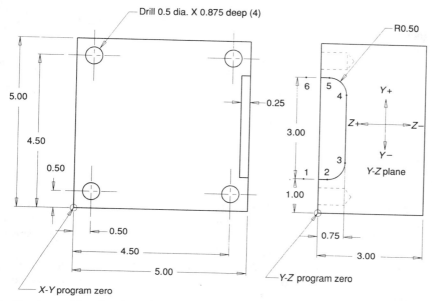

Figure 2.24 Drawing for right-angle head example program.

program zero is still specified as it would be for machining on the top surface of the workpiece. The end mill used to machine into the right side of this workpiece is held in the same attitude as shown in Fig. 2.23 (pointing in the X minus direction). For this example, we'll say the distance from the tip of the end mill to the spindle centerline is precisely 4.000 in.

Program:

O0016 (Program number)
(0.500-in-diameter drill)
N005 G17 G54 G90 S800 M03 T02 (Select X-Y plane, coordinate system, absolute mode, turn spindle on CW at 800 RPM, get tool 2 ready)
N010 G00 X.5 Y.5 (Move to first hole location)
N015 G43 H01 Z.1 (Rapid down to just above workpiece)
N020 G81 R.1 Z-.875 F5.0 (Drill lower left hole)
N025 Y4.5 (Drill upper left hole)
N030 X4.5 (Drill upper right hole)
N035 Y.5 (Drill lower right hole)
N040 G80 (Cancel cycle)
N045 G91 G28 Z0 M19 (Return to reference position, orient spindle for tool change)
N050 M01 (Optional stop)
N055 T02 M06 (Change tools to right-angle head)
(0.875-in-diameter end mill)
N060 G90 S400 M03 T01 (Select absolute mode, turn spindle on CW at 400 RPM, get tool 1 ready)
N065 G00 X8.75 Y1.75 (Rapid to first X-Y position)
N075 G43 H02 Z.75 (Rapid down to just above workpiece)

N080 G19 (Select *Y-Z* plane)
N085 G41 D32 Y1.0 (Instate cutter radius compensation, move to point 1)
N090 G01 Z-.25 (Feed to point 2)
N095 G03 Y1.5 Z-.75 R.5 (Circular move to point 3)
N100 G01 Y3.5 (Feed to point 4)
N105 G03 Y4. Z-.25 R.5 (Circular move to point 5)
N110 G01 Z.6 (Feed to point 6)
N115 G00 X9.1 (Move away in *X*)
N120 G40 (Cancel cutter radius compensation)
N125 G17 (Switch back to *X-Y* plane selection)
N130 G91 G28 Z0 M19 (Return to reference point in *Z*)
N135 M01 (Optional stop)
N140 T01 M06 (Put tool 1 back in spindle)
N145 G28 X0 Y0 (Return to reference point in *X* and *Y*)
N150 M30 (End of program)

This program requires further explanation. For all movements in *X* for the right-angle head, the 4.000-in tool length (distance from tool tip to spindle center) had to be considered. In line N065, the tip of the tool had to be positioned to an *X* of 4.75 in. But the spindle center (of the machine's spindle) is being programmed. The spindle center is 4.000 in away from the tool tip (in this case), so it had to be added to our desired position.

Notice the *Y-Z* plane selection command (G19) was not given until just before it was needed (in line N080). This assures that the plane selection will not affect other movements in an unexpected way. Also, note that the *X-Y* plane selection must be reinstated or else the G81 commands in the first tool will be affected by the G19 command after the first time the cycle is run. More on how plane selection affects canned cycles in a moment.

Keep in mind that this tool is pointing in the *X* minus direction. This means that both circular movements and cutter radius compensation are evaluated from the tool point side of the motion, making it relatively easy to determine which of G02/G03 and G41/G42 to use.

You may have a little trouble visualizing the motions these commands make under the influence of cutter radius compensation. You may be so used to thinking in *X-Y* that you can't easily adapt to other planes. But stick with it. These techniques will be necessary if you ever have to work with a right-angle head.

Using canned cycles with a right-angle head. As you know, canned cycles allow easy programming for hole machining by machining centers. One relatively simple command is given to specify machining for the first hole, telling the control what kind of cycle to use (drill, tap, counterbore, etc.) and the necessary information needed to machine the hole (rapid plane, hole depth, feed rate, etc.). Then the programmer simply lists the locations at which holes are to be machined. After the last hole, the canned cycle must be canceled by a G80.

There are a variety of canned-cycle types that allow the programmer to specify the kind of hole to be machined. Drilling, peck drilling, tapping, reaming, and boring are among the types most often used. Though the actual commands vary from one control manufacturer to the next, here is a list of common cycle types and their most popular G code designations.

G73 Chip-breaking peck-drilling cycle

G74 Left-hand tapping cycle

G76 Fine boring cycle

G80 Canned-cycle cancel command

G81 Standard drilling cycle

G82 Counterboring cycle

G83 Chip-clearing drilling cycle

G84 Tapping cycle

G85 Reaming cycle

G86 Boring cycle

Canned cycles are most often used for machining in the Z axis. That is, as a hole is being machined, the tool is moving in the Z axis. The hole's centerline coordinates are given in the X-Y plane (G17). However, if you are using a right-angle head, hole machining will no longer be along the Z axis. Instead, the right-angle head will require that machining be done in the X or Y axis, depending on how the right-angle head is held in the spindle of the machine.

When you are using the right-angle head, programming holes with canned cycles is much easier than trying to specify that holes be machined longhand with G00 and G01 (just as it is when machining in the X-Y plane). However, as with circular commands and cutter radius compensation, you must specify the plane you intend to be machining holes in *before* you attempt to use canned cycles. Also, the meaning of each canned-cycle word within the canned cycle itself will change if you are working in the X-Y plane.

The actual words used with canned cycles will vary from one CNC machine to the next. Here we show one common example of how canned-cycle use and plane selection work together. If you understand these presentations, you should be able to easily adapt to any variations you come across. For this discussion, we will discuss canned cycles only as they are used in the absolute mode (G90).

For X-Y plane hole drilling (the one most often used), the hole center coordinates are specified in the X-Y plane and machining takes place in the Z axis. Here is a list of words that are used on one popular control and their meanings in the X-Y plane (G17).

X Hole center coordinate in X axis

Y Hole center coordinate in Y axis

R Rapid plane in Z axis

Z Hole bottom position in Z axis (if the work surface is program zero in Z, this word is equal to hole depth)

F Feed rate

Q Peck depth for G73 and G83

P Pause time for G82

The functions of X, Y, R, and Z will change when you change the plane selection. Say, for example, you are going to use a right-angle head as shown in Fig. 2.25. Note that the drill is pointing in the X minus direction. In this case the Y-Z plane must be used (G19). The rapid plane (specified by R) will now be along the X axis. The X in the canned cycle will be the hole bottom position (along the X axis). Y and Z in the canned-cycle command will now specify the hole center coordinates.

For machining in the X-Z plane (G18), the rapid plane (specified by R) is now along the Y axis. The Y value in the canned-cycle command is the hole bottom position. The X and Z values will specify the hole centerline coordinates.

Here is an example program showing the use of a 0.375-in-diameter drill being held in the right-angle head shown in Fig. 2.25. To keep the example program simple, say the drill tip is precisely 4.000 in from the spindle centerline. Figure 2.26 shows the workpiece to be machined. Notice that this is the same workpiece shown earlier for

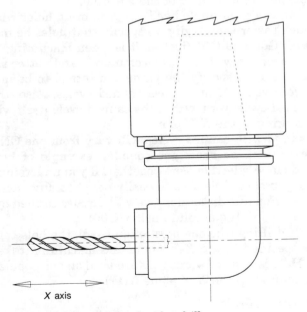

X axis

Figure 2.25 Right-angle head with a drill.

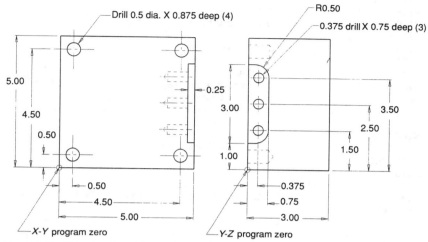

Figure 2.26 Drawing for right-angle head with canned-cycle example program.

the circular movement and cutter radius compensation example, with the addition of three 0.375-in-diameter holes. This program would, of course, require the use of two right-angle heads, one for the end mill and one for the 0.375-in-diameter drill.

Program:

O0017 (Program number)
(0.500-in-diameter drill)
N005 G17 G54 G90 S800 M03 T02 (Select *X-Y* plane, coordinate system, absolute mode, turn spindle on CW at 800 RPM, get tool 2 ready)
N010 G00 X.5 Y.5 (Move to first hole location)
N015 G43 H01 Z.1 (Rapid down to just above workpiece)
N020 G81 R.1 Z-.875 F5.0 (Drill lower left hole)
N025 Y4.5 (Drill upper left hole)
N030 X4.5 (Drill upper right hole)
N035 Y.5 (Drill lower right hole)
N040 G80 (Cancel cycle)
N045 G91 G28 Z0 M19 (Return to reference position, orient spindle for tool change)
N050 M01 (Optional stop)
N055 T02 M06 (Change tools to end-mill right-angle head) (0.875-in-diameter end mill)
N060 G90 S400 M03 T03 (Select absolute mode, turn spindle on CW at 400 RPM, get tool 3 ready)
N065 G00 X8.75 Y1.75 (Rapid to first *X-Y* position)
N075 G43 H02 Z.75 (Rapid down to just above workpiece)
N080 G19 (Select *Y-Z* plane)
N085 G41 D32 Y1.0 (Instate cutter radius compensation, move to point 1)
N090 G01 Z-.25 (Feed to point 2)
N095 G03 Y1.5 Z-.75 R.75 (Circular move to point 3)
N100 G01 Y3.5 (Feed to point 4)
N105 G03 Y4. Z-.25 R.75 (Circular move to point 5)

```
N110 G01 Z.6 (Feed to point 6)
N115 G00 X9.1 (Move away in X)
N120 G40 (Cancel cutter radius compensation)
N125 G17 (X-Y plane selection)
N130 G91 G28 Z0 M19 (Return to reference point in Z)
N135 M01 (Optional stop)
N140 T03 M06 (Put tool 3 in spindle)
N145 G54 G90 S1200 M03 T01 (Select coordinate system, absolute mode, turn
spindle on CW at 1200 RPM, get tool 1 ready)
N150 G00 X8.85 Y1.5 (Rapid to first X-Y position)
N155 G43 H03 Z-.375 (Rapid to hole center in Z)
N160 G19 (Select Y-Z plane)
N165 G81 Y1.5 Z-.375 R8.85 X8. F5. (Drill first hole)
N170 Y2.5 (Drill second hole)
N175 Y3.5 (Drill third hole)
N180 G80 G17 (Cancel cycle, return to X-Y plane)
N185 G91 G28 Z0 M19 (Return to reference point, orient spindle for tool change)
N190 M01 (Optional stop)
N195 T01 (Put tool 1 back in spindle)
N200 G28 X0 Y0 (Return to reference point in X and Y)
N205 M30 (End of program)
```

Notice once again how the plane selection commands were placed close to the actual motions requiring the Y-Z plane. We strongly recommend that you do this to avoid having unpredictable movements caused by the plane selection commands.

Other times you must use plane selection commands. Though plane selection commands are often required when you use a right-angle head, there are other times when they must be used. Any time you intend to make a two-axis circular motion command or use cutter compensation involving the Z axis (on a machining center), you must first instate the proper plane selection command (G18 or G19).

Milling with a ball end mill. One common occasion when this is necessary involves milling with a ball end mill. If you need to make circular motions when using a ball end mill, you must consider the proper plane selection command. Since a ball end mill is often used to plunge in Z as well as mill in X or Y, it can be used to make X-Z and Y-Z circular moves. Figure 2.27 shows a motion with a ball end mill that would require an X-Z plane selection (G18). Notice how the circular motion direction appears to be incorrectly specified (as G03). However, remember that the motion direction (G02 or G03) must be decided on by viewing the motion from the Y plus side (back of the machine on a vertical machining center).

If you intend to allow a range of ball end mill sizes to be used while milling in X-Z or Y-Z, cutter radius compensation must be used. This would also require that you first select the proper plane (even if circular motions are not commanded).

Plane selection with coordinate manipulation commands. Many CNC controls are equipped with coordinate manipulation features like polar

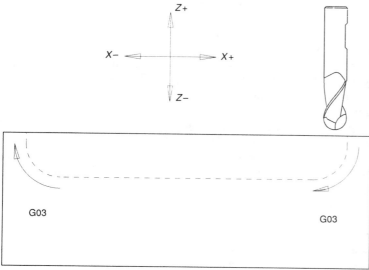

Motion requires *X Z* plane selection (G18).

Figure 2.27 The kind of ball-end-mill motion that requires plane selection commands.

coordinates, coordinate rotation, single-direction positioning, and scaling that make the calculation of motion positions much easier. Though these commands are most commonly used in the *X-Y* plane, you can also use them to manipulate motions in the *X-Z* and *Y-Z* planes.

As with canned cycles, you must exchange the direction of machining for the particular coordinate manipulation feature. Coordinate rotation in the *X-Z* plane, for example, would require that the center of rotation be a position in the *X-Z* plane, instead of in the *X-Y* plane.

Plane selection with a rotary axis to tilt the tool in the spindle. Some elaborate multiaxis machining centers (four- and five-axis machines) incorporate at least one rotary device, mounted in the machine's headstock, that tilts the tool in the spindle to the desired attitude relative to the *X-Z* plane and/or the *Y-Z* plane.

One application for this form of rotary axis is machining complicated and sculptured surfaces, such as the airfoil of an aircraft wing. In this case, at least one tilting axis is used to maintain the perpendicularity of the cutting tool to the surface being machined. In this application, the surface being machined is *not* along a simple plane but is an extremely elaborate surface. For this reason, this application requires a high-level computer-aided manufacturing system to produce programs.

A simpler application of a rotary axis to tilt the tool in the spindle is for more conventional machining operations done at a specified angle to the spindle. Normally the angle of rotation is somewhat limited; a full 90° rotation is not possible.

For example, the tool may be tilted to a 45° position (relative to the X-Z and/or Y-Z plane), and a hole may be drilled into a 45° angular surface. In this case, machining is *not* being done within any of the previously defined planes (X-Y, X-Z, or Y-Z). The plane for machining is now an angular plane, possibly even incorporating a combination of two angular planes.

At first glance, this application may seem very difficult to work with. However, most current CNC controls capable of tilting the tool held in the spindle offer a feature called *variable plane selection*. The commands used to evoke this feature vary substantially from one control to the next.

One popular control uses a G68 for the purpose of variable plane selection. In this command, the programmer specifies the angular plane's position, in effect aligning the plane selection with the tilted angle of the tool in the spindle. Once instated, all coordinate-related commands discussed in this section (canned cycles, cutter radius compensation, etc.) will behave in much the same way as previously described. This feature allows machining operations like milling and hole machining to be done with relative ease, even on angular surfaces of the workpiece.

Inch/metric implications

Most current CNC machines allow input in either the inch mode or the metric mode. Generally speaking, once either input is selected, it is maintained throughout the program. That is, seldom will you be required to use both modes in one program. In fact, most companies will use only one of these measurement modes for *all* programs written.

If the company comes across a part that happens to have been designed in the other input system, it will simply convert the print's dimensions and tolerances to the input mode with which it is most familiar and run the workpiece in that mode. Here are the conversion formulas.

$$\text{Inches} = \text{millimeters} \div 25.4$$

$$\text{Millimeters} = \text{inches} \times 25.4$$

For example, say you have a dimension of 16 mm on the print, but you are going to write your program in the inch mode. Simply divide 16 by 25.4 to come up with the inch equivalent (0.6299 in).

Though the metric mode is becoming more popular, the inch mode is, by far, the more common mode used in the United States. Since the United States has been working in the inch mode for two centuries, it has been difficult for the country to make the switch to metric.

Keep in mind that switching to the metric mode involves more than simply writing programs in metric. There are other considerations when making a switch from one mode to the other that will cost your company money. First, measuring devices like micrometers, calipers, height gauges, and dial indicators must be replaced when switching to the metric mode, since most of these tools are designed to show measured dimensions in only one of the two input modes. Second, most manual machines like engine lathes, turret lathes, and milling machines have their handwheel scale increments in inches. While most machine-tool builders offer replacement scales capable of converting the machine from inch to metric, many companies find this expense to be prohibitive. Third, all shop people must be reeducated to work in metric.

On the other hand, more and more European and Far Eastern companies (among others) are opening manufacturing facilities in the United States. These companies work exclusively in the metric mode. As time goes on, more and more American companies will be forced to conform. It is likely that you will have to work in the metric mode at some point in your CNC career.

How to select the inch or metric mode. Most CNC controls allow the measurement system (inch or metric) to be selected in two ways. First, the operator is usually allowed to select the inch or metric mode manually, through some kind of switch. The switch could be a physical toggle switch on the control panel, or more likely, a switch displayed and set through the display screen.

Second, the programmer can usually select inch or metric by a preparatory function (G code). On most controls, a G20 selects the inch mode and a G21 selects the metric mode. By this method, the input mode can be selected from within a program, or by manual data input mode (MDI).

The machine can usually be manipulated so the desired mode is initialized at power-up. If your company works exclusively in inches, the machine can be made to power-up in the inch mode. If your company works exclusively in metric, the machine can be made to power-up in the metric mode. This will keep the programmer from having to specify a G20 or G21 in the program if the desired mode is used. The control will automatically assume the correct mode when the machine is turned on.

You can easily tell which input mode is currently selected by looking at the coordinate positions on the display screen. In the inch mode, almost all CNC machines will display coordinate positions to four places of accuracy (down to 0.0001 in). In the metric mode, the control will display coordinate positions to three places of accuracy (0.001 mm). For example, if the position display page of the control screen shows these values:

```
X12.2500
Y11.3750
Z08.8750
```

you would know the machine was currently set to the inch mode because four places follow the decimal point. On the other hand, if the position display page of the control screen shows these values:

```
X150.500
Y280.250
X350.375
```

you would know the machine was currently in the metric mode because three places follow the decimal point.

There are a few companies that utilize their CNC machines in both input modes. It may be possible that about half of a company's workpiece prints are dimensioned in inches and the other half in metric. For this company, it may be best to work in the most convenient input mode. Keep in mind that this means a duplication of measuring devices. If your company is one of the few that runs programs in both modes, we recommend that you include the appropriate G20 (inch mode) or G21 (metric mode) at the beginning of *all* programs to avoid accidentally being in the wrong input mode. If no programmed command tells the control which input mode to use, of course the control will assume the input mode from the most recent program (if one exists) or the mode initialized at power-up.

If the control assumes the wrong mode, the results can be disastrous. If the program is written in the metric mode, but the machine is set to the inch mode, all coordinate position end points will be greatly enlarged. A value that was supposed to be taken as 5.0 mm (0.1968 in) will actually be taken as 5.0 *inches*.

On the other hand, if the program is written in the inch mode but, when it is run, the machine is set to the metric mode, coordinate position end points will be dramatically reduced. A value of 5.0 in will be taken as 5.0 mm (0.1968 in). In either case, being in the wrong input mode sets up potentially dangerous situations. The inclusion of the proper input mode G code at the beginning of *all* programs will let you avoid this possibility for disaster.

Other considerations in switching input modes. As you have seen, switching from one input mode to the other is not as simple as throwing a switch. Though the machine will assume the correct mode, your company's measuring devices and manual machine tools, and even the attitude of its employees, also affect the change from inch to metric and vice versa.

There are yet other considerations. You must work exclusively in the selected mode. For example, the measurement of the program zero point must be made in the selected mode. If working in metric, the distance from program zero to the machine's starting point must be entered in the metric mode.

Tool offsets must also be entered in the selected mode. Say you intend to work in metric. For machining centers, tool length offsets and cutter radius offsets must be entered in metric. For turning centers, offsets to control machining size as well as those to compensate for tool nose radius must be entered in metric.

Note that most types of cutting tools must also be supplied in the selected input mode. For example, if the design engineer dimensions a hole to be 10 mm in diameter, a 10-mm drill must be used. Though there are times when you will find tooling in inch equivalents that happen to match the metric tool requirements, these occurrences are purely coincidental.

The accuracy advantage of the metric mode. If your company is currently working exclusively in the inch mode, you may see little reason to change to metric. Surely, nothing presented to this point would have changed your mind. It would take quite an investment of time and money to switch to metric. You will probably want to continue machining workpieces in the inch mode and convert those few metric prints you come across to inches and run the parts in the inch mode.

However, there is one advantage of working in the metric mode that is not very obvious. It has to do with the least input increment of the machine tool in the selected input mode. The *least input increment* is the smallest departure movement possible on the CNC machine. For most CNC machines, the least input increment in the inch mode is 0.0001 in. In the metric mode, the least input increment is 0.001 mm.

When converted to the inch mode, 0.001 mm is equal to 0.00003937 in (0.001 divided by 25.4), so 0.001 mm is less than half of 0.0001 in. This means the machine has a much finer resolution or movement grid when you are working in the metric mode. You can target the end point of each movement command to a more precise position when working in the metric input system. Figure 2.28 shows the grid for the

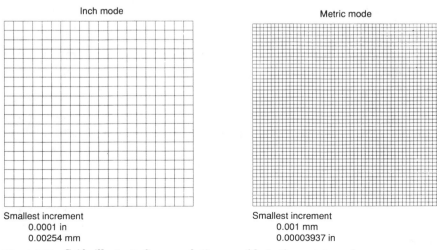

Inch mode

Smallest increment
   0.0001 in
   0.00254 mm

Metric mode

Smallest increment
   0.001 mm
   0.00003937 in

Figure 2.28 Grids illustrate finer resolution possible in the metric mode.

inch mode as it compares to the grid for the metric mode (0.0001-in grid versus 0.001-mm grid). This is a graphic illustration of how much more precise you can be with the specification of end points in the metric mode. As you can see, the machine's resolution (set of possible end points for each command) is much finer in the metric mode.

We are *not* saying that the machine is more accurate in the metric mode. The CNC machine will perform to its quoted specifications in either mode. In the metric mode, you can simply target your end points to a finer location.

Compare this to an indexing device mounted on the table of a vertical machining center. If you have a 5° indexer, you can specify angular indexes every 5°. If you have a 1° indexer, you can specify angular index every 1°. The 5° indexer will have only 72 positions, while the 1° indexer will have 360 positions. With the 1° indexer, you can target angular end points to a much finer location.

However, this fact by itself does *not* make the 1° indexer more accurate. It is possible that the 5° indexer is just as good at attaining the proper angularly commanded position as the 1° indexer. The 1° indexer simply allows the selection of more rotational locations.

In a similar way, the metric mode will allow the possible end points along a linear axis to be more than doubled. Actually there will be 2.54 times the number of end points for any linear axis in the metric mode than in the inch mode. For a linear axis that is 10 in long, there would be 100,000 possible end points in the inch mode. For the same linear axes, there would be 254,000 possible end points in the metric mode.

Note that this statement does not apply to a rotary axis. Since all true rotary axes are commanded in angular increments, there is no difference in the number of possible end points from the inch mode to the metric mode. A position of 45° is the same in both modes.

Selecting the mean dimension for the specified tolerance. There are times when having the ability to select finer increments of motion will make the difference between success and failure with a program. For example, when you are trying to hold extremely critical tolerances on a workpiece, it may be helpful (if not mandatory) to target each motion as precisely as possible.

When programming any workpiece, most programmers will select the mean dimension of the tolerance for use as the programmed coordinate. This allows any cutting condition problems to slightly affect machining yet be within the given tolerance. For example, for the dimension

$$3.2500 \text{ in} + 0.0004 - 0.0002$$

the programmer would use 3.2501 as the programmed coordinate, since it represents the mean value of the specified tolerance (3.2500 + 0.0004 − half the overall tolerance 0.0003).

However, there are times when the programmer cannot specify the precise value of the mean tolerance in the inch mode because of the resolution grid limitations discussed earlier. For example, for the dimension

$$3.2500 + 0.0003 - 0$$

the mean value is 3.25015 in. Since the least input increment in the inch mode is 0.0001 in, the desired end point of the motion command cannot be commanded in the inch mode. In this mode, either the dimension would have to be rounded up to 3.2502 in or rounded down to 3.2501 in. Either way, the programmed value would be 0.00005 in from the needed program value.

However, if the dimension is converted to metric, the mean dimension end point can be much more precise. The value 3.25015 in in metric is 82.5538 mm (3.25015 × 25.4), which can be rounded to 82.554 mm. This coordinate is within 0.0002 mm (or 0.0000079 in) of being precisely the desired mean value coordinate. When you compare this value to the best possible inch mode value (within 0.00005 in), you can see how much better the metric mode lets you target end points.

Offset considerations. Another time when the metric mode will help with critical tolerances is when you use offsets. When an operator is trying to adjust the size of the workpiece with tool offsets, the machine's least input increment will again be a limitation. If working in the inch mode, the operator will be limited to making offset adjustments in increments of 0.0001 in. In the metric mode, the operator is allowed to make much finer adjustments in 0.001-mm (0.00003937-in) increments. This can sometimes mean the difference between being able to hold size or *not* being able to hold size for critical tolerances.

Though the points made here are true for all kinds of CNC machines, this kind of tolerance problem occurs most frequently on turning centers when you are trying to hold close diameter tolerances. For example, say this inch input mode diameter and tolerance must be held on a turning center:

$$3.1250 \text{ in} + 0.0001 \text{ in} - 0$$

In this case, the operator would have little or no chance of adjusting the offset perfectly if working in the inch mode. Also note that the programmer would have to program the value as either 3.1250 or 3.1251. In either case, the programmed coordinate would be on a tolerance limit. The best the operator could hope for is to be very lucky when adjusting the offset. By luck alone will the dimension come out to the mean dimension of the tolerance.

However, when converted to the metric mode, 3.1250 in is 79.375 mm. The tolerance band of 0.0001 in is 0.00254 mm when converted. This means the mean dimension of the tolerance would be 79.376 mm (3.21505 × 25.4 rounded down to the next 0.001 mm). If running in the metric input system, the operator will have a much better chance of adjusting the offset to conform to this dimension.

Admittedly, the tolerances we have been discussing are minute indeed, and, in reality, most companies will not have to work to such close tolerances. But when the task of handling them arises, it is good to know the implications of working in the metric mode. In these cases, you can convert the dimensions on the drawing to metric and machine the workpiece in the metric mode.

How the control generates axis departures (inch versus metric).   Depending on the control manufacturer, the resolution of the CNC control will sometimes determine how smoothly motion will occur. By resolution, we mean the size of the smallest single-axis departure when a movement of more than one axis is commanded. When linear and circular commands (G01, G02, and G03), are given, the actual motion occurs along a series of tiny single-axis motions (Fig. 2.29). For most applications, these motions will be so tiny that the end result will appear to be a perfectly straight line or a perfectly round circle. The size of each step is determined by the control's resolution. The better the resolution, the smaller the step, hence the smoother the motion will be.

For some current CNC controls, the control's resolution is exactly the same (and the best it can be) no matter which input mode is selected (inch or metric). However, the resolution of some (especially older CNC controls) is dramatically affected by which input mode is selected. In fact, many times the least input increment is the actual step value determined by the control's resolution.

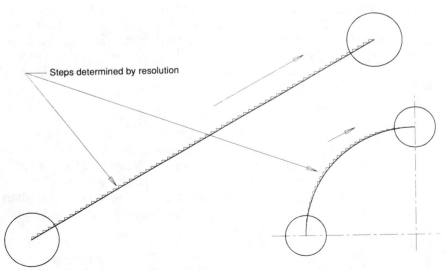

Steps determined by resolution

Figure 2.29   How the control's resolution affects steps in linear and circular motions.

If this is the case, the control's motion capabilities are directly affected by whether the control is in the inch or the metric mode. That is, in the inch mode the resolution (step size) is 0.0001 in. In the metric mode, the resolution is 0.001 mm (or 0.00003937 in). This means the control can make smoother movements in the metric mode than in the inch mode.

For most applications, there would be no indication of this limitation in the inch mode. The tiny 0.0001-in steps would seldom be detectable. Also, newer controls have the same resolution in either mode; you would never be faced with any problems stemming from resolution differences based on the input mode.

But we wish to warn you about one kind of problem you may come across at some point in your career. Figure 2.30 shows a workpiece to be machined on a turning center that requires a very tiny taper on the face of the part (though not to scale). If this part is to be programmed in inch mode, and if the resolution of the control is set by the least input increment (0.0001 in in this case), the desired motion could not be generated.

Figure 2.31 shows what *would* happen. Notice that, since only 0.0002-in taper is generated on the face in the Z axis, the control would simply divide this motion by the least input increment and break the command down into a number of steps equal to the result—in this case, two steps, since 0.0002 ÷ 0.0001 = 2. No true taper could be generated.

6.00

Figure 2.30 Drawing of a tiny taper desired on the face of the workpiece.

0.0002

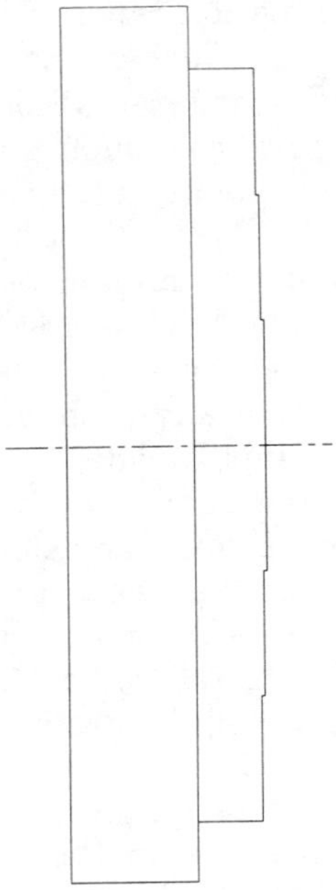

Figure 2.31 With some controls, the machine's resolution is equal to the least input increment. Taper is shown here for the inch mode.

Figure 2.32 Better taper resolution possible in the metric mode.

In the metric mode, since the least departure increment is less than half of that in the inch mode, the motion would be much better, though still not perfect. Figure 2.32 shows the same motion made in the metric mode.

Keep in mind that some (especially newer) CNC controls do not base the control's resolution on the least input increment. With this kind of control, the resolution (step size) is even smaller than the least input increment, even in the metric mode. This means the above-mentioned problem may never occur.

Program copy techniques

Program copy is a feature that allows a series of commands within a program to be repeated. Though not available on all CNC controls, it is quite useful.

Program copy is normally commanded by a G25. Within the G25 command, the programmer will include a P word and a Q word that point to sequence numbers (used as statement labels) corresponding to commands within the same program to be executed. For example, the command

    N095 G25 P025 Q055

tells the control to go to line N025 and execute from there until line N055. On completing the execution of line N055 the control would return to the command immediately *after* line N095 and continue executing the program from this point.

Note that much of what can be accomplished by program copy can also be done with another programming feature called *subprogramming*. Though some discussions of subprogramming have already been given, we will discuss subprogramming techniques in detail a little later in this chapter.

Note that some controls even allow program copy to scan to and execute commands from other programs. However, most are limited to executing commands only within the current program. Even so, this feature dramatically reduces the number of commands necessary to write programs.

Besides shortening programs, program copy also helps ensure correctness. If the series of commands executes properly the first time through, it will also be correct when repeated with program copy command.

Keep in mind that sequence numbers (N words) are being used as statement labels whenever program copy is being used. This means that the sequence numbers specified by the P and Q word of the G25 command must exist in the program, and must be used only one time within the program. Here are some examples of when program copy can be reduced to reduce program commands.

Program copy with canned cycles. Whenever you are required to machine holes with multiple operations on a machining center, program copy can help. For example, say a workpiece required that 10 holes be center-drilled, drilled, and tapped. Without program copy, at least 30 commands would be required just to machine the holes (one command for three operations times 10 holes). With program copy, the machining commands can be reduced to about 14. Also, as long as program copy is used, if the holes are center-drilled in the correct locations, so will they be drilled and tapped.

Figure 2.33 shows the print for an example program stressing the use of program copy. In this case, 25 holes are to be center-drilled, drilled, and tapped.

Program:

O0018 (Program number)
(Center drill)
N005 G54 G90 S1200 M03 T02 (Select coordinate system, absolute mode, turn spindle on CW at 1200 RPM, get tool 2 ready)
N010 G00 X1. Y1. (Rapid over to lower left-hand hole)
N015 G43 H01 Z.1 (Rapid down to just above work surface)
N020 G81 X1. Y1. R.1 Z-.25 F3. (Center-drill first hole)
N025 Y2. (Second hole)
N030 Y3. (Third hole)
N035 Y4. (Fourth hole)
N040 Y5. (Fifth hole)

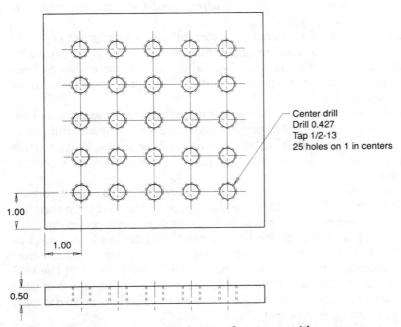

Center drill
Drill 0.427
Tap 1/2-13
25 holes on 1 in centers

1.00

1.00

0.50

Figure 2.33 Drawing for canned-cycle example program with program copy.

N045 X2. (Sixth hole)
N050 Y4. (Seventh hole)
N055 Y3. (Eighth hole)
N060 Y2. (Ninth hole)
N065 Y1. (10th hole)
N070 X3. (11th hole)
N075 Y2. (12th hole)
N080 Y3. (13th hole)
N085 Y4. (14th hole)
N090 Y5. (15th hole)
N095 X4. (16th hole)
N100 Y4. (17th hole)
N105 Y3. (18th hole)
N110 Y2. (19th hole)
N115 Y1. (20th hole)
N120 X5. (21st hole)
N125 Y2. (22nd hole)
N130 Y3. (23rd hole)
N135 Y4. (24th hole)
N140 Y5. (25th hole)
N145 G80 (Cancel cycle)
N150 G91 G28 Z0 M19 (Return to reference position, orient spindle for tool change)
N155 M01 (Optional stop)
N160 T02 M06 (Change to tool 2)
(0.427-in drill)
N165 G54 G90 S800 M03 T03 (Select coordinate system, absolute mode, turn spindle on CW at 800 RPM, get tool 3 ready)
N170 G00 X1. Y1. (Rapid back over to first hole)
N175 G43 H02 Z.1 (Rapid down to just above work surface)
N180 G81 X1. Y1. R.1 Z-.7 F4.5 (Drill first hole)
N190 G25 P025 Q145 (Repeat lines N025 through N145 to drill all holes)
N195 G91 G28 Z0 M19 (Return to reference point, orient spindle for tool change)
N200 M01 (Optional stop)
N205 T03 M06 (Change to tool 3) (½-13 tap)
N210 G54 G90 S229 M03 T01 (Select coordinate system, absolute mode, turn spindle on CW at 229 RPM, get tool 1 ready)
N215 G00 X1. Y1. (Rapid back over to first hole)
N220 G43 H03 Z.25 (Rapid down to just above part)
N225 G84 X1. Y1. R.25 Z-.75 F17.6 (Tap first hole)
N230 G25 P025 Q145 (Repeat lines N025 through N145 to tap all holes)
N240 G91 G28 Z0 M19 (Return to reference point, orient spindle for tool change)
N245 M01 (Optional stop)
N250 T01 M06 (Place tool 1 back in spindle)
N255 G91 G28 X0 Y0 (Return to reference point in *X-Y*)
N260 M30 (End of program)

The very first tool in this program (the center drill) requires all hole positions to be programmed. But after that, each tool uses the same set of coordinates as the first tool. In lines N180 and N225, notice how the cycle is established for the drill and tap *before* the G25 program copy command is given. This lets the programmer set up the canned cycle in any desired way. Then the hole coordinates are simply repeated with G25.

One minor limitation of using this technique is that the order by which holes are machined must be the same from one tool to the next.

This means each tool must make a rapid motion in X and Y back to the starting hole. In our example, this was not too detrimental to cycle time. However, the longer this distance back to the first hole, the more wasted time. For extreme cases, when cycle time is of utmost importance, it may be wise to reverse the order by which the holes are machined, minimizing the benefits gained by using program copy commands.

Using program copy with cutter radius compensation. Another helpful application of program copy is when cutter radius compensation is used to rough- and finish-mill a surface. Cutter radius compensation allows the programmer to use the same series of coordinates to finish-mill the contour that was used to rough-mill the contour. With this technique, the offset for the roughing pass must be bigger than the actual cutter radius by the amount of stock to be left for finishing. For example, if you use a 1-in roughing end mill and intend to leave 0.030-in stock for finishing, the offset for roughing must be set to 0.530 in (as long as workpiece coordinates are used in the program).

Figure 2.34 shows the drawing for an example program. Notice that we are even using arc-in and arc-out techniques to make this program more realistic.

Program:

O0019 (Program number)
(0.500-in roughing end mill)

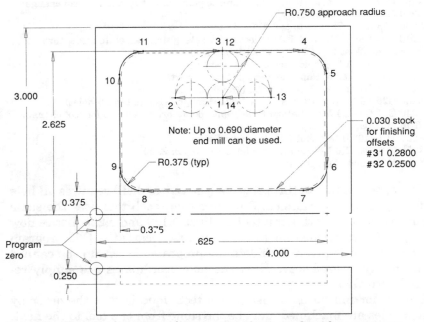

Figure 2.34   Drawing for cutter radius compensation example with program copy.

N005 G54 G90 S750 M03 T02 (Select coordinate system, absolute mode, turn spindle on CW at 750 RPM, get tool 2 ready)
N010 G00 X2. Y1.875 (Rapid to point 1)
N015 G43 H01 Z.1 (Rapid down to just above work surface)
N020 G01 Z-.245 F3.5 (Feed down to pocket bottom leaving 0.005-in stock)
N025 G42 D31 X1.25 (Instate cutter radius compensation, move to point 2, offset 31 must be set to 0.030-in more than actual cutter radius)
N030 G02 X2. Y2.625 R.75 (Arc-in to point 3)
N035 G01 X3.25 (Straight move to point 4)
N040 G02 X3.625 Y2.25 R.375 (Circular move to point 5)
N045 G01 Y.75 (Straight move to point 6)
N050 G02 X3.25 Y.375 R.375 (Circular move to point 7)
N055 G01 X.75 (Straight move to point 8)
N060 G02 X.375 Y.75 R.375 (Circular move to point 9)
N065 G01 Y2.25 (Straight move to point 10)
N070 G02 X.75 Y2.625 R.375 (Circular move to point 11)
N075 G01 X2. (Straight move to point 12)
N080 G02 X2.75 Y1.875 R.75 (Arc-out to point 13)
N085 G40 G01 X2. (Cancel cutter radius compensation on straight move to point 14)
N090 G00 Z.1 (Rapid up to above work surface)
N095 G91 G28 Z0 M19 (Return to reference point in Z, orient spindle for tool change)
N100 M01 (Optional stop)
N105 T02 M06 (Change tools)
(0.500-in finishing end mill)
N110 G54 G90 S800 M03 T01 (Select coordinate system, turn spindle on CW at 800 RPM, get tool 1 ready)
N115 G00 X2. Y1.875 (Rapid to point 1)
N120 G43 H01 Z.1 (Rapid down to just above work surface)
N125 G01 Z-.25 F3.5 (Feed down to pocket bottom)
N128 G42 D32 X1.25 (Instate cutter radius compensation, move to point 2, offset 32 must be set to the actual cutter radius)
N130 G25 P030 Q090 (Repeat lines N030 through N090 for finish-milling cutter)
N135 G91 G28 Z0 M19 (Return to reference return position, orient spindle for tool change)
N140 M01 (Optional stop)
N145 T01 M06 (Place tool 1 back in spindle)
N100 G28 X0 Y0 (Return to reference point in X and Y)
N105 M30 (End of program)

Notice how line N130 repeats the same commands used by the rough-milling cutter, keeping these commands from having to be repeated in the program. Note also that if the rough-milling cutter machines the contour correctly, and if program copy is used, the finish-milling cutter will also machine the contour correctly.

While there are other helpful techniques possible with program copy, we will stop our discussion here. Later, when we discuss subprogramming techniques, you will find more applications of how redundant commands can be repeated. Keep in mind that almost anything possible with subprogramming techniques can be accomplished with program copy and vice versa.

Handling cutter radius compensation problems

Cutter radius compensation is one of the CNC programmer's most helpful programming tools when it is correctly applied. It keeps the programmer from having to calculate the tool's centerline coordinates, it allows the easy specification of roughing commands, and it allows a variety of cutter sizes to be used. If you work with CNC machining centers, you have probably used this extremely helpful tool and know these benefits firsthand.

Yet there are many times when cutter radius compensation may not behave as expected. If not correctly programmed, the control may cause odd motions or generate alarms. We all dread cutter radius compensation alarms because they can be the most difficult alarms to diagnose and correct. In some cases, the programmer will be tempted to give up on cutter radius compensation altogether and program centerline coordinates.

While programming centerline coordinates is sometimes the fastest way around a cutter radius compensation problem, it leaves the programmer with a great deal of frustration and hesitant to use cutter radius compensation in the future. Because it can sometimes be frustrating to work with this extremely useful tool, and because so many programmers give up on it prematurely, we will give a lengthy presentation on how to handle problems with cutter radius compensation. This section will show you some of the reasons why you may have had problems with cutter radius compensation in the past. You will also see how to avoid problems with cutter radius compensation in the future.

The first point we want to make is this: there is nothing magical about how cutter compensation behaves! There are logical and understandable rules that govern how cutter compensation behaves for every CNC control. Though the rules may change slightly with the control manufacturer, *every time* cutter compensation behaves unexpectedly, there is a logical reason and solution. If you understand the basic points we make in this section, you should be able to solve most cutter radius compensation problems. Your determination will be the key factor that determines how quickly you can find and correct the problem.

The two ways to use offsets.   Before discussing possible cutter radius compensation problems, we will examine the two ways by which the cutter radius compensation offset can be used. With one method, the programmer generates the program using part surface coordinates in the program. This method often allows the programmer to use print dimensions, and is the method of choice of most manual CNC programmers. In this case, the offset used with cutter radius compensation represents the *radius* of the cutter for most CNC controls (on some controls, the diameter of the cutter input is the offset). For example, if you are using a 1-in-diameter cutter, the offset will be 0.500 in, since the radius of a 1-in cutter is 0.500 in.

With the second method, the programmer uses the cutter's centerline coordinates in the program, and bases the programmed coordinates on a planned cutter size. In this case, the tool offset will be the difference in radius from the planned cutter size to the cutter size actually being used. For example, if the program were developed for a 1-in-diameter cutter, all programmed dimensions would reflect the 0.500-in radius of the tool, and would be calculated accordingly. If a 1-in-diameter cutter is used during machining, the offset value would be zero. If a 1-in-diameter cutter is not available, the offset must reflect the difference in radius *from* the 1-in planned cutter size to the size actually being used. For example, if a 0.875-in-diameter cutter is actually used with the program, the offset would be *minus* 0.0625 in.

Generally speaking, fewer problems present themselves when the value of the tool offset used with cutter radius compensation is kept small. This is evidenced by the fact that almost all cutter radius compensation alarms do not activate if the offset value is set to zero. While this does not actually fix the problem, it does show that the cutter radius compensation problem is related to the size of the offset. The second method of assigning offsets reduces the possible problems that are encountered with cutter radius compensation because the radius offset is kept smaller. For this reason, and since CAM systems can generate cutter centerline coordinates as easily as workpiece surface coordinates, many CAM system programmers prefer to have their CNC programs created in this manner.

Since more problems occur when the offset used with cutter radius compensation is large, all examples given in this section will be related to the first method of assigning offset values, where the offset is the radius of the cutter. However, if you use the second method of assigning offsets (programming cutter centerline coordinates), the same basic rules will apply when you have problems.

How cutter radius compensation works.   Understanding how your CNC control interprets cutter compensation commands will be your first step in solving any cutter radius compensation problem. Though there are some minor differences related to how each control manufacturer internally handles cutter radius compensation, the basic points we make in this section will apply to most current CNC controls.

Using cutter radius compensation involves three basic programming steps.

1. Instate cutter radius compensation
2. Make movements to machine workpiece
3. Cancel cutter radius compensation

Cutter radius compensation is instated with a command that tells the control how to position the cutter relative to the surfaces being machined throughout its movements. Either the cutter will be positioned to the left of the surface (with a G41) or to the right of the surface (with a G42). You can easily remember G41 and G42 if you know the difference between climb milling and conventional milling. If using a right-hand cutter (spindle rotating clockwise with M03), climb milling is instated with G41 and conventional milling is instated with G42.

Once instated, the control will keep the cutter to the left or right side of a series of lines and circles generated with straight-line (G01) and circular (G02 and G03) commands. These lines and circles represent the actual surfaces being machined.

Cutter radius compensation will remain in effect until canceled. That is, the cutter will be kept on the left side or right side of all motion commands until cancellation. The command to cancel cutter radius compensation is G40.

To begin to solve any cutter radius compensation problem, you must first be able to visualize what is really happening while the cutter is making its movements around the surfaces being machined. As stated, the surfaces programmed are a series of lines and circles commanded by G01, G02, and G03 (and even G00).

Figure 2.35 shows the motions during a series of motion commands under the influence of cutter radius compensation. As you can see, each movement the control generates after cutter radius compensation is instated is based on how cutter radius compensation was instated (right or left), the size of the milling cutter (in the offset), and the coordinates used in the program. In the example in Fig. 2.35, the control is being told to keep the cutter on the left side of all programmed surfaces. The motions will be adjusted automatically. For example, in the movement to point 2, the control cuts short the motion

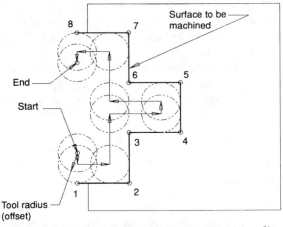

Figure 2.35 Motions under the influence of cutter radius compensation.

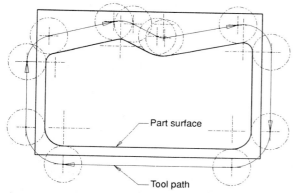

Figure 2.36   How cutter compensation can be used for very complicated contours.

by a value equal to the radius of the cutter. In the motion to point 3, the control lengthens the motion by the radius of the cutter, and so on.

Though the drawing in Fig. 2.35 illustrates only straight-line motions (G01), the same idea is true for circular motions. Also, the motions in Fig. 2.35 are quite simple, just a series of straight-line motions, each along only one axis. Figure 2.36 shows that a CNC control can just as easily compensate for the radius of the cutter even with more complex shapes involving angular and circular motions. Notice how precisely the control can generate tangency points between angular and circular movements. Indeed, this is one of the main reasons for using cutter radius compensation in the first place.

Almost all cutter radius compensation problems stem from one of two possible causes. Either the control is unable to drive the cutter through your defined motions without violating the workpiece, or the motions commanded in the program are not possible. When either of these two problems is encountered, one of two things will happen. Either the control will generate an alarm, stopping the program's execution, or the actual motions generated by the program will not be as desired. Let's start by looking at those problems that generate alarms.

Alarms and possible causes.   Most CNC controls handle cutter radius compensation problems with only a few cryptic alarms. That is, most controls do very little to help you diagnose cutter radius compensation problems. They may show you the general area of the program that is generating the alarm, but most will not even specify which command is actually causing the problem. The most common catchall alarm is the *overcutting will occur* alarm.

Diagnosing the overcutting alarm.   This alarm is the most common alarm you will receive when working with cutter radius compensation. While the actual wording for this alarm varies from one control to the next, here is a common definition: *Overcutting will occur during cutter radius compensation.* Because this alarm can be generated from a variety of problems, it is also the most difficult cutter radius compensation alarm to diagnose.

Whenever you receive this alarm, the control is trying to tell you that the cutter will violate the programmed path (and usually the workpiece) if the program is allowed to run. However, it will not point you in any direction that will help you fix the problem or even tell you how the surface is being violated. For this reason, and since it could be the result of several problems, it is one of the most feared alarms a CNC control can generate. We sympathize with this dreadful feeling.

As stated, there are several conditions that will cause this alarm. If you know them, you will be much better prepared to diagnose your specific problem. Most have to do with the size of the tool offset value as it relates to the surfaces being machined.

Insufficient clearance for the starting position.   Almost all CNC controls require that the cutter be at least a tool radius away from the surface you will be milling *before* you instate cutter radius compensation. Figure 2.37 shows this relationship. To send the tool to its approach position, centerline coordinates must be used. In this example, the value in the tool offset *must* not exceed 0.600 in (1.200-in-diameter cutter). If it does, most controls will generate the overcutting alarm. If you receive the overcutting alarm early on in the cutter's motion, this would be the first thing to check.

Offset value is too large.   *All* programs using cutter radius compensation will have limitations as to how large the cutter can be. As the cutter size grows, the control will have to keep the generated centerline coordinates for the cutter farther and farther away from the surfaces to be machined. Depending on the contour, there may be

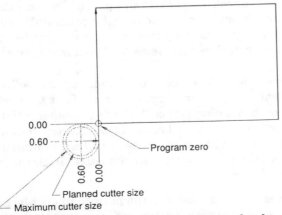

0.00

0.60

Program zero

0.60   0.00

Planned cutter size

Maximum cutter size

Figure 2.37 How the maximum cutter size is related to the starting point for cutter radius compensation.

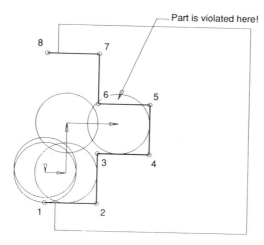

Part is violated here!

Figure 2.38 How the workpiece can be violated if offset is too large.

times when the compensated motion along one surface will actually violate another. If this happens, the control will generate the overcutting alarm *before* the violating motion occurs. Figure 2.38 demonstrates this. Notice that this is the same series of motions in Fig. 2.35, but this time the cutter size has been increased. It may not be apparent to the programmer (or operator) at the time the offset is entered that the tool to be used is too large to fit into the recess of this part. In this case, the overcutting alarm would occur.

This can be the hardest kind of cutter radius compensation problem to find, for two reasons. First, the blueprint can sometimes be very deceiving if it is not to scale. For this reason, as you attempt to solve any cutter radius compensation problem, it helps to ignore the blueprint and use only the programmed coordinates as your way of viewing the motions. If viewing the blueprint, you may be tempted to make certain assumptions about the correctness of your programmed coordinates. If you put the blueprint aside and plot coordinates *to scale* from the program, many times you will see a basic mistake related to this form of overcutting problem. You can use techniques similar to the drawing shown in Fig. 2.38, actually drawing in the exact cutter size being used.

Second, since the program will behave properly if the offset is small enough to allow the programmed motion, this overcutting problem may not present itself the first time the program is run. It is possible that the program may be run several times, then the operator may change cutter sizes (to a larger cutter), and then the overcutting problem occurs. Say, for example, the operator is using a 1-in-diameter end mill to mill a surface generated with cutter radius compensation. After several workpieces, the cutter becomes dull and has to be replaced. However, the operator finds that there are no more 1-in end mills left in stock, so a 1.25-in diameter end mill is used instead. When the offset is changed to that needed for the 1.25-in diameter end mill, an overcutting alarm may be generated since an overcutting problem may now crop up somewhere along the contour that did not occur with the smaller 1-in end mill.

Attempting to machine multiple contours in one series of motions. The biggest cutter radius compensation problem for beginners seems to be telling how much can be done with cutter radius compensation during one series of motions. You must remember that cutter radius compensation remains in effect until canceled. This means the control will continue to keep the tool on the left side or right side of *all* motions, once cutter radius compensation is instated. Beginners have the tendency to instate cutter radius compensation one time and then try to machine several separate contours without concern for the (rapid) motions from one contour to the next. While moving from one contour to the next, the control will remain under the influence of cutter radius compensation and try to compensate cutter motions accordingly. While there are times when this will work (only by coincidence or cautious planning), in most cases the motions between contours will cause the overcutting alarm. Even if no alarm is generated, unless the programmer has planned each motion carefully, the motions the control makes from one contour to the next will probably be incorrect.

When machining multiple contours, you must instate cutter radius compensation, machine with it, and finally, *cancel it*. Then go on to the next contour. Instate, machine, cancel. This must be repeated for each of the contours to be machined.

By *contour*, we mean a surface made by a series of motions while the cutter remains in contact with the work. Of course, several commands could make up one contour. However, if you have to rapid in X and Y to begin machining again, you must consider the next series of cutting motions as a separate contour.

It can sometimes be difficult to keep instating cutter radius compensation for every contour if there are many contours to be machined. But to reap the benefits of cutter radius compensation, you must adhere to its rules.

Forgetting to cancel cutter radius compensation. Once instated, cutter radius compensation *must* be canceled. One common cause for the overcutting alarm is forgetting to cancel cutter radius compensation. Because the control is still under the influence of cutter radius compensation, the subsequent motions after the contour is machined should eventually cause this alarm. However, we must warn you here. If the subsequent motions do not break the rules of cutter radius compensation (only by sheer coincidence), it is possible that the next tool (maybe a drill) will make motions still under the influence of the last tool's cutter radius compensation. In this case, some very strange things can happen. If the next tool is a drill (or any hole-machining tool), the tool will *not* go to the correct coordinates to machine the hole. This can be a very difficult problem to diagnose. In this case, you will be looking for the problem in the drill's commands. You may not see that the problem is in the previous tool!

Maximum cutter size exceeded alarm. The second common alarm with cutter radius compensation is related to the maximum cutter diameter possible with inside radii. Though the wording of the alarm varies from one control to the next, here is one popular version: Cutter diameter tool large for inside radius. This alarm has to do with circular commands when you are machining an inside radius. For inside radii, the cutter radius compensation offset value *must* be smaller than or equal to the radius to be machined. Figure 2.39 shows an example. In this case, the maximum cutter size would be 1 in in diameter.

Other limitations of cutter radius compensation. Unfortunately, there are other times when cutter radius compensation can behave poorly. In some cases, no alarm is generated, but the motions are not correct. The control may be doing its best to interpret what you want, but its interpretation of what you want does not match your actual requirement. Because the control is not generating any alarm, and because the amount of error in generated motion may be very small, it can be hard to detect this kind of problem until after a workpiece is machined. For this reason, this can be the hardest kind of cutter radius compensation problem to find and diagnose. Here are some things to watch for when using cutter radius compensation that may cause this kind of problem.

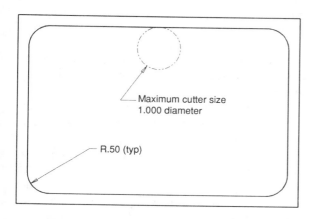

Figure 2.39 Relationship between inside radii and maximum cutter size.

Two moves in the same direction. With most CNC controls, there is a severe limitation with regard to change in motion direction. In order to compensate correctly, the CNC control requires that some detectable change in motion direction occur from one command to the next. That is, two consecutive motions in the same direction are *not* allowed. This can be frustrating, since there are times when this kind of motion is necessary. For example, say you're machining a weldment. When the tool comes close to the weld flash (the joint of the weld itself), you may want to slow the feed and speed, then continue machining the flash area. (The weld area is usually much harder than the workpiece material if the part has not been annealed.) Once the weld flash area has been cleared, you would want to increase the feed and speed to their original values and continue. These three motions could all occur along the same motion direction. With most CNC controls, the easiest way around the problem is to program centerline coordinates (not using cutter radius compensation). Unfortunately, if you must use cutter radius compensation, on most controls no change in speed and feed will be allowed since it will not be possible to make two consecutive movements in the same direction.

Note that some CNC controls allow something called *directional vectors* to be programmed within cutter radius compensation commands. With directional vectors, the programmer is allowed to point in the direction of the next movement within the current command. If your control allows directional vectors (usually P and Q words), two consecutive moves in the same direction are easily possible.

Nonmotion commands during cutter radius compensation. A CNC control is constantly looking ahead in the program to see what kind of motion is coming up next. For cutter radius compensation, this look-ahead feature allows the control to select the ending point of the current command on the basis of what it sees in the next command. The ending point for the current command will be different, depending on whether an inside intersection, outside intersection, or tangency is coming up relative to the next command.

Every CNC control has a limited look-ahead feature. The look-ahead buffer (especially for older controls) may be quite small. If nonmotion data like feeds and speeds are programmed during cutter radius compensation, the look-ahead buffer can become filled with nonpertinent data, and the control will not be able to calculate the end point of the current command correctly. What will happen in this case can be difficult to predict. While some controls will generate an alarm, others will do their best to determine what you want, but motions may not be as desired. For this reason, we recommend keeping unrelated commands away from cutter radius compensation movements.

Angles under 90°. Some CNC controls (especially older controls) do *not* allow angles of under 90° to be programmed. With this type of control, if you attempt to command a movement forming an angle under 90° (forming an inside or outside surface) while under the influence of cutter radius compensation, an alarm will be generated. Current CNC controls have no limitation related to the size of an angle that can be generated.

Reversal in motion direction.   There are times when you will be deceived during programming motions under the influence of cutter radius compensation. Look at Fig. 2.40. Notice that the slot in this workpiece is the same width as the cutter diameter. You might think that, as you write the commands for movement around this part, you could simply move to point 3 and immediately back to point 2. But reversing motion direction will *never* give you the motions you desire.

Figure 2.41 shows what will happen if a reversal in direction is programmed. Since the control will be keeping the tool on the right side of the surface programmed (in this case), the workpiece will be badly violated, yet no alarm would occur.

In this case, the programmer would need to program the motions around the contour of the slot. As long as the cutter is equal to or smaller than the slot width, the program will execute properly, generating the desired cutter path.

Hints on how to cancel cutter radius compensation.   After all cutting motions are completed, you must cancel cutter radius compensation with a G40 command. However, there are times when your last cutting motion may leave the cutter in a condition that makes you prone to error in the cancellation command. Figure 2.42 shows a series of motions generated by the program that follows.

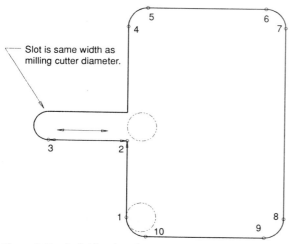

Figure 2.40   A slot having the same width as cutter diameter.

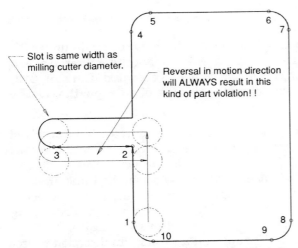

Figure 2.41 Reversal in motion direction under the influence of cutter radius compensation will generate undesired motion.

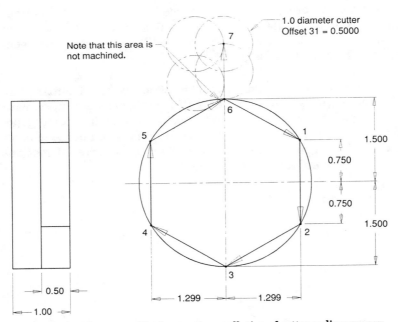

Figure 2.42 Problem caused by incorrect cancellation of cutter radius compensation.

Program:

O0020 (Program number)
N005 G54 G90 S350 M03 (Select coordinate system, turn spindle on CW at 350 RPM)
N010 G00 X0 Y2.2 (Rapid to point 7)
N015 G43 H01 Z.1 (Rapid down to just above work surface)

```
N020 G01 Z-.5 (Fast-feed to work surface)
N025 G41 D32 Y1.5 F5.0 (Feed to point 6)
N030 X1.299 Y.75 (Feed to point 1)
N035 Y-.75 (Feed to point 2)
N040 X0 Y-1.5 (Feed to point 3)
N045 X-1.299 Y-.75 (Feed to point 4)
N050 Y.75 (Feed to point 5)
N055 X0 Y1.5 (Feed to point 6)
N060 Y2.2 (Feed to point 7)
N065 G40 (Cancel cutter radius compensation)
N070 G91 G28 Z0 (Return to reference position in Z)
N075 G91 G28 X0 Y0 (Return to reference position in X-Y)
N080 M30 (End of program)
```

Notice how the last motion of the program under the influence of cutter radius compensation (movement to point 7) is a clearance movement away from the workpiece. But since the motion is still under the influence of cutter radius compensation (compensation is not canceled until line N065), the tool will continue to stay on the left side of the surface and the workpiece will not be machined correctly. There is still stock to be removed on the last surface machined, as the drawing shows.

This kind of problem can be very difficult to foresee as you prepare to write the program. Many programmers will be deceived and prepare the program as we have shown. The problem will not be obvious even during a dry run, but appears only after a workpiece has been machined (and possibly must be scrapped).

To correct this problem you must understand how the control will interpret a cancellation command (G40) within a straight-line motion command. When most controls see the G40 within a G01 motion command, they will bring the cutter's *centerline* to the line generated by the canceling G01 motion as part of the last machining motion *before* the cancellation command is executed. This is hard to visualize, so Fig. 2.43 shows the motions generated by the corrected program to follow.

Program:

```
O0021 (Program number)
N005 G54 G90 S350 M03 (Select coordinate system, turn spindle on CW at 350
RPM)
N010 G00 X0 Y2.2 (Rapid to point 7)
N015 G43 H01 Z.1 (Rapid down to just above work surface)
N020 G01 Z-.5 F30 (Fast-feed to work surface)
N025 G41 D32 Y1.5 F5.0 (Feed to point 6)
N030 X1.299 Y.75 (Feed to point 1)
N035 Y-.75 (Feed to point 2)
N040 X0 Y-1.5 (Feed to point 3)
N045 X-1.299 Y-.75 (Feed to point 4)
N050 Y.75 (Feed to point 5)
N055 X0 Y1.5 (Feed to point 6)
N060 G40 Y2.2 (Cancel compensation during feed move to point 7)
```

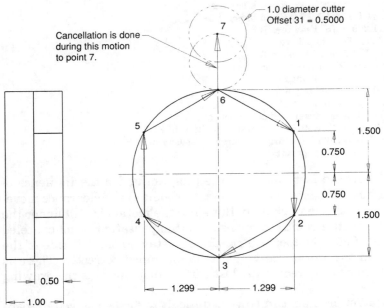

Figure 2.43   Tool path generated by corrected cutter radius compensation cancellation.

N065 G91 G28 Z0 (Return to reference position in Z)
N070 G91 G28 X0 Y0 (Return to reference position in X-Y)
N075 M30 (End of program)

Notice in line N060 that the G40 command is now included with the movement to point 7. This time, as the control looks ahead to line N060 (during the angular move in line N055), it will see the cancellation command (G40) within the next motion command. For this reason, the control will continue to bring the cutter along the angular motion commanded by line N055 until its centerline is precisely on the (vertical) line generated by N060, in effect canceling the compensation for the X axis. During the actual motion in line N060, the cutter center will move to Y2.2, and finalize the cancellation of cutter radius compensation.

As stated, this is difficult to visualize, especially before the program is actually running at the machine. But this kind of cancellation problem is a common one and one you will have to be prepared to deal with.

Conclusion to handling cutter radius compensation problems.   While we cannot hope to prepare you for every possible problem you could ever encounter with cutter radius compensation, the problem areas we have discussed should point you in the right direction for those times when problems arise. If you come across problems with cutter radius compensation that you cannot seem to solve, we encourage you to stick with it until you find the reason why cutter radius compensation is behaving poorly. If you are too quick to give up and go back to programming centerline coordinates, you will never truly master this very helpful and powerful feature.

Techniques with mirror image

One of the most commonly misunderstood features of a CNC control is mirror image. While there are limitations to the use of this feature, it is quite handy to know how to use it for those times when the need arises. In this section, we will discuss the limitations as well as possible applications for this helpful feature.

General explanation of mirror image. As the name implies, mirror image is used to generate a series of movements that represent the reflection of a programmed path. The first thing to point out with mirror image is that there is nothing magical about it. In its most basic form, only one very simple thing happens when mirror image is activated: the sign of each coordinate in the mirrored axis is reversed. For example, an X-axis coordinate of X2.0 before mirror image would be taken as X-2.0 after mirror image is turned on for the X axis. Figure 2.44 demonstrates this. Notice how the mirror image in this example is taking place about the program zero point. Keep in mind that, with

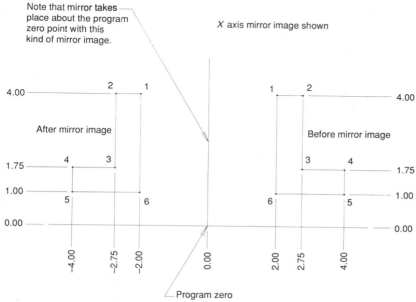

Figure 2.44 Mirror image in its simplest form.

some CNC controls, this is the only possible way to apply mirror image.

Some CNC controls will allow you to also specify the center of the mirror image in the command turning on mirror image. With this form of mirror image, more happens than a simple sign reversal. In this case, the control will take the distance from the coordinate (before mirror) to the center of mirror image into account when the calculation of the mirrored coordinate is made. Figure 2.45 shows this kind of mirror image. In this example, the X-axis is being mirrored about the X-axis position of 7 in. This is a more powerful version of mirror image, since the programmer is not limited to mirroring around only the program zero point.

Some controls that do not allow the center of mirror image to be specified in the program do still allow the programmer to mirror about a location other than program zero. With this type of control, the center of the spindle in the axis to be mirrored must be physically moved to the center of mirror image *before* mirror image can be turned on. While this technique is more cumbersome and wastes machine time, at least it allows mirror image to take place about any desired position in the mirrored axis.

Note that it is possible to mirror more than one axis at a time. Figure 2.46 shows both the X and Y axes being mirrored. In this example, we are simply mirroring about the program zero point. Though this is the case, if the control allows the center of mirror image to be specified in the program, both an X and Y center can be specified.

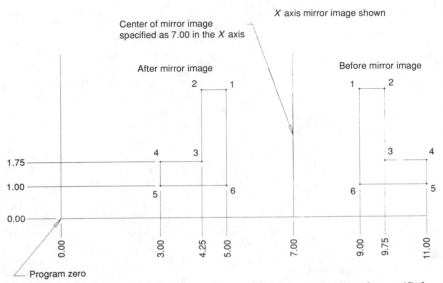

Figure 2.45   Some forms of mirror image allow center of mirror image to be specified.

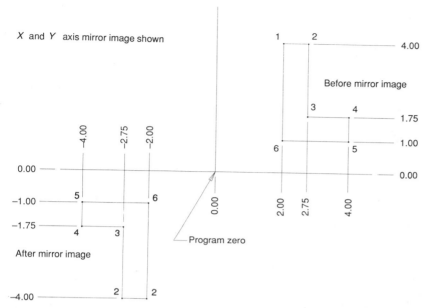

Figure 2.46 Both X and Y mirror image activated at the same time.

Applications for mirror image. For general-purpose use, mirror image applies best to machines that have the ability to contour in the X-Y plane, like machining centers and wire electric-discharge machining (EDM) equipment, though we will show two possible times when it is also useful on turning centers.

Using mirror image when machining holes. For machining centers, mirror image can be very helpful for machining holes in left-hand and right-hand workpieces. Many manufacturing companies make side frames for their products which require a left-side and a right-side frame. Depending on the side frame's applications, there are times when the right-hand and left-hand side frames are identical, except that one is the mirror image of the other. In this case, the use of mirror image would allow the same program that machines the right-hand side frame to also machine the left-hand side frame.

Figure 2.47 shows two workpieces (left hand and right hand) to be used for the following example program. Remember, this program can be used to produce both workpieces.

Program:

O0022 (Program number)
N005 G54 G90 S800 M03 (Select coordinate system, absolute mode, and turn the spindle on CW at 800 RPM)
N015 G00 X.5 Y.5 (Rapid over to lower left hole)

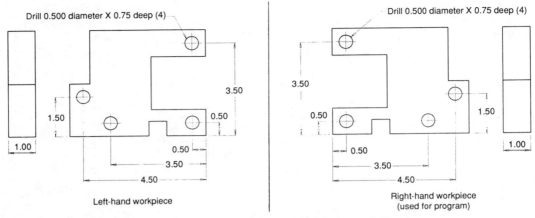

Figure 2.47 Drawing for hole-machining example program using mirror image.

N020 G43 H01 Z.1 (Rapid down to just above workpiece)
N025 G81 R.1 Z-.75 F3.5 (Drill first hole)
N030 Y3.5 (Drill upper left hole)
N035 X4.5 Y1.5 (Drill upper right hole)
N040 X3.5 Y.5 (Drill lower right hole)
N045 G80 (Cancel cycle)
N050 G91 G28 Z0 (Return to reference position in *Z*)
N055 G28 X0 Y0 (Return to reference position in *X-Y*)
N060 M30 (End of program)

When the right-hand workpiece is run, the setup will be made as usual. No special consideration must be given. As a normal part of the setup, the operator will measure the distances from program zero to the machine's reference point and inform the fixture offset (or G92 command) accordingly. Then the job can be run.

However, when the left-hand workpiece must be run, mirror image must be turned on for the *X* axis. For this kind of application, some controls require that the machine be positioned at the reference point before mirror image is turned on, since the reference position is actually the center of mirror image in this case.

Also, most CNC controls would require that the operator reverse the sign for the program zero measurement for the axis to be mirrored. For example, if fixture offsets are being used, the sign of the *X* fixture offset used to machine the right-hand part must be reversed. If it was originally minus for the right-hand workpiece, it must be changed to plus for the left-hand workpiece. This measured distance (with a reversed sign for the mirrored axis as compared to the right-hand workpiece) from the left-hand workpiece's program zero point to the machine's reference position is entered into the fixture offset (or G92 command).

Even though this example program is very simple, remember that the mirror image technique will still work with more complicated workpieces, when more machining operations must be performed.

Limitations of mirror image when milling. A severe problem exists when mirror image is used for milling operations. This problem has nothing to do with how well mirror image will perform. It is related to basic machining practice. If only one axis is mirrored (*X or Y*, not both), whatever surfaces have been milled by conventional milling techniques will switch to climb milling when mirror image is turned on (and vice versa). Figure 2.48 demonstrates this.

As you can see, the part on the right shows what will happen when the mirror image in *X* is turned off. The original program (for this right-hand workpiece) uses conventional milling techniques to mill around the contour in a generally counterclockwise direction. However, as the workpiece on the left shows, when mirror image is turned on, and the left-hand workpiece is milled, the form of milling will switch to climb milling and the general direction around the workpiece will be in a clockwise direction.

Truly, the cutter will follow the proper programmed path, and physically make an opposite-hand workpiece, but the witness marks left from conventional milling will always be different from those left by climb milling. This means the actual finish of the surface will be different from one workpiece to the other. You may also find differences

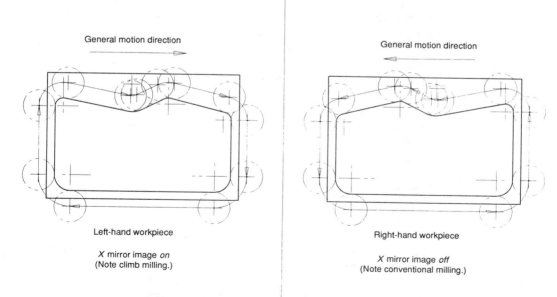

Figure 2.48 How conventional milling and climb milling become reversed when mirror image is turned on in only one axis.

in actual workpiece size from right-hand to left-hand part. If these conditions are unacceptable, the only solution to this problem is to generate two separate programs, one for the left-hand part and another for the right-hand part, and use the same climb or conventional milling technique for both.

The two ways to activate mirror image.   For most CNC controls, mirror image can be turned on manually and by programmed command (usually by a G or M code). The application determines which way you will need to do it.

Manually turning on mirror image.   Say you have 500 right-hand workpieces and 500 left-hand workpieces to run. You intend to run all of the right-hand workpieces in one setup, and then tear down the setup for the right-hand workpiece and set up to run the left-hand workpieces. In this case, there is absolutely no need to turn mirror image on in the program. To run the workpiece for which the program has been written (right *or* left hand), you measure the distance from program zero in *X, Y,* and *Z* to the reference position (as usual) and input those values into the fixture offset or G92 command. So far, there is no difference from how you would normally run any job.

However, as you make the setup to run the opposite hand, when you measure the distances from program zero to the machine's home position you *must* remember to reverse the sign for the axis you are intending to use mirror image with before you enter it into the fixture offset or G92 command. (This was discussed earlier.) Then, when you turn mirror image on manually, you will be allowed to use the same program used for the first version of the workpiece (without mirror image).

The key to making the same program work with both parts is remembering to change the sign of the axis that is being mirrored in the fixture offset or G92 command. If, for example, you intend to mirror the *X* axis, and the original sign of the *X*-axis measurement in the fixture offset is minus, this sign must be changed to plus when mirror image is turned on (note that the actual measured distances will probably be different). If you do not do this, it will be an easy problem to spot during a dry run of the program. On its first movement toward the workpiece, the machine will go the wrong way, and probably overtravel.

One more *very* important point. When turned on manually, most CNC controls will assume the center of mirror image to be the *current location* along the mirrored axis. With the above technique, you *must* turn mirror image on while the machine is resting at its reference position. If you turn on mirror image while the mirrored axis of the machine is anywhere else, the motions generated by the mirrored program will not be correct.

Turning mirror image on from within the program. There is a possibility that you will be running *both* the left-hand workpiece and the right-hand workpiece *in the same setup*. On a vertical machining center, for example, you may elect to run a left-hand workpiece on the left side of the table and a right-hand workpiece on the right side of the table. After the operator loads both workpieces, and internal to one program, you wish to machine both workpieces.

As mentioned earlier, most CNC controls have a G or M code that turns on mirror image. This command word will vary from control to control, so you must check your control's programming manual to find the words related to mirror image for your particular machine. One popular machining-center control uses G05 for X-axis mirror image, G06 for Y-axis mirror image, G07 for Z-axis mirror image (seldom used), and G09 to turn mirror image off (in all axes).

The level of power available with the commands to turn mirror image on also varies dramatically from one control to the next. Some controls only allow mirror image to be turned on and off. For these types of control, the center of mirror image will be assumed to be the current location of the mirrored axis. For example, if G05 is given to turn on X-axis mirror image, the center of mirror image would be taken as the machine's current position along the X axis. This form of mirror image can be cumbersome to use, requiring the programmer to physically move the machine to center of mirror image before mirror image can be turned on. Also, this motion to the center of mirror image is usually an extra movement that does waste cycle time.

Other controls that allow the programmer to specify the center of mirror image from within a program also allow the center of mirror image to be specified within the mirroring command. This dimension is taken from the program zero point of the program (relative to the off or canceled state of mirror image), and makes the specification of the mirror image center much easier. Also, no cycle time is wasted since there is no need to physically move the machine to the center of mirror image. With this form of mirror image command, the programmer is allowed to specify the axis position of the center of index from within the mirror image command. For example, the command

N065 G05 X-5.

tells the control to turn on mirror image for the X axis and that the center of mirror image is 5 in to the left (minus) of the program zero point.

Figure 2.49 shows a print for the right-hand workpiece to be used in the example program that follows. Figure 2.50 shows how the right-hand and left-hand workpieces will be held on the table of a vertical machining center for machining by this program. To keep from having to repeat coordinates, we are using the program-copy technique (G25) shown earlier in this section. Note that subprogramming techniques

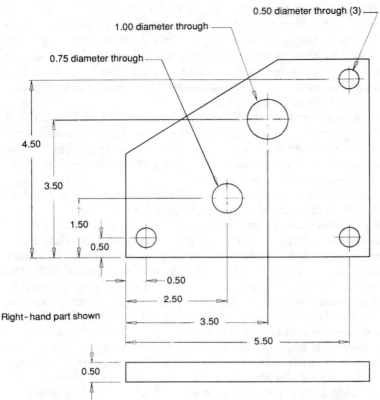

Figure 2.49 Drawing for example program demonstrating mirror image activation in a program.

could also be used to accomplish the same thing. However, without these command-repeating techniques, notice that it would be almost as difficult to use mirror image to machine these two workpieces in the same setup as it would be to program them without the use of mirror image.

Program:

O0022 (Program number)
(0.500-in drill)
N005 G54 G90 S800 M03 T02 (Select coordinate system, absolute mode, turn spindle on CW at 800 RPM, get tool 2 ready)
N010 G09 (Be sure mirror image is off)
N015 G00 X.5 Y.5 (Rapid to lower left hole)
N020 G43 H01 Z.1 (Rapid down to just above work surface)
N025 G81 X.5 Y.5 R.1 Z-.70 F4.0 (Drill lower left hole)
N030 X5.5 (Drill lower right hole)
N035 Y4.5 (Drill upper right hole)
N040 G80 (Cancel cycle)
N045 G05 X-2. (Turn on mirror image, set center 2 in to the left of rightmost workpiece)

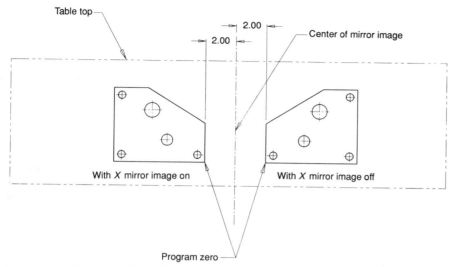

Figure 2.50 Table setup for workpiece to be machined by mirror image example program.

N050 G25 P025 Q040 (Repeat lines N025 through N040)
N055 G91 G28 Z0 M19 (Return to reference point in Z, orient spindle for tool change)
N060 M01 (Optional stop)
N065 T02 M06 (Change to tool 2)
(0.75-in drill)
N070 G54 G90 S600 M03 T03 (Select coordinate system, turn spindle on CW at 600 RPM, get tool 3 ready)
N075 G05 X-2. (Assure that mirror image is still on)
N080 G00 X2.5 Y1.5 (Rapid to hole location)
N085 G43 H02 Z.1 (Rapid down to just above work surface)
N090 G81 X2.5 Y1.5 R.1 Z-.75 F5. (Drill hole)
N095 G80 (Cancel cycle)
N100 G09 (Turn off mirror image)
N105 G25 P090 Q095 (Repeat lines N090 through N095)
N110 G91 G28 Z0 M19 (Return to reference position in Z, orient spindle for tool change)
N115 M01 (Optional stop)
N120 T03 M06 (Change to tool 3)
(1.00-in drill)
N125 G54 G90 S350 M03 T01 (Select coordinate system, absolute mode, turn spindle on CW at 350 RPM, get tool 1 ready)
N130 G09 (Assure that mirror image is turned off)
N135 G00 X3.5 Y3.5 (Rapid to hole location)
N140 G43 H03 Z.1 (Rapid down to just above work surface)
N145 G81 X3.5 Y3.5 R.1 Z-.8 F6.5 (Drill hole)
N150 G80 (Cancel canned cycle)
N155 G05 X-2. (Turn on mirror image, set center 2 in to the left of rightmost workpiece)
N160 G25 P145 Q150 (Repeat lines N145 through N150)
N165 G09 (Cancel mirror image)
N170 G91 G28 Z0 M19 (Return to reference position in Z, orient spindle for tool change)

N175 M01 (Optional stop)
N180 T01 M06 (Change tools)
N185 G91 G28 X0 Y0 (Return to reference point in *X-Y*)
N190 M30 (End of program)

As you study this program, the techniques shown will become clear. You should be able to see from this example that mirror image does not help a great deal when activated in the program. It is *much* more helpful when one entire part is machined at a time (as shown earlier).

In lines N010, N075, and N130, you may be wondering why we included the current status of the mirror image. These commands are required to assure that the current state of mirror image will be known should the operator wish to rerun only one of the tools. For example, if the operator must rerun only tool 2, mirror image must be on before any motion occurs.

Warning about mirror image. As you have seen, though mirror image has its limitations, it can be a very helpful programming tool. However, when mirror image is not desired, if it is unintentionally turned on (without the operator's knowledge), the machine will behave unexpectedly. When mirror image is on for any axis, motions along that axis will be reversed.

For example, if a tool has been commanded to go in the plus direction, but instead it is going minus, mirror image has somehow been turned on for the axis moving the wrong way. It is possible that the programmer meant to use a G60 in the program (possibly to select single-direction positioning mode), but instead typed G06 by mistake (mirror image on in *Y*). When this command is activated, mirror image will come on in the *Y* axis and stay on until it is canceled. It is likely that neither the programmer nor the operator will notice it. This kind of problem can be very frustrating to diagnose and can sometimes take hours to find.

Some machine-tool builders place an indicator light on the control panel to alert you to when mirror image is on for each axis. This light would be very helpful in the above example, for without the indicator light, the operator could waste a great deal of time trying to figure out why the machine is moving in the wrong direction.

Turning-center applications for mirror image. Most programmers would never consider using mirror image on a turning center. There just aren't any general-purpose applications that come to mind. But there are two special cases when knowing the effects of mirror image in the *X* axis on a turning center can really help.

Making turning centers compatible. Almost all turning-center manufacturers specify plus and minus for the *X* axis in a manner corresponding to diameter. That is, the larger the diameter, the more plus the position. For this type of machine, as a part is being faced to center, the X axis is moving minus. A diameter of 3 in would be specified by the X word:

X3.0

By far, this is the most popular method used to designate plus and minus for turning centers.

However, there are some turning-center manufacturers who reverse the X axis. That is, for this kind of machine, as a workpiece is being faced to center, the X axis is going plus. A diameter of 3 in for this kind of machine would be specified as

X-3.0

If the X axis has been reversed for the turning center, there are other things that reverse as well. The way you evaluate circular commands (G02 and G03, as discussed much earlier in this chapter) and the way you evaluate tool nose radius compensation (G41 and G42) also change. On a turning center which has the X axis reversed, G02 is *counter*clockwise and G03 is clockwise. G41 is tool right, G42 is tool left. How the operator sets tool offsets is also reversed. If an outside-diameter turning tool is cutting a diameter too large, the offset must be made bigger.

If you only have one turning center, and if you have learned how to interpret the X axis (no matter which way the X axis is situated), you will never run into a compatibility problem. But if your company owns two or more turning centers, and if one or more of the machines has the X axis reversed from the others, compatibility becomes much more important. It can be very difficult indeed to program and work with both methods.

In this case, mirror image can help. To make the turning centers compatible with regard to the X axis, simply turn mirror image in X on for those machines you wish to switch. For example, if you want all machines to have the X axis direction set so that facing to center is minus, turn mirror image on in the X axis for those machines that have the X axis reversed. From that point on, all functions of the X axis will be compatible, including X-axis direction, circular commands, tool nose radius compensation, and offset setting.

To turn mirror image on, most turning-center controls allow you to do so through the control screen manually. Mirror image turned on in this manner is usually permanent; you will have to do it only once.

Two turrets on the same cross-slide. While today's turning centers are trending toward a slanted bed configuration, there are still turning centers being used that resemble engine lathes. That is, the bed of the machine is flat and a cross-slide that is mounted on top of the bed controls the X axis.

One common configuration for this kind of machine has two (four-position) turrets mounted on the same cross-slide, one on the front side and one on the back side. Though only one of these turrets can be machining at a time, this configuration doubles the number of tools the machine can hold.

When the front turret is programmed, the X axis plus and minus directions are like those of a normal turning center. That is, when facing a workpiece to center, the tool is moving in the minus direction on the X axis. However, when the back turret is programmed, the X axis is reversed (as is the way you interpret circular commands, tool nose radius compensation, and offset setting).

This reversal of the X axis makes programming the back turret rather difficult. The use of X-axis mirror image in programming the back turret will allow the front-turret and back-turret programming method to be the same.

Coordinate system shifting

The coordinates going into each program you write are taken from a logical location, called the *program zero point*. The wise selection of your program zero point can make calculating the coordinates needed for your program much easier. In many cases, if the program zero point is well-selected, most program coordinates can be taken right from the print, eliminating calculations altogether.

For the majority of applications, once the program zero point is located, *all* dimensions for the program are simply taken from this one location, therefore this method is sufficient. However, there are times when it is helpful to be able to shift the program zero point, which in effect, shifts the entire coordinate system.

Fixture offsets. One time when it is helpful to use more than one coordinate system is when you are working with machining centers. For example, if you must machine two or more workpieces in the same setup on a vertical machining center, it will be helpful to assign one program zero point for each workpiece. If you must machine more than one side of the same workpiece with the help of a rotary device (indexer or rotary axis), having the ability to assign multiple program zero points will also help.

Most current machining-center controls have a standard feature called *fixture offsets* which allows the assignment of multiple program zero points. While the number of fixture offsets available varies from one control to the next, one popular control comes standard with six fixture offsets (and more can be purchased as an option). Here we intend to discuss applications for this helpful programming feature.

Two ways to assign fixture offsets. How fixture offsets are assigned varies from one control to the next. In all cases, the control must be told where each program zero point is located by one means or another. With one popular method, the operator measures the distances from the machine's reference position to each fixture offset in each axis. These measured values are then entered into the corresponding fixture offset. Figure 2.51 shows this method of inputting fixture offsets. Note that most controls require the distance *from* the reference position *to* each program zero point. As the figure shows, this means all values will be minus, usually.

This method is most helpful when the workpieces have no known relationship from one to the next. For example, if the workpieces are held in vises, and if the vises are simply placed on the table in convenient locations, the operator will have no idea as to precisely how far it is from one vise to the next. A measurement in each axis must be taken for each vise.

Another popular method of inputting fixture offsets requires the operator to measure the distance from the machine's reference position to one (the base) program zero point. Each fixture offset is then taken from this base position. Figure 2.52 shows this method.

This method of inputting fixture offsets is helpful when the distance from one program zero point to the next is known. For example, if one fixture is used to hold the workpieces to be machined, or if a fixture subplate is used to hold vises, the dimensions from one workpiece to the next may be right on the fixture drawing.

When fixture offsets are used to assign multiple program zero points, the operator must, of course, enter each set of fixture offset measured values as shown in Fig. 2.51 or 2.52. Note that if the method

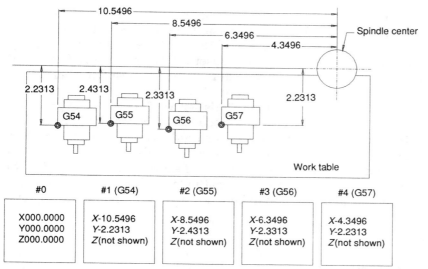

Figure 2.51 Method of assigning all fixture offsets from the machine's reference position.

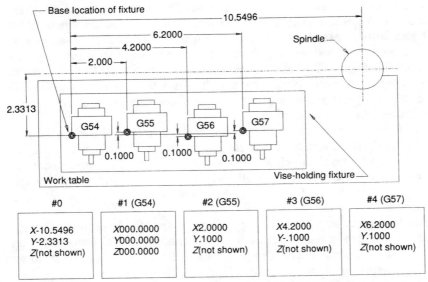

Figure 2.52 Method of assigning fixture offsets from a base location.

shown in Fig. 2.51 is used, the operator must make several measurements for the setup [at least three measurements (*X*, *Y*, and *Z*) per program zero point]. This could be considered the one negative side to using this very helpful programming tool. While programming becomes much easier, setting up becomes slightly more difficult.

Programming with fixture offsets. A series of G codes are used to instate the desired fixture offset. Most machining center controls use the series of G codes from G54 through G59 to instate fixture offsets numbered 1 through 6 (G54 for fixture offset 1, G55 for fixture offset 2, and so on). The various coordinate system numbers as well as their corresponding G codes are shown in Figs. 2.51 and 2.52.

To instate a fixture offset with this series of G codes, the programmer simply includes the desired G code (G54 through G59) in or before the first motion command needed within the coordinate system. That is, any motion commands in the absolute mode will utilize the currently instated fixture offset. Figure 2.53 shows a simple workpiece to be used for the example program that follows. Figure 2.54 shows how two of these workpieces are to be machined in the same setup by one program.

Program:

O0023 (Program number)
(Center drill)
N005 G54 G90 S1200 M03 T02 (Select coordinate system, absolute mode, turn spindle on CW at 1200 RPM, get tool 2 ready)

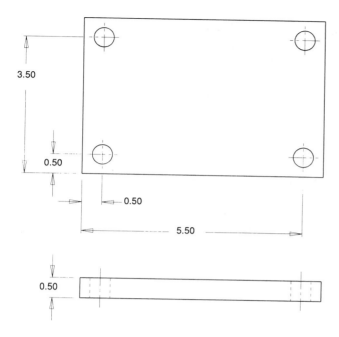

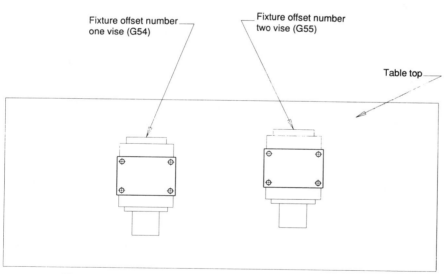

Figure 2.54 How two workpieces are held in the setup for fixture offset example program.

N010 G00 X.5 Y.5 (Rapid to lower left hole relative to fixture offset 1)
N015 G43 H01 Z.1 (Rapid down to just above work surface)
N020 G81 R.1 Z-.25 F4. (Center-drill lower left hole of left part)
N025 Y3.5 (Center-drill upper left hole of left part)
N030 X5.5 (Center-drill upper right hole of left part)

N035 Y.5 (Center-drill lower right hole of left part)
N040 G55 X.5 Y.5 (Center-drill lower left hole of right part, note G55)
N045 Y3.5 (Center-drill upper left hole of right part)
N050 X5.5 (Center-drill upper right hole of right part)
N055 Y.5 (Center-drill lower left hole of right part)
N060 G80 (Cancel cycle)
N065 G91 G28 Z0 M19 (Return to reference position in the Z axis, orient spindle for tool change)
N070 M01 (Optional stop)
N075 T02 M06 (Change tools)
N0080 G55 G90 S550 M03 T01 (Select coordinate system, absolute mode, turn spindle on CW at 550 RPM, get tool 1 ready)
N085 G00 X5.5 Y.5 (Rapid over to lower right hole of right part)
N090 G43 H02 Z.1 (Rapid down to just above work surface)
N095 G81 R.1 Z-.7 F4.5 (Drill lower right hole of right part)
N100 Y3.5 (Drill upper right hole of right part)
N105 X.5 (Drill upper left hole of right part)
N110 Y.5 (Drill lower left hole of right part)
N115 G54 X5.5 Y.5 (Drill lower right hole of left part, note G54)
N120 Y3.5 (Drill upper right hole of left part)
N125 X.5 (Drill upper left hole of left part)
N130 Y.5 (Drill lower left hole of left part)
N135 G80 (Cancel cycle)
N140 G91 G28 Z0 M19 (Return to reference position in the Z axis, orient spindle for tool change)
N145 M01 (Optional stop)
N150 T01 M06 (Change tools)
N155 G91 G28 X0 Y0 (Return to reference position in X-Y)
N160 M30 (End of program)

Though this program is very simple, machining two identical workpieces, it stresses how fixture offsets can be used to assign multiple-program zero points. Note how easy it is to change from one coordinate system to another. The above program even does so within a canned cycle (G81).

Keep in mind that the workpieces being machined do *not* have to be identical to use this method. Truly, any combination of workpieces can be machined as long as the program is written accordingly.

Also note that it is necessary to include the proper fixture-offset G code at the very beginning of each tool's use. Especially when using more than one coordinate system, the control must know which one to use for positioning movements. This word in each tool's start-up format (G54–G59) assures that the control will use the proper fixture offset even when the operator picks up in the middle of the program, and runs from the beginning of a tool.

Watch out for the Z axis! The simple example program shown above machines two identical workpieces held in two identical vises. It just so happens that the surface being machined in both workpieces is at the same Z location. This means the program can rapid from one workpiece to the other without concern for interference in the Z axis.

If the tool clears one workpiece in the Z axis, it will clear the other. This, however, will not always be the case.

There will be times when the surfaces you expect to machine (in Z) will *not* be the same for all the workpieces on the table. If for example, one of our workpieces is 0.500 in thick while another is 0.750 in thick, you would have to be careful when moving from the thinner workpiece to the thicker workpiece. You would have to be sure that the tool came up high enough to clear the 0.750-in-thick workpiece *before* you position the tool to any coordinate above the thick workpiece. For some controls this may mean breaking out of the canned cycle in order to clear the thicker workpiece. If you are not careful in this regard, the tool will crash into the 0.750-in-thick workpiece. Of course, when going from above the thicker workpiece to the thinner one, this problem does not exist.

How tool length compensation affects fixture offsets.   There are two popular methods for coming up with offsets used with tool length compensation. Most companies will use one method or the other for all of their CNC machining centers. With one method, the value stored in the offset is the *length* of the tool. (This is our recommended method.) With the other method, the distance *from* the tip of the tool while the machine is resting at its Z-axis reference position *to* the program zero point is stored as the tool offset. Figure 2.55 shows both methods.

How each fixture offset Z value for each coordinate system is determined varies according to which tool length compensation offsets are stored and how fixture offsets are being assigned. There are four possibilities (two methods of storing offsets times two ways of assigning fixture offsets). Here are the possibilities and instructions on how to assign the fixture offset Z:

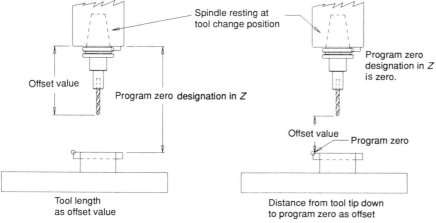

Figure 2.55   Two popular ways to apply offsets for tool length compensation.

1. If you store the length of the tool in the tool length compensation offset (our suggested method) and if you are assigning fixture offsets as shown in Fig. 2.51, the Z-axis value for each fixture offset will be the distance *from* the spindle nose *to* the program zero point (as the left drawing of Fig. 2.55 depicts). With this method, the operator will make similar Z-axis measurements to determine the Z-axis designation for all fixture offsets being used within the program.

2. If the length of the tool is stored as the offset used for tool length compensation (our recommended method) and you assign fixture offsets as shown in Fig. 2.52, the operator measures the Z-axis distance *from* the nose of the spindle while the machine is resting at its reference position *to* the Z surface used for the *base* fixture offset (shown in Fig. 2.52 as #0). This value is entered into the Z position of the base fixture offset. From this point, the distance *from* the base fixture offset *to* each fixture offset used in the program is measured and stored in each fixture offset Z designation. Plus and minus for these values must be considered; thus, if a surface is above the base fixture offset surface, its fixture offset Z value will be plus.

3. If you are storing the distance from the tip of the tool to program zero as the offset value used with tool length compensation and assigning fixture offsets as shown in Fig. 2.51, you must touch the tip of each tool to one of the program zero points in Z (it does not matter which one). For whichever workpiece you use for this purpose, its corresponding fixture-offset Z value will be zero. For every other fixture-offset Z value, you must store the distance *from* this first fixture offset Z position *to* each subsequent fixture offset you use. Plus and minus for these values must be considered.

4. If you are using the distance from the tip of the tool to program zero as the offset for tool length compensation and assigning fixture offsets as shown in Fig. 2.52, each tool tip must be touched to the Z surface used as the base fixture offset. The distance from the tip of the tool while the machine is resting at its Z-axis reference position to this surface in Z is stored as the offset for tool length compensation. For each fixture offset, the distance in Z *from* the base fixture offset *to* each fixture offset must be stored as each fixture offset's Z value.

All of this may sound a little confusing. To keep it as simple as possible, we strongly recommend that you use the first situation discussed. With this method, the tool's length is stored as the tool-length compensation offset value, and the operator measures the distance from the nose of the spindle to each program zero position in Z. Since all measurements remain consistent from one fixture offset to the next, the operator will be less likely to make mistakes.

Shifting the coordinate system of a turning center.   Though shifting coordinate systems is not as popular a method as it is for machining-center applications, there are times when it is helpful with a turning center. The program zero point selected by the programmer is, from the programmer's viewpoint, the most convenient position on the workpiece from which to work. Normally, the programmer will base the program zero point on the location on the workpiece from which most (or all) dimensions are taken.

In the Z axis, since many drawings for turned workpieces show dimensions coming from the very end of the workpiece being machined, this surface is a very popular location for the program zero point in Z.

In the X axis, the center of the workpiece is chosen as the program zero point in all cases. Figure 2.56 shows this popular location for program zero on a workpiece being held in the turning center.

Though this location is a very convenient one from which to work from the programmer's viewpoint, when it comes to setting up it is not so convenient for the operator or setup person. It is very likely that the workpiece's overall length will change from one setup to the next. For example, the workpiece being machined may be 4.500 in long, but the workpiece to be run in the next setup may be 5.500 in long.

When an operator or setup person makes a setup for a turning center, the control is told the location of program zero for *every tool* being used in the program. Since the cutting edge of each tool will vary dra-

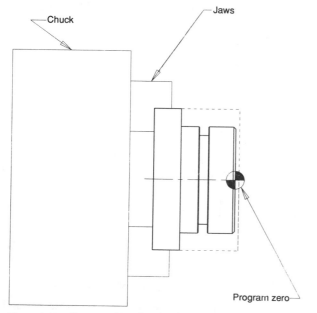

Figure 2.56   Common location for the program zero point for a turning-center program.

matically from one tool to the next on most turning centers, this means measurements must be made for *every tool* used in the setup. Though specific techniques vary from one turning center to the next, these measurements are made to come up with the distances in X and Z from the program zero point to the tip of the tool while the machine is resting at its reference position.

If the length of the workpiece changes from one setup to the next, as it almost always will, a measurement (in Z) must be made to determine the program zero point for *each tool* in each new setup. A measurement must even be made for those tools remaining in the turret that were used in the previous setup. This requires tedious and error-prone measurements to be repeated for every tool in every setup. Of course, this extra effort causes wasted setup time in every setup.

Shifting the Z axis. This feature (equipped on most current turning centers) lets the programmer work from the end of the workpiece (as shown in Fig. 2.56), yet gives the operator a more consistent Z surface from which to work. The operator will measure the distance from the fixed location to the tip of each tool while the machine is resting at its reference point. It will be as if the fixed Z surface is the program's zero point.

The coordinate system will then be shifted in the Z axis by the distance from the fixed position to the program zero point. Figure 2.57 shows an example.

In this case, the location marked as program zero in Fig. 2.57 is the Z surface the operator will use to touch all tools in Z. The distance

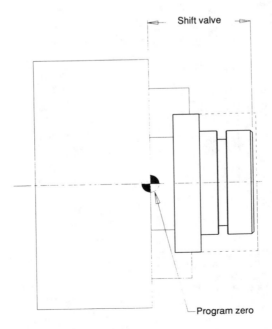

Shift valve

Program zero

Figure 2.57 How program zero can be assigned at a fixed position and the coordinate system can be shifted.

from the end of the workpiece to the program zero point is entered as the shift value. Once the shift value is entered through the control screen, the coordinate system will be in synchronism with the program.

If you are working with a turning center that has a three-jaw chuck or collet chuck, the face of the chuck makes an excellent fixed location in the Z axis. In this example, the setup person will measure the distance from the face of the chuck to the tip of *all* tools used in *all* setups. When going from setup to setup, this means no measurement will be needed for those tools used in the previous setup.

The setup person then informs the control as to the shift amount. For some controls, this technique is identical to the previous discussion of fixture offsets on a machining center. On other controls, there will be a special shift page that comes up on the display screen. Though the physical techniques vary from one control to the next, once this value is input, all coordinates used in the program will be manipulated by the shift amount, putting the program back in sync with the setup.

The coordinate system shifting technique allows the best of both worlds. Programming remains as simple as possible, since the programmer can come up with the best location from which coordinates will be taken for the program. Operation remains simple and efficient, since the setup person will be working from a common touch-off point for all tools used in all programs.

Single-direction positioning

All forms of CNC equipment will experience wear and tear, even with normal use. As the axes move back and forth, the ways of the CNC machine are constantly being rubbed, and wear is constant. While the CNC machine is designed to combat this kind of wear, as time goes on, the machine will develop noticeable backlash. Backlash is the amount of nonmovement that occurs during a reversal in axis direction. For example, if a machining center has 0.0005-in backlash in its X axis, whenever the X axis reverses direction (going from plus to minus, for example), the motion in the reversed direction will be 0.0005 in shorter than commanded. As the amount of backlash becomes larger, the machine tool will lose accuracy, and will not be as rigid during machining operations.

Backlash compensation. Most current CNC machines have a control feature called *backlash compensation*. With this feature, once the control is told how much backlash exists in a particular axis, the control will add this amount to any axis reversal movement. For positioning (noncutting) movements, this may be acceptable, but the rigidity of an axis that is experiencing backlash will be poor. Generally speaking, backlash compensation will help only when the amount of backlash is

very small. Excessive backlash must be corrected by physical mainte-
nance on the machine tool.

Using single-direction positioning to correct for backlash. If your machining center is experiencing backlash in the X and/or Y axis, and if
you must machine holes at critical X-Y locations within a close tolerance, the backlash may cause your holes to be out of the tolerance
band. Knowing this, you can use the single-direction positioning technique to assure that backlash will not affect the motion to the hole
location in X and Y.

If you ensure that the X and Y axes always approach the hole location from the same direction, you can rest assured that backlash will
not affect your hole location. Figure 2.58 shows an example of these
movements.

In this case, the tool always approaches the hole location from the X
minus and Y minus side. However, approaching the hole locations
from any direction consistently will have the same effect. When deciding on the direction from which to approach, it is wise to take into consideration the machine's natural tendencies. For example, on a horizontal machining center, the machine's natural tendency for the Y
axis is to drop or fall in the negative direction, because of the weight of
the machine's headstock. In this case, it is best to make the single-
direction approach from the Y minus side.

To manually program the machine to move to these approach posi-

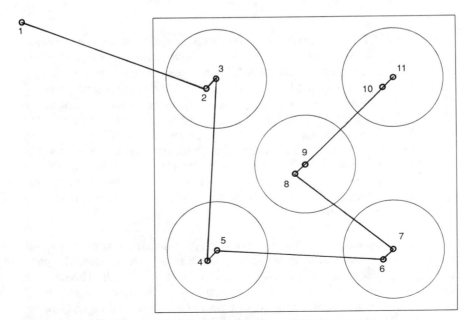

Figure 2.58 Motions commanded by single-direction positioning techniques.

tions with G00 can be somewhat tedious. For this reason, many control manufacturers give you a preparatory function (G word) called *single-direction positioning*. One popular control uses a G60 for this purpose. Once the G60 is instated, the control will always approach an ending position from the same direction in *X* and *Y*. The actual direction the control will use to make each approach is usually set by the control builder at the factory. It can normally be changed, either by programmed command or through the control's set of parameters. A G64 is used to cancel this modal command and return the control to normal movement.

Hints for using hole-machining canned cycles

For machining-center application, canned cycles allow one complete hole to be machined per command. Machining multiple holes is as simple as listing the *X-Y* coordinates for the holes to be machined. The hole can be machined by a variety of techniques, including drilling, tapping, boring, counterboring, and reaming. Though more commonly equipped on machining-center controls, this series of canned cycles is also found on some turning-center controls. Each cycle type performs slightly differently, but the actual programming format for each kind of cycle remains quite consistent.

Before we discuss some rather advanced implications of how to use canned cycles, let's first look at the programming words involved on one popular CNC control. For this particular control, here is a list of the canned-cycle types and the corresponding G codes:

G73 Chip-breaking drilling cycle (breaks chips)

G74 Left-hand tapping cycle

G76 Fine boring cycle (leaves no drag line in hole)

G80 Cancel canned-cycle command

G81 Standard drilling cycle

G82 Counterboring cycle

G83 Deep-hole drilling cycle (clears chips)

G84 Right-hand tapping cycle

G85 Reaming cycle

G86 Standard boring cycle

Now, here is a list of the programming words used with canned cycles. These words mean essentially the same thing with all canned cycles, so that once you know their meaning in one, you will know how they function in all. Note that some of these words are required only with certain canned cycles.

Word	Cycle	Meaning
X-Y	All cycles	Specifies the hole center coordinate
R	All cycles	Specifies rapid plan position above work surface in Z
Z	All cycles	Specifies hole bottom position in Z
F	All cycles	Feed rate for machining
L	All cycles	Number of holes to machine (if left out of the canned-cycle command, one hole will be machined)
Q	G73, G83	Feed-in amount per peck
I-J	G76 only	Specifies move-over direction and amount at hole bottom
P	G82 only	Pause time at hole bottom
G98	All cycles	Rapid out of the hole to the initial plane
G99	All cycles	Rapid out of the hole to the R plane

If you work with machining centers and perform hole-machining operations, you are probably quite familiar with the various hole-machining canned cycles as they are used on your particular control. However, here we will show you some new twists on their usage.

Canned-cycle modal warning.   Since canned cycles are modal, they will remain in effect until canceled. This means that a hole will be machined in *every* command, regardless of whether there is a coordinate position included in the command. This can lead to some strange machine movements if you do not understand what is going on. It is possible that a hole will be machined twice (or more) if you are not careful. For example, the following program includes a mistake in this regard:

```
O0024 (Program number)
N005 G54 G90 S500 M03 (Select coordinate system, absolute mode, turn spindle on CW at 500 RPM)
N010 G00 X.5 Y.5 (Rapid to first hole location)
N015 G43 H01 Z.1 (Rapid down to just above work surface)
N020 G81 R.1 Z-.85 F5. (Drill first hole)
N025 Y2.5 (Drill second hole)
N030 S550 (Change spindle speed to 550 RPM)
N035 X4.5 (Drill third hole)
N040 Y.5 (Drill fourth hole)
N045 G80 (Cancel canned cycle)
N050 G91 G28 Z0 (Return to reference position in Z)
N055 G91 G28 X0 Y0 (Return to reference position in X-Y)
N060 M30 (End of program)
```

Notice the spindle speed change in line N030. Possibly this workpiece is made from two different materials, the left side of the workpiece requiring one spindle speed and the right side requiring another. Though the spindle speed change may be required, it will cause a peculiar hole-machining motion. The hole commanded in line N025 (X.5 Y2.5) will be machined twice. This is because the canned cycle is modal, and will machine a hole in *every* command. In this particular example, probably the S550 command could easily be moved into the next command to fix this problem. However, there may be times when you must break out of the canned cycle (cancel it with G80), before you have the machine do some function not related to canned cycles, to avoid machining a hole more than once.

One other problem related to the fact that canned cycles are modal has to do with physically skipping lines in the program. Some programmers like to make their programs more readable by allowing extra space at certain places in the program. For example, the programmer may elect to skip two spaces at the beginning of each tool, making it easier to spot each tool's beginning. This is done by including an end-of-block (EOB) command on a line by itself.

In most cases, when the control reads an end of block on a line by itself, it will simply skip the command. However, if the control reads and executes an end-of-block command in a line by itself during the execution of a canned cycle, it will machine another hole at the same *X-Y* location as the last hole, meaning two holes will be drilled in the same location.

Using polar coordinates to specify hole locations.   The rectangular coordinate system is but one of the ways to specify coordinate locations for a CNC program. Since it is so universally accepted as the best coordinate system for most CNC applications (because it matches the method of dimensioning techniques used by most design engineers), you may not even know about other coordinate system possibilities.

There are times, however, when dimensions given on the print do not conform to the rectangular coordinate system. Figure 2.59 shows an example.

It would be better if the design engineer would dimension coordinates in the rectangular coordinate system. In the drawing shown in Fig. 2.59, *everyone* working with this print, including the programmer, operator, setup person, and inspector would have to use trigonometry to come up with the coordinates for the holes on the bolt hole circle. This opens the door to mistakes on everyone's part.

Unfortunately, this is the way many design engineers still dimension bolt-hole patterns for the drawings they make. While most manual programmers simply use trigonometry to calculate the center coordinates and continue to use the rectangular coordinate system, most current controls offer a feature called polar coordinates that makes the specification of hole locations in a bolt-hole circle much easier. For the drawing shown in Fig. 2.59, if the polar-coordinates feature is used, the programmer can still use print dimensions to specify the hole locations.

As we give an example, keep in mind that there is quite a difference from one control to the next as to how polar coordinates are programmed. You must check in your control's programming manual to find the specific words related to your particular control.

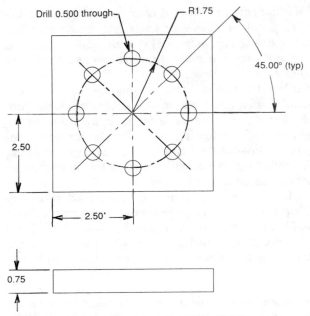

Figure 2.59 Example of when rectangular coordinates are not used for dimensioning purposes.

One popular control uses a G16 to instate the polar-coordinates mode of programming. G15 is used to cancel polar coordinates (return to the rectangular-coordinate system). From the point where the G16 is executed, the control will assume all coordinate values to be polar. Included in the actual motion command will be the center of the rotation, the radius, and the angle at which the desired coordinate is located. With the control used for our example program, when the polar-coordinates mode is instated, the X and Y represent the center of rotation (in rectangular coordinates). The radius is specified by a U word, and the angle is specified by an A word. For example, the commands

```
N050 G16 (Instate polar-coordinates mode)
N055 G00 X2.5 Y2.5 U1.75 A45. (Motion command with polar)
N060 G15 (Cancel polar-coordinates mode)
```

would specify that the tool would move over to the upper right-hand hole in Fig. 2.59.

Once polar coordinates are instated, they will remain in effect until canceled (as shown in line N060 in the example above).

Using polar coordinates with canned cycles. The most popular use for polar coordinates is with hole-machining canned cycles when bolt-hole patterns are specified as in Fig. 2.59. When polar coordinates are used with canned cycles, no trigonometry is needed to calculate hole positions. The programmer can simply specify dimensions right from the print. Here is a program to drill the 0.500-in holes shown in Fig. 2.59:

Program:

```
O0025 (Program number)
N005 G54 G90 S500 M03 (Select coordinate system, absolute mode, turn spindle on
CW at 500 RPM)
N050 G00 X2.5 Y2.5 (Rapid over to workpiece in X-Y)
N055 G43 H01 Z.1 (Rapid down to just above work surface)
N060 G16 (Instate polar coordinates mode)
N065 G81 X2.5 Y2.5 U1.75 A0 R.1 Z-.85 F5. (Drill first hole)
N070 A45. (Drill second hole)
N075 A90. (Drill third hole)
N080 A135. (Drill fourth hole)
N085 A180. (Drill fifth hole)
N090 A225. (Drill sixth hole)
N095 A270. (Drill seventh hole)
N100 A315. (Drill eighth hole)
N105 G80 G15 (Cancel canned cycle and polar-coordinates mode)
N110 G91 G28 Z0 (Return to reference position in Z)
N115 G91 G28 X0 Y0 (Return to reference position in X-Y)
N1120 M30 (End of program)
```

With most current controls, the words involved with polar coordinates (X, Y, U, and A in our example) are also modal. This means they can be left out of subsequent commands if they do not change. As you can see in the above example, once the first hole of the bolt-hole circle is completely described in line N065, all that changes from that point is the angle for each subsequent hole. This means only the A word is required in each subsequent hole-machining command to specify the new angular hole position on the bolt-hole circle.

Using canned cycles in the incremental mode.   Though we normally recommend programming exclusively in the absolute mode, there is one canned-cycle-related technique requiring incremental programming that can dramatically reduce the number of commands in a program. This technique is available on most current CNC machining-center controls.

When evenly spaced holes must be programmed, one command can machine any number of evenly spaced holes along a line. Before we can show an example, we must discuss how the various canned-cycle words are handled when you work in the incremental mode (incremental mode is specified by G91 on most controls).

In the incremental mode, X and Y are the distances from the current position to the hole center. R is the distance from the current position in Z down to the rapid plane. Z is the distance from the rapid (R) plane to the hole bottom. L is the number of holes to machine. All other canned-cycle words (G98, G99, P, Q, F, I, and J) mean exactly the same thing as in the absolute mode.

Figure 2.60 shows a series of holes along the X axis. Here is a short

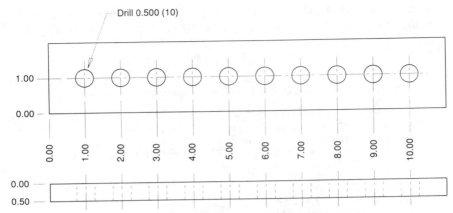

Figure 2.60   Drawing for first incremental canned-cycle example program.

program that shows how all holes can be machined in one command:

Program:

```
O0026 (Program number)
N005 G54 G90 S500 M03 (Select coordinate system, absolute mode, turn spindle on
CW at 500 RPM)
N010 G00 X0 Y1. (Move to the left of first hole location by the distance between
the holes)
N015 G43 H01 Z.1 (Rapid down to just above work surface)
N020 G91 (Select incremental mode)
N025 G81 X1. R0 Z-.75 F5. L10 (Drill all 10 holes)
N030 G80 (Cancel cycle)
N035 G91 G28 Z0 (Return to reference position in Z)
N040 G91 G28 X0 Y0 (Return to reference position in X-Y)
N045 M30 (End of program)
```

In line N010, notice how the tool is sent to a position to the left of the leftmost hole. The distance to the left is equal to the equal distance between the holes (1.00 in in this example). In line N025, since the canned cycle is given in the incremental mode, first the tool will move the distance specified by X (1.00 in). Since the R word is set to zero, no motion will occur to the R plane (the tool is already 0.100 in above the work surface as specified by line N015). Next the tool will plunge incrementally down 0.750 in from the R plane. The tool will actually traverse 0.650 in below the top surface of the workpiece. Last, the tool will rapid out of the hole, and one hole is thus machined.

Note the L word in line N025. It is set to 10. The canned cycle will be repeated nine more times, meaning 10 total holes will be machined, 1 in apart in X.

If the holes are along the Y axis, of course, the first position would be above or below the first hole in Y. A Y word would be included in the canned-cycle statement. If the holes are along an angular line, both an X and Y must be included in the canned-cycle command and the starting position must be adjusted in both axes accordingly.

Using the incremental mode to make a grid pattern of holes. The incremental technique just shown can be easily expanded to form a grid of holes. When programming holes in the incremental mode, just keep in mind that a hole will be machined in each command. In the incremental mode, you tell the control how far it is from the current position to the next hole's location. Figure 2.61 shows an example in which 100 holes must be machined in the form of a grid pattern. In the absolute mode, of course, this would require 100 commands. Here is a program that uses the incremental mode to substantially shorten the program:

Program:

O0027 (Program number)
N005 G54 G90 S500 M03 (Select coordinate system, absolute mode, turn spindle on CW at 500 RPM)

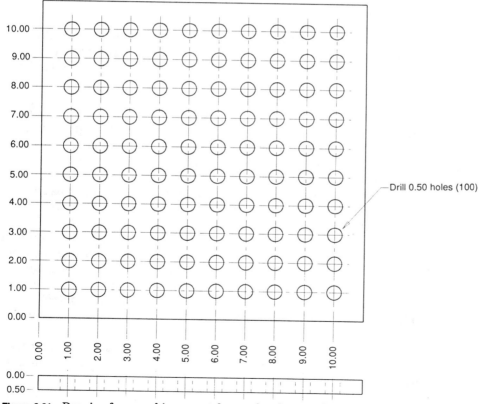

Drill 0.50 holes (100)

Figure 2.61   Drawing for second incremental canned-cycle example program.

```
N010 G00 X0 Y1. (Move to the left of first hole location by the distance between
the holes)
N015 G43 H01 Z.1 (Rapid down to just above work surface)
N020 G91 (Select incremental mode)
N025 G81 X1. R0 Z-.75 F5. L10 (Drill 10 holes in first row)
N030 Y1. (Drill first hole in second row)
N035 X-1. L9 (Drill second row)
N040 Y1. (Drill first hole in third row)
N045 X1. L9 (Drill third row)
N050 Y1. (Drill first hole in fourth row)
N055 X-1. L9 (Drill fourth row)
N060 Y1. (Drill first hole in fifth row)
N065 X1. L9 (Drill fifth row)
N070 Y1. (Drill first hole in sixth row)
N075 X-1. L9 (Drill sixth row)
N080 Y1. (Drill first hole in sixth row)
N085 X1. L9 (Drill seventh row)
N090 Y1. (Drill first hole in eighth row)
N095 X-1. L9 (Drill eighth row)
N100 Y1. (Drill first hole in ninth row)
N105 X1. L9 (Drill ninth row)
N110 Y1. (Drill first hole in tenth row)
N115 X-1 L9 (Drill tenth row)
N120 G80 (Cancel canned cycle)
N125 G91 G28 Z0 (Return to reference position in Z)
N130 G91 G28 X0 Y0 (Return to reference position in X-Y)
N135 M30 (End of program)
```

You can see how much the incremental mode with canned cycles can shorten your program. Only 20 commands were needed to machine all 100 holes. As stated, the absolute mode would have required 100 commands.

Hole pattern commands.   Some (but not many) CNC controls provide the programmer with a series of hole pattern commands to keep the number of commands needed to machine standard configurations of holes to a minimum. Among the most popular hole pattern commands are bolt-hole pattern, line pattern, box pattern, and grid pattern. The use of these types of commands varies widely for those controls that offer this feature.

If the control you will be working with offers this feature, we strongly recommend that you learn its function. It will make the programming of standard hole configurations very easy. For example, if your control has a grid pattern command, the pattern of holes shown in Fig. 2.62 could be machined in two commands (one to specify the canned cycle type and one to specify the grid pattern).

As stated, this function varies dramatically from one control to the next, so we must refer you to your particular control's programming manual for more information.

One popular control manufacturer uses a G70 to specify a bolt-hole pattern. That is, one G70 command will machine the entire bolt-hole pattern of holes. For example, the command

```
N050 G70 X2.5 Y2.5 I1.75 J45. L8
```

would specify that the machine move through the *X-Y* positions needed in Fig. 2.59. X and Y are the bolt-hole center coordinates. I is the bolt-hole circle radius. J is the starting angle. L is the number of equally spaced holes.

When used in conjunction with canned cycles, the G70 command forces all holes on the bolt-hole pattern to be machined. However, there is one problem that may not be obvious. The G70 command does *not* tell the control how to machine the holes (cycle type, R plane, depth, etc.). It simply forces the control to calculate and move through the series of required *X-Y* coordinates at which holes are to be machined.

To specify the machining information, a canned-cycle command must be given prior to the hole pattern command. However, if only the holes in the bolt-hole pattern are to be machined (no others), the programmer must specify that the canned-cycle command itself does not actually machine a hole (as it normally does). This is done with the L word (number of repeats) in the canned-cycle command. If L is set to zero in the canned-cycle command, the control will *not* machine a hole during the canned-cycle command. It will simply be informed as to *how* the holes are supposed to be machined in subsequent coordinate commands. In essence, the control is being told to wait until the next command to find the actual hole positions. Here is an example program that machines the bolt-hole pattern shown in Fig. 2.59:

Program:

    O0028 (Program number)
    N005 G54 G90 S500 M03 (Select coordinate system, absolute mode, turn spindle on
    CW at 500 RPM)
    N010 G00 X2.5 Y2.5 (Rapid over to workpiece center)
    N015 G43 H01 Z.1 (Rapid down to just above work surface)
    N020 G81 R.1 Z-.85 F4.5 L0 (Inform the control as to how the holes should be
    machined, but machine *no hole*)
    N025 G70 X2.5 Y2.5 I1.75 J45. L8 (Machine bolt-hole pattern of holes)
    N030 G80 (Cancel cycle)
    N035 G91 G28 Z0 (Return to reference position in Z)
    N040 G91 G28 X0 Y0 (Return to reference position in X-Y)
    N045 M30 (End of program)

Again, notice the L0 in line N020. It tells the control not to machine a hole at the present time. It is not until line N025 (the bolt-hole circle pattern command) is read that a hole is drilled.

Incremental programming techniques

In most cases, we strongly recommend working in the absolute mode only. The absolute mode provides numerous advantages over the incremental mode:

1. Coordinates going into the program are easier to calculate.

2. If a mistake is made for one coordinate value in the absolute mode,

only one command of the program will be incorrect. In the incremental mode, all motions from the point of the incorrect command
will be incorrect.

3. A program written in the absolute mode makes sense to look at. It
will be very clear as to where the tool is in any command. In the
incremental mode, the entire program is nothing more than a
whole series of motions from the current tool position and is very
difficult to read.

These are but three of the reasons why working in the absolute
mode makes a better way of programming. If you have been programming for any length of time, it is likely you have been programming
exclusively in the absolute mode.

Though the absolute mode is so much better for general-purpose
programming, there are times when it can be very helpful to temporarily program in the incremental mode within a program. We have
previously presented at least two such times in this chapter (trial boring with optional block skip and machining multiple holes with
canned cycles). Here, we intend to show more.

Multiple identical pockets on a machining center.   Incremental programming can minimize programming commands when multiple identical
pockets are machined. This technique also requires either program
copy or subprogramming techniques to be used.

Figure 2.62 shows a workpiece that requires five identical pockets.
Programming these pockets in the absolute mode would require *many*
redundant programming commands. In the incremental mode the motions only have to be programmed one time.

The programmer will position the tool in a consistent way relative

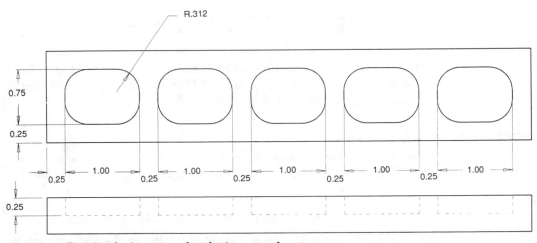

Figure 2.62   Drawing for incremental pocketing example programs.

to each pocket to be machined while still in the absolute mode. For our example, this consistent position is the center of the pocket in *X-Y* and 0.100 in above the top of the pocket in *Z*. This consistent position is left totally to the programmer's discretion. From this position, the incremental commands needed to machine the pocket can simply be repeated with program copy (G25) or with subprogramming techniques (M98, M99). Here is the program that machines the five pockets with a 0.500-in-diameter tool. (Though cutter radius compensation can also be used with the incremental mode, note that the tool's centerline coordinates are used in this program for positioning movements.)

Program:

```
O0029 (Program number)
(0.500-in end mill)
N005 G54 G90 S750 M03 (Select coordinate system, absolute mode, turn spindle on
CW at 750 RPM)
N010 G00 X.75 Y.625 (Rapid to center of leftmost pocket)
N015 G43 H01 Z.1 (Rapid down to just above work surface)
N020 G91 (Select incremental mode)
N025 G01 Z-.1 F2. (Feed to work surface)
N030 G01 Z-.25 F2. (Plunge to pocket bottom)
N035 Y.063 F5. (Feed up in Y)
N040 X-.188 (Feed over in X)
N045 Y-.126 (Feed down in Y)
N050 X.376 (Feed back in X)
N055 Y.126 (Feed up in Y)
N060 X-.188 (Feed back to center in X)
N065 Y.062 (Feed up in Y)
N070 X-.188 (Feed over in X)
N075 G03 X-.062 Y-.062 R.062 (Form upper-left radius)
N080 G01 Y-.126 (Feed down in Y)
N085 G03 X.06 2 Y-.062 R.062 (Form lower-left radius)
N090 G01 X.376 (Feed over in X)
N095 G03 X.062 Y.062 R.062 (Form lower-right radius)
N100 G01 Y.126 (Feed up in Y)
N105 G03 X-.062 Y.062 R.062 (Form upper-right radius)
N110 G01 X-.188 (Feed back to center in X)
N115 Y-.125 (Feed back to center in Y)
N120 G00 Z.25 (Rapid to top surface)
N123 Z.1 (Rapid 0.100 above work surface)
N125 G90 (Reset absolute mode)
N130 G00 X2. Y.625 (Rapid over to center of second pocket)
N135 G25 P020 Q125 (Repeat lines N020 through N125 for second pocket)
N140 G00 X3.25 Y.625 (Rapid over to center of third pocket)
N145 G25 P020 Q125 (Repeat lines N020 through N125 to machine third pocket)
N150 G00 X4.5 Y.625 (Rapid over to center of fourth pocket)
N155 G25 P020 Q125 (Repeat lines N020 through N125 to machine fourth pocket)
N160 G00 X5.75 Y.625 (Rapid over to center of fifth pocket)
N165 G25 P020 Q125 (Repeat lines N020 through N125 to machine fifth pocket)
N170 G91 G28 Z0 (Return to reference position in Z)
N175 G91 G28 X0 Y0 (Return to reference position in X and Y)
N180 M30 (End of program)
```

If you are used to working exclusively in the absolute mode, it may be difficult for you to figure out how the motions are occurring between lines N020 and N125. Rest assured that these commands will incrementally machine one pocket from solid stock. Though more difficult to program than absolute commands, once these commands are calculated one time, they are simply repeated for each pocket.

We recommend that you get in the habit of leaving the tool back at the starting point at the completion of the series of incremental movements (as our example program does). This will assure that you know where the tool will be left whenever the series of incremental commands is required.

Also, keep absolute motion commands out of the series of incremental movements (even in Z). If absolute commands in the Z axis are included in this series, the machining motions will not work if the Z surface to be machined is not consistent from one pocket to the next. Note that the series of incremental commands shown in the program above could be used for a pocket at any Z position. As long as the programmer rapids the tool to the center of the pocket in X-Y, and 0.100 in above the top surface of the pocket in Z, this series of incremental commands will work in every case, properly machining a 0.75- by 1.0- by 0.25-in-deep pocket with a 0.500-in end mill.

Since not all controls utilize the G25 program copy command, we will also show how to handle this problem with subprogramming techniques. Note that the consistent starting position for the pocket is still the center of the pocket in X-Y, and 0.100 in above the top surface of the pocket in Z.

Main program:

```
O0030 (Program number)
(0.500-in end mill)
N005 G54 G90 S750 M03 (Select coordinate system, absolute mode, turn spindle on
CW at 750 RPM)
N010 G00 X.75 Y.625 (Rapid to center of leftmost pocket)
N015 G43 H01 Z.1 (Rapid down to just above work surface)
N020 M98 P1000 (Jump to subprogram and machine first pocket)
N025 G00 X2. Y.625 (Rapid over to center of second pocket)
N030 M98 P1000 (Jump to subprogram and machine second pocket)
N035 G00 X3.25 Y.625 (Rapid over to center of third pocket)
N035 M98 P1000 (Jump to subprogram and machine third pocket)
N040 G00 X4.5 Y.625 (Rapid over to center of fourth pocket)
N045 M98 P1000 (Jump to subprogram and machine fourth pocket)
N050 G00 X5.75 Y.625 (Rapid over to center of fifth pocket)
N055 M98 P1000 (Jump to subprogram and machine fifth pocket)
N060 G91 G28 Z0 (Return to reference position in Z)
N065 G91 G28 X0 Y0 (Return to reference position in X and Y)
N070 M30 (End of program)
```

Subprogram:

```
O1000 (Subprogram number)
N1 G91 (Select incremental mode)
N2 G01 Z-.1 (Feed to work surface)
N3 G01 Z-.25 F2. (Plunge to pocket bottom)
```

N4 Y.063 F5. (Feed up in Y)
N5 X-.188 (Feed over in X)
N6 Y-.126 (Feed down in Y)
N7 X.376 (Feed back in X)
N8 Y.126 (Feed up in Y)
N9 X-.188 (Feed back to center in X)
N10 Y.062 (Feed up in Y)
N11 X-.188 (Feed over in X)
N12 G03 X-.062 Y-.062 R.062 (Form upper-left radius)
N13 G01 Y-.126 (Feed down in Y)
N14 G03 X.06 2 Y-.062 R.062 (Form lower-left radius)
N15 G01 X.376 (Feed over in X)
N16 G03 X.062 Y.062 R.062 (Form lower-right radius)
N17 G01 Y.126 (Feed up in Y)
N18 G03 X-.062 Y.062 R.062 (Form upper-right radius)
N19 G01 X-.188 (Feed back to center in X)
N20 Y-.125 (Feed back to center in Y)
N21 G00 Z.25 (Rapid to top surface)
N22 Z.1 (Rapid 0.100 above work surface)
N23 G90 (Reselect absolute mode)
N24 M99 (Return to main program)

With subprogramming techniques, the subprogram to machine this 0.750- by 1.00-in pocket could be left in the control's memory. Whenever this size pocket is required, this subprogram can be called. The same technique could be repeated for all common pocket sizes your company machines. Eventually, programming time for pocketing operations would be almost nothing.

In both cases (program copy and subprogramming), incremental techniques must be used to produce multiple pockets with the same commands. If you were to use absolute coordinates (in the G90 mode) to machine the first pocket, if the commands are repeated, the *first pocket* would be machined again. While there are ways around this problem if you shift the coordinate system, most programmers like to reserve coordinate shifting commands for more important functions. (Coordinate system shifting was discussed earlier in this chapter).

Multiple identical grooves on a turning center.   In a similar way, the incremental mode can help when you are machining multiple identical grooves on a turning center. Figure 2.63 shows an example of when the same groove must be machined five times on the workpiece. If programmed in the absolute mode, the grooving commands could not be repeated, since the groove would be made in the same location five times.

By using the techniques we show, the programmer can position the tool to a consistent location relative to each groove and then execute the incremental commands to actually machine one groove (by using program copy or subprogramming techniques). For the example program, the consistent position will be flush with the left side of each groove in Z and 0.100 in above the groove in X (0.200-in diameter).

Here is the program using program copy to repeat the incremental grooving commands. [For the control we use for this example, note

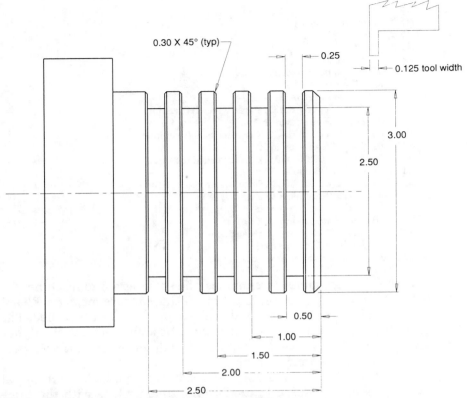

Figure 2.63 Drawing for incremental grooving example program.

that incremental movements are specified with U and W. U is an incremental change in diameter (*X* movement), while W is an incremental *Z* movement.] Only the grooving tool portion of the program is shown.

Program:

O0031 (Program number)
(⅛-in-wide grooving tool)
N005 G50 X _____ Z _____ (Set coordinate system)
N010 G00 T0303 M42 (Index to station three, select high spindle range)
N015 G96 S400 M03 (Turn spindle on CW at 400 SFM)
N020 G00 X3.2 Z-.5 (Rapid to consistent position for rightmost groove)
N025 G00 W.0625 (Rapid to groove center in *Z*)
N030 G01 U-.7 F.005 (Feed to groove bottom)
N035 G04 P500 (Pause for 0.500 second)
N040 G00 U.7 (Rapid out of groove)
N045 W-.0925 (Rapid to left side of chamfer)
N050 G01 U-.2 (Feed down flush with groove diameter)
N055 U-.06 W.03 (For chamfer on left side of groove)
N060 U-.440 (Feed to groove bottom)
N065 G04 P500 (Pause for 0.500 second)
N070 G00 U.7 (Rapid out of groove)

N075 W.155 (Rapid to right side of right chamfer)
N080 G01 U-.2 (Feed flush with groove diameter)
N085 U-.06 W-.03 (Form right chamfer)
N090 U-.440 (Feed to groove bottom)
N095 G04 P500 (Pause for 0.500 second)
N100 G00 U.7 (Rapid out of groove)
N105 W-125 (Rapid back to consistent starting point in Z)
N110 G00 X3.2 Z-1. (Rapid to second groove position in Z)
N115 G25 P025 Q105 (Repeat lines N025 through N105 for second groove)
N120 G00 X3.2 Z-1.5 (Rapid to third groove position in Z)
N125 G25 P025 Q105 (Repeat lines N025 through N105 for third groove)
N130 G00 X3.2 Z-2. (Rapid to fourth groove position in Z)
N135 G25 P025 Q105 (Repeat lines N025 through N105 for fourth groove)
N140 G00 X3.2 Z-2.5 (Rapid to fifth groove position in Z)
N145 G25 P025 Q105 (Repeat lines N025 through N105 for fifth groove)
N150 G00 X _____ Z _____ T0300 (Return to tool change position, cancel tool offset)
N155 M30 (End of program)

As with the pocket-milling example, the incremental movements within lines N025 through N105 may be hard to follow. Keep in mind that all U values are *diameter* value changes in the X axis. Also note that, at the completion of the incremental commands, the tool is left back where it started (flush with the left side of the groove). This is a good habit to get into, making it possible for everyone involved with the program to predict the tool's ending position.

Though all grooves for the above workpiece happen to be on the same diameter, the series of incremental movements would form the same 0.25-in-wide by 0.25-in-deep groove on any diameter as long as the programmer sends the grooving tool to a consistent starting position prior to repeating the incremental commands.

The groove machined in this example program is quite simple. It has straight walls and requires only three passes to depth. However, this same technique can be used for more complicated grooves, like pulley grooves, that have angular walls and require more passes.

If your company machines grooves on a regular basis, and if the grooves remain consistent from one program to the next, using this technique can dramatically shorten your long-term programming effort. Instead of using G25, store the incremental commands as a subprogram (as shown in the pocket-milling example). Keep the subprograms for all popular grooves in the control's memory permanently and keep track of the related program numbers. Whenever you must machine a groove, it will be as simple as rapiding the tool to its consistent starting position and calling the correct subprogram.

Shifting the coordinate system with incremental techniques

Older CNC controls do not allow a convenient way to shift coordinate systems. They have nothing like fixture offsets (discussed earlier) to allow the programmer to easily assign more than one program zero per program. With these older controls, it becomes more difficult to handle applications that require coordinate system shifting, though, in most cases, it is still possible with somewhat unorthodox methods.

If your control has fixture offsets, or some other form of coordinate system shifting, the information given here will be of little value. You already have a better and easier-to-use way of shifting coordinate systems. But if you have no special form of coordinate system shifting commands, the information should be helpful.

CNC controls have always had a way of assigning program zero from within a program. On machining centers, for example, a G92 command is the most popular command for this purpose. Turning centers will use either a G50 or a G92 for this purpose. With either method, the program zero setting command tells the control how far it is *from* program zero *to* the machine's current position. Normally, when this program zero setting command is read, the machine will be resting at its reference position, meaning the distances given in the G92 or G50 command will be from program zero to the machine's reference position.

However, the machine does not have to be at its reference position when the G50 or G92 command is given. When the program zero setting command is given, the control will take the axis values included in the command as the distance from program zero to the machine's *current* position. (This technique was discussed in the presentation on how to move the program's starting position earlier in this chapter.) When you need to run more than one workpiece in the same setup by the same program, there are times when you will need to reassign the program zero point after making an incremental movement equal to the distance from one workpiece to the next.

Figure 2.64 shows a series of six workpieces to be machined from the same piece of rough stock on a turning center. After the program machines and cuts off one workpiece, the program will machine the next workpiece, and the next, until all workpieces are machined.

One easy way to handle this kind of program is to shift the coordinate system after each workpiece is completely machined and then to run the program again. In Fig. 2.64, the shift distance from one part to the next (0.780 in) will be the amount of incremental shift distance between parts.

Since the same program must be run six times, this also makes an excellent application for subprogramming techniques. The entire program that actually machines the workpiece will be in the form of a subprogram. The main program will simply call it and repeat it six times. While we do not show the entire machining program for this workpiece, here is the basic structure required for the two programs.

Main program:

```
O0032 (Main program)
N005 G28 U0 W0 (Ensure that machine is at the reference position)
N010 M98 P1000 L6 (Machine six workpieces)
```

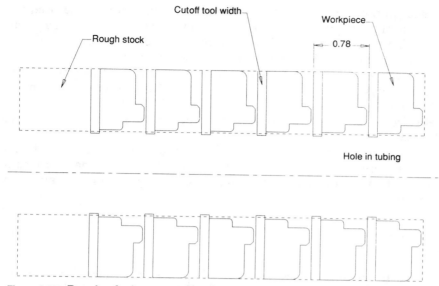

Figure 2.64 Drawing for incremental-mode program-zero-shifting example program.

N015 G28 U0 W0 (Return to reference position)
N020 M30 (End of program)

Subprogram:

O1000 (Subprogram number)
N1 G50 X _____ Z _____ (Set program zero for first tool)
N2 G00 T0101 M41 (Index to tool number one, select low spindle range)
N3 G96 S500 M01 (Turn spindle on CW at 500 SFM)
  .
  .
  .
N234 G00 X _____ Z _____ T0500 (Return last tool to tool change position, cancel tool offset)
N235 M01 (Optional stop)
N236 G00 W-.780 (Move over the incremental distance between workpieces)
N237 M99 (Return to main program)

Though the subprogram is only the skeleton of the required machining program, you should be able to see what is happening. In line N005 of the main program, we assure that the machine is at its reference position. In line N010, we call the machining subprogram and tell the control to execute it six times.

The first time the control executes the subprogram, the machine is resting at the reference position. The G50 commands for all tools in the subprogram reflect the distance *from* program zero *to* the tip of each tool while the machine is resting at the reference position. The first part is run in this manner.

At the end of the subprogram but before the M99, we make an incremental movement equal to the distance from one workpiece to the next (in the minus direction). When the subprogram is executed the second time, the machine is, in effect, out of position by the incremental movement amount (0.780 in). When the control reads the various G50 commands in the machining subprogram this time, it will assume the distances given are from program zero to the tip of each tool at the *current* position. In effect, we have shifted the coordinate system by the incremental distance moved at the end of the subprogram. This shifting is repeated each time the subprogram is executed (in our case, six total times).

After the subprogram is executed the sixth time, the control returns to the main program. Prior to the M30 command, the main program sends the machine back to its original starting position, the reference position.

Advanced Implications of Other Programming Words

There are several programming words that have special implications. Many can be used in two ways, depending on the format of the given command. While you may know the primary purpose for the word, the secondary purpose we give may be new to you.

Accuracy of feed rate for threading

For turning-center applications, the feed rate can be specified in two ways: either as feed per minute or as feed per revolution. A G code will specify which mode is in effect. Normally, G98 specifies feed per minute, while G99 specifies feed per revolution.

For most operations, the accuracy of the feed rate is not critical. Especially if constant surface speed is used, the spindle will be constantly changing speed while the tool is machining the workpiece. The control will do its best to maintain the feed rate as programmed.

However, threading requires a very precise synchronization between spindle rotation and feed rate because the pitch of the thread determines whether the thread will fit into its mating part, and because the control must be able to trace over its motions as the thread is being machined. While you are threading, we recommend using the feed per revolution mode to specify feed rate. In this way, the programmed feed rate will be equal to the pitch of the thread. In the inch system, the pitch of any thread is equal to 1 divided by the number of threads per inch. In the metric system, the thread pitch is actually given as part of the thread's designation. Our point in this section will apply *only* to threads designated in the *inch* system.

The most common feed-rate word is the F word. In the inch mode, F.005 is equal to 0.005 in per revolution. Keep in mind that most CNC turning-center controls limit the number of places that can be programmed to the right of the decimal point to four.

If programming a ⅜-16 thread, the number of threads per inch is 16. The pitch of this thread is precisely 0.0625 in (1 divided by 16). In this example, the F word could be used to precisely specify the exact value of the pitch (as F.0625).

On the other hand, if a ½-13 thread is to be programmed, the required pitch is 0.0769231 (1 divided by 13). If using the F word to specify thread pitch, you will be limited to only four places of accuracy and the above pitch must be rounded to four places (F.0769).

Admittedly, this very small deviation from the programmed feed rate to the required feed rate will have only a small effect on the quality of the workpiece. In most cases, this small deviation will not even be noticed. For example, if making the thread to mate with the thread of another workpiece, you simply need to program the same F word for both threads.

However, for certain applications, the pitch of the thread is more critical. If machining any kind of lead screw, for example, the traverse motion rate of the mating part is critical. In this case, the F word may not be acceptable. You may need to specify thread pitch more precisely.

Most CNC turning center controls allow a more accurate way of specifying pitch. An E word is used in place of the F word for pitch designation with threading commands. With most controls, the E word allows six digits to be programmed to the right of the decimal point (gaining you two more places of accuracy as compared to the F word). In the case of the ½-13 thread, the pitch could be specified as E.076923. Though still not perfect, this designation of pitch is much more precise than that specified with the F word.

Even if your particular control does not allow the E word to specify six-place pitch accuracy, you still have a way of specifying a more precise pitch. If the pitch of the thread is critical, and if the four-place accuracy of the F word in the inch system is not acceptable, you can always attain better results by switching to the metric mode and programming the workpiece in metric. (A lengthy discussion of other accuracy benefits of the metric system was given earlier in this chapter.)

In the inch mode, if the ½-13 thread pitch is programmed with the F word, the 0.0769231-in pitch must be rounded to 0.0769 in, meaning the deviation from the programmed pitch to the desired pitch is 0.0000231 in. Again, this small deviation will not usually affect the quality of the workpiece if the thread is being machined to simply fit with a mating workpiece.

To convert from inches to metric, simply multiply the inch value by the 25.4 value constant. In our example of the ½-13 thread, the calculated pitch is 0.0769231 in. When converted to metric, the pitch becomes 1.9538462 mm (0.0769321 times 25.4), which must be rounded to 1.954 mm. In this case, the difference between the programmed pitch (1.954 mm) and the desired pitch (1.9538462 mm) is only 0.0001538 mm, which is equivalent to 0.0000061 in. This deviation is much smaller than the 0.0000231 in deviation resulting from using the F word in the inch mode.

Since the pitch of a metric thread is always given as an even number in the thread's designation, this problem does not exist with metric threads. For example, in the metric mode, a thread may be given as with a 60-1.5 designation. The 60 is the thread's major diameter (in millimeters) and the 1.5 is the pitch of the thread (in millimeters).

We say again that this pitch deviation will usually cause *no* major problems if you are simply making mating threads. Only when the thread pitch is critical should you consider this alternative. Another example of when thread pitch is critical is the thread within a micrometer. As the handle of a micrometer is turned, the thread must cause a very precise and predictable linear motion.

Limiting spindle speed in the constant-surface-speed mode

Turning centers boast a very helpful feature called *constant surface speed*. This feature lets the programmer specify speed in either surface feet per minute (inch mode) or meters per minute (metric mode). From then, the control constantly and automatically calculates the required RPM on the basis of the current machining diameter.

For single-point operations like turning, boring, and grooving, this provides three major advantages over programming in RPM. Since the programmer does not have to make RPM calculations, programming is much simpler. Since the control is constantly maintaining the perfect RPM and synchronizing it with the (inches per revolution) feed rate, surface finish is better. And, since cutting speed remains consistent relative to the cutting edge of the tool, tool life improves.

Once activated, constant surface speed will maintain the programmed speed according to the current diameter of the cutting tool in the X axis. As the tool comes closer to the spindle centerline, RPM increases. As the tool moves to larger diameters, RPM decreases. If the tool is brought to the spindle center in the X axis (as would be required for facing the end of a solid workpiece), the RPM would increase to the maximum RPM allowed in the current spindle range. In some cases, this can cause severe problems.

For example, if the workpiece is not perfectly round (as would be the case with poorer-grade castings), as the spindle RPM increases there will be a tendency for vibration to occur. If left uncorrected, it is possible that the workpiece would eventually vibrate out of the workholding device, causing damage to the workpiece and machine, and possible injury to the operator.

For this reason, control manufacturers that offer constant surface speed must also allow the programmer a way to limit the maximum RPM in the constant surface speed mode from within the program. Most use the G50 command for this purpose. If the programmer includes an S word within the G50 command, the control will use this value as the limiting RPM. For example, if the control read the command

N050 G50 S1000 (Limit RPM to 1000)

it would not allow the spindle to rotate faster than 1000 RPM from that point on, no matter what speed in RPM the constant surface speed feature calculates for the operation. Normally the spindle limiter is modal and will remain in effect until changed, or until the machine is turned off (when it is reset to the machine's maximum).

To determine the maximum RPM for any one workpiece requires caution on the operator's part. If you have a workpiece that you feel will be prone to vibration if rotated at too fast an RPM, here is what you should do:

1. After setting/boring jaws, load the workpiece in the chuck in the normal manner.

2. By manual or manual data input (MDI) mode, turn the spindle on at a very slow RPM.

3. Slowly, and by small increments, increase the RPM. At the first sign of vibration, immediately turn the spindle off.

4. Repeat steps 1 to 3 for several workpieces to determine any variance in maximum RPM. Determine your maximum RPM for the worst condition.

5. Once you determine the maximum allowable RPM, *reduce* this value by at least 10 percent to come up with your spindle limiter for the program.

Offset cancellation with the T word on turning centers

As you know, offsets on turning centers are canceled with the last two digits of the T word. Throughout this text, you will see this cancellation during each tool's return to the tool change position.

During offset cancellation, most programmers repeat the tool station number followed by two trailing zeros. For example, in the command

N055 G00 X _____ Z _____ T0200

the offset used with tool 2 (probably offset 2) is being canceled. However, as you continue reading, keep in mind that the above command will cancel *any* tool offset.

One major problem that has always existed relates to how this technique is used to cancel offsets on turning centers. It has to do with repeating the tool station number. If the programmer makes a mistake with regard to the tool station number when canceling an offset on the tool's return to tool change position, the results could be disastrous. For example, say tool 2 is currently being used in the program, but, on the retraction to tool change position, the programmer makes a mistake and programs a T0300 instead of T0200. The T0300 will cause an index while the turret is still very close to the workpiece, probably taking the turret index into the workpiece or chuck.

Another possible problem that comes up from this form of offset cancellation has to do with changing tool stations. For example, say a program was written to use a rough turning tool in station 3. While setting up, the programmer notices that the rough turning tool is currently in station 2. Rather than move it in the turret, it is easier to simply change the program. However, if tool offsets are canceled by restating the tool station number followed by two trailing zeros, the programmer must change *two* commands in the program in order to change tool station numbers. If the second change during the offset cancellation is overlooked, the same index problem mentioned above will occur.

As you may have guessed, there is a way to avoid these two terrible problems. Most current CNC controls allow insignificant leading digits to be suppressed. In the case of the T word used with offset cancellation, the (redundant) tool station number is unnecessary in the tool offset cancellation command. If this technique is allowed by your control, in the command

N055 X _____ Z _____ T0

the T0 will cancel *any* tool's offset. Since the tool station number is not repeated, the programmer can rest assured that there will *never* be an unwanted tool index during a tool offset's cancellation.

To find out whether your particular control allows this technique may take some digging. This kind of information is (at best) difficult to find in the programming manual. You may have to cautiously test this technique to confirm that it is possible on your particular control. It will be well worth your time to find out.

3

Techniques with Tool Offsets

All forms of compensation utilize tool offsets. For a machining center, tool length compensation uses offsets to store the tool's length value. Cutter radius compensation uses offsets to store the cutter's radius value. Fixture offsets use a set of offsets to store the distances from the machine's reference position to the program zero point.

For a turning center, tool nose radius compensation uses offsets (R and T) to store the tool's radius and type. Dimensional offsets (X and Z) are used to allow the operator to size the workpiece.

If you currently work with any form of CNC equipment, you have probably been exposed to the primary purposes for those offsets which your CNC machine uses. Each compensation type requires knowledge of offsets in one way or another. In this chapter, we will expand your knowledge to include advanced uses of the various kinds of offsets. In most cases, the techniques we show will simply be an extension of what you already know, yet you may be surprised at how much these techniques can help when it comes to holding size on a workpiece.

Understanding Turning-Center Dimensional Tool Offsets

The primary purpose for dimensional offsets (also called simply *offsets*) on a turning center is to allow the operator to adjust for imperfections between the intended tool position and the actual tool position. This imperfection in the tool's position could result from improper setting in the tool-holding device or from tool wear.

It is impossible for the operator to perfectly place every tool into the machine. And even if this could be accomplished, as each tool begins machining workpieces, it will begin to wear. This tool wear will affect the size of the workpiece machined by the tool and must be adjusted for by dimensional tool offsets.

Even a tiny deviation from the tool's desired position to its actual position can cause a workpiece to be out of tolerance. For example, say a turned diameter on the workpiece is specified with a tolerance of $+0.002$ in, -0. In this case, if the tool were more than 0.001 in out of position (since X is specified in diameter), it would not machine the diameter within the specified tolerance.

For this reason, all CNC turning-center control manufacturers supply the dimensional offset feature. When a tool offset is instated, the current coordinate system is shifted by the amount of the offset. Once shifted, motion occurs as usual.

You can think of dimensional offsets as having the ability to instantaneously and accurately move the tool in its tool holder by the precise amount of imperfection. In effect, this is what happens when an offset is instated. The X and Z axes are shifted by the amount of the offset, as if the tool had been physically moved in its holder by the offset amount.

How tool offsets are instated on turning centers

Most turning-center controls use a T word to specify both the tool station number to be indexed to and the offset to be used with the tool. To accomplish this, the T word is usually a 4-digit command. The first 2 digits specify the tool station number and the second 2 digits specify the offset to be used. For example, the command

    N045 G00 T0101

tells the control to rotate the turret to station 1 and instate offset 1.

Though it is not mandatory to do so, we recommend that you use the same offset number as the tool station number to which your are indexing (tool 1 and offset 1, tool 2 and offset 2, tool 3 and offset 3, and so on). This makes it easy for the operator to know which offset is being used for each tool.

We call the offset being instated with the tool indexing command the *primary offset*. In most applications, this will be the only offset needed for the tool. Later, we will show several times when it will be necessary to use a second or third offset with one tool.

As stated, when the T command is executed, the turret indexes to the tool station specified and the offset is instated. Turning-center manufacturers are not consistent with exactly what will happen when an offset is instated. Most will make the axes move immediately by the amount stored in the offset.

For example, say offset 1 has the value 0.010 in currently stored in the X position of the offset and 0.005 in stored in the Z position. When the command

    N010 G00 T0101

is executed, the X axis will immediately move in the plus direction by the value of 0.005 in, increasing the diameter the tool will machine by 0.010 in (if the control uses diameter programming). At the same time, the Z axis will move plus by 0.005 in. Since G00 is the current motion type, the motion will occur at rapid. You can think of the offset-instating command used in this manner as commanding an incremental move by the amount stored in the tool offset.

Some turning-center manufacturers will not make the axes compensate for the amount in the offset until the next motion command. These controls will automatically adjust the ending position for the next motion command by the amount stored in the offset. For example, say offset 1 currently has the value 0.010 in stored in the X position and 0.005 in stored in the Z position when this series of commands is executed:

Program:

    O0033 (Program number)
    N005 G50 X _____ Z _____ (Assign program zero)
    N010 T0101 (Index to station 1, instate offset 1)
    N015 G96 S500 M03 (Turn spindle on CW at 500 SFM)
    N020 G00 X3. Z.1 (Move to first position)
    ...

With this kind of control, line N010 will index the turret, but cause no axis motion. In line N020 (the next motion command), the end point of X3. and Z.1 would be adjusted by the amount of the offset. In this case, the tool would actually move to a position of X3.010 and Z.105, the new end point. From there, motion would continue as usual, as if the tool were really positioned at X3.000 and Z.100 in each axis.

This method of instating offsets in each tool's first motion command is better for three reasons. First, since no motion occurs at the T word, the time taken for the movement will be saved. Though this is a very short time savings per index, when multiplied by the number of indexes made during the machine's life, this time will be substantial. Second, this method makes for a cleaner program. The turret will not be jumping around at each tool change. Third, many turning-center manufacturers make the reference position (commonly used for tool changing) very close to the axis overtravel limits. If this is the case, and if the turret does move during the instating of a tool offset, it is likely that an axis will overtravel if a large positive offset is given for either axis.

Even if the axes of your machine will move when an offset is instated, rest assured that it is possible to keep the offset from being instated until the first motion command. Here is a series of commands that accomplishes this with a machine that *will* move the axes when an offset is instated:

Program:

```
O0034 (Program number)
N005 G50 X _____ Z _____ (Set program zero)
N010 T0100 (Index to station 1, but do not instate offset)
N015 G96 S400 M03 (Turn spindle on CW at 400 SFM)
N020 G00 X3. Z.1 T0101 (Move to first position, instate offset)
    ...
```

This time, in line N010, the offset is not instated. The turret simply indexes to station 1. Later, in line N020, when the motion command is made, the offset is instated. Since station 1 is already in position, no index will occur. All that will happen because of the T word in this command is that the offset will be instated. This will achieve the same results as a control that does not instate an offset until the next motion command. If you have a turning center that moves the axes immediately when an offset is instated, we recommend that you use this technique for all programmed tool changes to minimize cycle time, make for a cleaner program, and avoid the possibility of an overtravel during indexing.

It may be a little confusing to truly picture what is happening when an offset is instated. Keep in mind that the primary purpose for offsets is to allow for deviations in the tool's setting position. Once the imperfection has been compensated for, the machine continues through its programmed path in the normal manner. If the tool is perfectly set, and if there is no tool wear, the offset would not be necessary. Since it is impossible to achieve this condition for all practical purposes, an offset *must* be used for every tool of every program you write.

Offset cancellation

While there are turning-center controls that do not require that the tool offset be canceled, most do. When the tool has finished its machining operation, most controls require that the offset used for that tool be canceled. If it is not, the offset will remain in effect, possibly causing problems with the next tool (depending on how program zero is defined). During the tool's return to the tool change position, the offset should be canceled. One way to cancel offsets is to repeat the tool station number with two trailing zeros. For example, the command

```
N050 G00 X _____ Z _____ T0100
```

returns the machine to its tool change position and cancels the offset value used with offset 1.

This technique requires that you be *very* careful to repeat the tool station number correctly. If you make a mistake and state a different tool station, most turning centers would start indexing at the beginning of the motion command, possibly causing the turret to index into the workpiece.

Also, if you make changes to your tool station numbers at the machine, you must be careful to change the program in two positions (where the tool is first commanded to index and where the tool offset is canceled). For example, suppose you intend to place a rough-turning tool in station 1. When the program is written, you index the turret to station 1 and instate offset 1 for this tool. When the tool is finished, you cancel with the command T0100.

However, when it comes time to run the program, you discover that the rough-turning tool happens to be in station 3. Rather than move the tool to station 1, you decide to leave it in station 3 and change the program. In this case, you *must* change the program in at least two places. If you forget to change the cancellation command, on tool 3's return to tool change position, the turret will index to station 1!

For this reason, we recommend using a slightly different method to cancel offsets. Since most turning-center controls allow leading insignificant digits to be suppressed, the command T0 will work on most controls to cancel the offset for *any* tool station. This means in the command

N050 G00 X _____ Z _____ T0

the T0 will cancel the offset, but will not consider the turret station number at all. The turret will *not* index.

Before using this technique in production, you must check your programming manual to see if this is allowed or test it at the machine. If you test at the machine, place a large offset in offset 1 (large enough to see the movement). Then make this series of commands (by MDI or in a program):

```
N005 G00 T0101
N010 G00 U0 W0
N015 T0
N020 G0 U0 W0
```

In line N005, the turret will index to station 1 and instate offset 1. If your machine moves the axes as soon as an offset is instated, the machine will also move immediately by the amount of the offset. If not, you will see a movement equal to the offset in line N010. This motion command is telling the machine to move nothing (increment zero) in both axes. But since it is a motion command, the offset will be added in the movement.

In line N015, you will determine whether the T0 technique is allowed. The turret should remain at the same index position (no index should occur). If your machine moves immediately when an offset is canceled, the turret will move back to its original *X-Z* position. If your machine does not consider the offset cancellation until the next move, you will see the turret move back to its original position in line N020.

The two key things to watch for during this test are that the turret does not index during line N015 and that the turret is positioned back where it started from at the end of this sequence. If these two conditions exist, you can confidently use the word T0 to cancel any tool's offset.

Holding Size with Dimensional Tool Offsets

When you run the very first workpiece, it is impossible to tell if offsets are properly set, especially with new tools that have been recently placed in the turret. Though you try your best to load the tools as precisely as possible, there is really no way of telling if you did so perfectly. Also, as any tool machines a workpiece, it will be under the influence of tool pressure. This tool pressure has the tendency to push the workpiece away from the cutting edge, and it is next to impossible to predict how it will affect the size of the workpiece before actually performing a machining operation.

Given this problem, you would be amazed at the number of operators who run the first part without concern for offsets. They hope luck is on their side and the workpiece comes out to size. In most cases, luck is not on their side and the first workpiece will be scrapped.

There is *never* an excuse for scrapping the first workpiece because of improperly set tool offsets. While this may sound like a bold statement, if you follow the suggestions we make in this section, you will have a very good chance of making even the first workpiece you run for each setup come out on size.

If you were working on an engine lathe, turning a 3.0-in diameter down to 2.875 in, how would you ensure that the 2.875-in diameter comes out to size? Would you crank the cross-slide to where you hoped it would machine a 2.875-in diameter and begin machining at this point? Of course not. You would first machine only a small amount of stock from the 3.0-in diameter. Once this preliminary machining is done, you would stop the spindle and measure the workpiece to see where you currently stand. After the measurement, you would know precisely how much more stock must be removed to bring the 2.875-in diameter to size, and in turn, you would know precisely how much more to turn the handwheel to reach this diameter.

With offsets, the same basic technique can be used on a turning center. *Before* a new tool machines the workpiece, its offset can be adjusted in a way that forces the tool to leave excess stock. Once the tool machines the workpiece, the program can be stopped and the measurement taken. After the measurement, you will know exactly how to adjust the offset to make the tool machine to the proper size. After the adjustment, the tool must be made to run again. This time it will machine precisely to the size required.

Here is a simple example. Say you have two turning tools (a rough-turning tool and a finish-turning tool) that are to be used to machine a 3.0-in diameter. The rough-turning tool is to leave 0.040 in of stock for the finish-turning tool. In this case, the rough-turning tool's target diameter is 3.080 in. *Before* the rough-turning tool is allowed to machine the workpiece, its offset can be adjusted in the *plus* direction (since this is an outside diameter) by a safe amount. In our case, say you adjust the X offset to +0.050 in.

After this rough-turning tool machines the 3.0-in diameter, you measure the workpiece and find it to be 3.128 in. Since this diameter is currently supposed to be 3.08 in, it is 0.048 in oversize (3.128 − 3.08). At this time, you reduce the offset for the rough-turning tool (by 0.048 in) and rerun the tool. This time it will come out precisely to 3.08 in.

As with the rougher, *before* you run the finish-turning tool, you adjust its X offset to force it to also leave excess stock. In this example, we'll say it is adjusted to +0.030 in. After the finisher machines the workpiece, the program is stopped and the diameter measured. Say it comes out to 3.028 in. You know you now must reduce the offset for the finish-turning tool by 0.028 in and rerun it. This time the 3-in diameter will come out precisely to size.

While this example was for a critical diameter, the same technique can be used to sneak up on critical Z surfaces (faces). Adjust the offset to leave excess stock. Machine with the tool. Measure what the tool did. Adjust the offset. Rerun the tool, making it machine the surface to size.

The same technique can be used for inside diameters, when machining with boring bars. In this case, however, the trial X offset must be made negative, to allow excess stock on the inside surface.

One important point is that you *must* make each tool machine to the proper size (rerun the tool after adjusting the offset) *before* going on to the next tool. It would be foolish (and possibly dangerous) to let subsequent tools run, knowing that a previous tool has not yet machined to size.

Leaving proven offsets alone

When you go from one setup to the next, there will almost always be some tools used in the last setup that are needed in the next setup. For those tools that were used in the last job, the offsets have already been proven. Since these tools machined the last workpiece to size, you can be sure that the current offset values will make the same tools machine the next workpiece to size. For tools used in the previous setup, you need not make the tool machine with excess stock and sneak up on the final size as suggested in the previous discussion.

The only exception to this rule has to do with tool pressure as it is affected by workpiece material. If a drastic change in machinability is experienced from one setup to the next (maybe you are changing from aluminum to tool steel), it will be necessary to size *all* tool offsets as if they had not been used before.

When to clear tool offsets

Some operators clear tool offsets (make the values zero) for all tools before any new job is set up. But as the previous discussion pointed out, you should not arbitrarily clear offsets for all tools for each setup you make. Our recommendation is this: get in the habit of clearing offset values as you remove a tool from the turret. With this technique, for those tools in the turret, you will know their tool offsets are proven. If they are required for a future job, you will not have to size them.

Grooving flush with a face

Without exception, trial machining can be used for every kind of tool on a turning center. However, there are some machining operations that make it somewhat more difficult to use this technique. Look at Fig. 3.1 to see an example.

In this case, a groove must be machined perfectly flush with the next shoulder. Also, the grooving tool is the same width as the groove to be machined. In this case, the Z offset for this tool must be adjusted perfectly before the groove can be plunged. If too negative, the grooving tool will gouge the shoulder (possibly damaging the tool). If too positive, the left side of the groove will not be flush with the shoulder. And, since the groove width is the same as the tool width, you will have only one chance to plunge the groove. If it is out of location, and you try to adjust the Z offset and rerun the tool, the groove will be machined too wide.

At first glance, this may seem like an unsolvable problem. It is exactly this kind of problem that makes most operators give up on trial machining and run the grooving tool anyway, hoping it will machine to size. But with a little ingenuity, you can overcome even this difficult problem. Figure 3.2 shows the tool path we would recommend for the actual grooving tool's motion. Notice that the grooving tool is positioned (at rapid) to within 0.100 in of the shoulder and also within 0.100 in (on the side) above the diameter to be grooved. Then it is fed flush to the shoulder and diameter simultaneously (at a 45° angle). The groove is then plunged and the tool retracted.

Of course, the diameter and shoulder have been machined to size by another tool prior to this grooving operation. *Before* the grooving tool

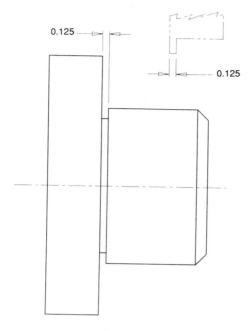

0.125

0.125

Figure 3.1   Drawing for grooving example stressing the use of sizing offset.

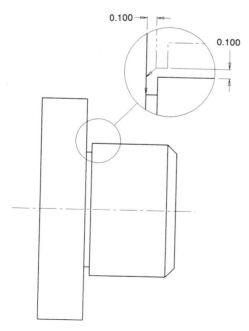

0.100

0.100

Figure 3.2   Path of grooving tool for grooving example.

is run, its X offset is set to 0.050 in (to force excess stock to be left at the groove bottom). But nothing is done (yet) to the Z offset.

In the single-block mode, the tool is commanded to move into position step by step. When it reaches the clearance position 0.100 in away from the shoulder, the cycle is stopped. In the *manual mode,* a measurement can be made to determine how far it is from the leading edge of the grooving tool to the shoulder. Of course, the tool should be precisely 0.100 in from the shoulder. If it is not, an offset adjustment must be made.

One easy way to take this measurement is to set the axis display for the Z axis to zero after the tool reaches the 0.100-in clearance position commanded by the program. Then, using the machine's handwheel, or other manual technique, cautiously move the grooving tool in the Z axis to touch the shoulder. When the tool touches the shoulder, the Z-axis display will be showing you how far it is from where the tool was positioned by the program to the shoulder.

Say, for example, the measured distance comes out to 0.105 in. In this case the offset for the Z axis must be adjusted in the minus direction by 0.005 in. If the measured distance comes out to 0.094 in, the offset for the Z axis must be adjusted in the plus direction by 0.006 in.

After the offset change for the Z axis, the grooving tool is run again (from the beginning of the grooving tool). This time, the programmer can be assured·that, when the tool feeds to the shoulder in the angular movement, it will come perfectly flush with the shoulder. Since the X-axis offset is still set to leave excess stock, when the groove is plunged, it will not be to depth. After the grooving tool is finished, the depth of the groove can be measured, and the X-axis offset adjusted accordingly. Finally, when the grooving tool is run the third time, it machines to the proper depth, flush with the adjacent shoulder.

While all of this may sound a little difficult and time-consuming, consider the alternatives. Without knowing where you stand in the Z axis for the grooving tool, it is possible that the grooving tool could gouge into the shoulder as it approaches the groove to be machined. Even if the shoulder is not gouged, the groove could still come out too wide if the Z-axis offset is not perfectly adjusted and if the tool has to be run twice. Considering the consequences of a scrapped workpiece, a damaged tool, and possible injury, the time taken to confirm your offset settings is time well spent.

Threading up close to a shoulder

Similar techniques can be used when threading is required to within a very close distance to a shoulder. Figure 3.3 shows an example. If the thread recess is very narrow, it may be necessary to thread to within a very small distance from the shoulder. Yet you will want to be care-

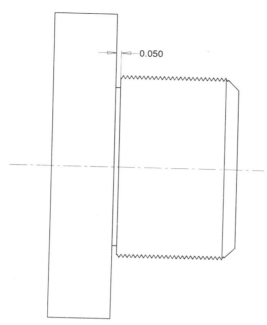

0.050

Figure 3.3 Drawing for threading example stressing the use of sizing offset.

ful not to crash the threading tool into the shoulder by coming too close.

For the example shown in Fig. 3.3, it will be necessary to bring the threading tool very close to the adjacent shoulder. Say, for example, the programmer wishes the threading tool to come within 0.010 in of the shoulder. This extremely small distance must be confirmed before production is run. To do so, the operator can first store a large plus value in the Z offset for the threading tool, say 0.100 in. In the X axis, an even larger value will be stored in the offset to assure that the first threading pass will not actually touch the diameter to be threaded. More than twice the thread depth will be required for the X offset.

Figure 3.4 shows the programmed movement of the threading tool during its first pass. We assume at this point that the diameter to be threaded, the groove, and the adjacent shoulder have been previously machined to size by other tools. In the single-block mode, the threading tool is allowed to make its first threading pass. Because of the large X offset, the operator can be sure that the tool will not touch the diameter to be threaded. Because of the large Z offset, the operator can be sure that the tool will not touch the adjacent shoulder.

After the tool has reached its final Z position and begins coming up in X, the operator can stop the cycle with feed hold. At this time, the distance from the leading edge of the threading tool to the shoulder is measured (as for the grooving tool in the previous example). The Z offset can then be adjusted accordingly to attain the desired 0.010-in

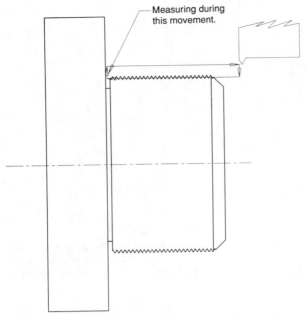

Measuring during
this movement.

Figure 3.4 Path of threading tool for threading example.

clearance. For example, if the measured distance from the leading
edge of the tool to the adjacent shoulder is measured to be 0.117 in,
the Z offset must be reduced by 0.107 in to attain the 0.010-in clearance.

From this point, the operator can be sure that the desired clearance
of 0.010 in will be held, and that the tool will not crash into the adjacent shoulder while threading. No more Z-axis offsets will be made for
this tool (as long as the Z value of the offset for the tool machining the
adjacent shoulder is not changed).

The threading tool must be rerun from the beginning. Before this is
done, the operator can reduce the X offset and actually machine the
workpiece. We still recommend leaving excess stock for the first time
the threading tool is run, so the X-axis offset can be set to +0.030 in.
The threading tool is run, and the diameter of the thread is measured
(with a thread gauge over the pins) to determine how much stock is
left to machine. The offset is then adjusted accordingly and the
threading tool is run a third time. This time the thread will come out
right to size.

Other offset considerations for threading

Once a threading tool has actually machined on the workpiece, you
can *not* adjust the Z-axis offset by any value other than the pitch of
the thread. Doing so would cause the workpiece to be cross-threaded,
since the Z starting position for the thread is not maintained. Of

course, after the workpiece is removed and before another is threaded, the Z offset can be changed. For this reason, we strongly recommend that you use the techniques shown above to determine the Z-axis offset *before* you allow the thread to be machined.

As stated earlier, the X offset can be changed during the machining of a single workpiece as many times as necessary. The change in X offset will not affect the positioning of the Z axis, and no cross-threading will occur.

However, there is one warning we give related to changing the X offset. If you sneak up on the final thread depth in very small increments, as would be the case if you use a go/no-go thread gauge, you must be careful with the *next* workpiece you run. Since the small offset changes brought the threading tool down to its final diameter slowly, the workpiece will not have been machined with the programmed number of passes and depths of cut per pass. When the next part is run, and the X offset is correctly set from the very beginning, the depth of the first threading pass will be *much* greater than when the X offset had a large value. If the programmed threading cycle is not correct relative to the first pass depth, this first pass may be too deep, causing damage to the threading tool.

Conclusion to sizing workpieces with offsets

If the techniques shown here are new to you, read this section until you thoroughly understand our presentations. As stated earlier, there is no excuse for scrapping your first workpiece because of improper offset settings. In *all* cases, there will be a way to assure that the tool machines correctly, making the workpiece come out on size. Though we have shown several specific techniques related to sizing workpieces, in some cases, you will have to think through the offsetting problem completely before a method to size the workpiece will come to you. The ingenuity you exercise while proving offsets will pay dividends in good workpieces.

Using Secondary Offsets on a Turning Center

As stated earlier, most turning-center applications require but one offset per tool. Normally, the offset number for each tool is made the same as the tool station number, and we call this offset the tool's *primary offset*.

There are times, however, when two or more offsets are required for a tool. When required, we call these offsets *secondary tool offsets*. Before we give applications for secondary tool offsets, you must fully understand what happens when a tool offset is instated or changed during a motion command.

As stated earlier, if a tool offset is instated during a motion command, the control alters the end point of the motion by the value stored in the offset and the motion occurs to this new end point. If included in a rapid command (G00), this altered motion occurs in the rapid mode, as if the altered end point were the actual command given. Figure 3.5 shows an example in the rapid mode.

In the straight-line cutting mode (G01), the control does much the same thing. The recalculation of the end point of the motion is made in the same way as for rapid. However, the motion to the end point will now be along a perfectly straight line. Figure 3.6 shows this.

Knowing how the end point of a straight-line motion command is altered by instating an offset has fantastic implications. As you can see from Fig. 3.6, the motion of straight-line commands can be changed by offsets. A straight turn can be made into a tapered move, and vice versa.

Keep in mind that offset changes are *not* accumulative. For example, say offset 1's X value is 0.005 in and offset 21's X value is 0.003 in when the control reads and executes this program:

```
O0035 (Program number)
N005 G50 X _____ Z _____ (Set program zero)
N010 G00 T0101 (Index to tool 1, instate offset 1)
N015 G96 S500 M03 (Turn spindle on CW at 500 SFM)
N020 G00 X3. Z.1 (Rapid to machining position)
N025 G01 Z0 F.005 (Feed flush with face)
```

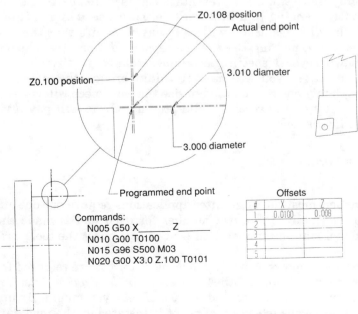

Z0.108 position
Actual end point
3.010 diameter
Z0.100 position
3.000 diameter
Programmed end point

Commands:
  N005 G50 X_____ Z_____
  N010 G00 T0100
  N015 G96 S500 M03
  N020 G00 X3.0 Z.100 T0101

Offsets

#	X	Z
1	0.0100	0.008
2		
3		
4		
5		

Figure 3.5 How the end point is changed when a tool offset is instated during a rapid motion command.

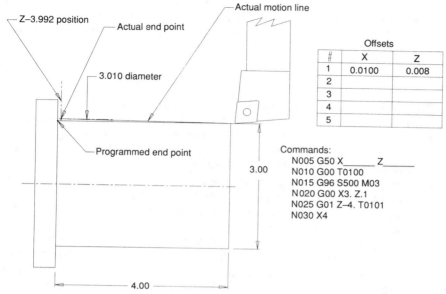

Figure 3.6 How motion changes when a tool offset is instated during a straight-line cutting command.

N030 G01 Z-5. T0121 (Turn diameter, instate offset 21)
N035 X3.2 (Feed off workpiece)
N040 G00 X _____ Z _____ T0100 (Return to tool change position,
cancel offset)
N045 M30 (End of program)

In line N010, when the control instates offset 1, the X axis will be under the influence of a 0.005-in offset. This means the end point in X of line N020 will actually be 3.005 in. Of course, this offset is intended to allow for tool setting imperfections. In this case, the tool will move to a position 0.005 in in diameter larger than if offset 1 were zero, making the tool machine precisely to the 3.000-in diameter when the tool-setting imperfection is considered.

What do you think will happen when offset 21 in line N030 is instated? The value of offset 21 is 0.003 in. As it moves to the Z-5. position, do you think the tool will move to a larger diameter or a smaller one?

Since offsets are *not* accumulative, the tool will be under the influence of 0.003-in offset at the end of line N030. The recalculated end point for this command will be *smaller* in diameter by 0.002 in (0.005 − 0.003). In this case, it will be as if line N030 were actually

N030 G01 X2.998 Z-5.

Though this may sound a little complicated, it is important that you understand this principle before you attempt to apply secondary offsets for *any* purpose. If necessary, repeat this section until you feel comfortable with the presented information. In order for you to understand the following presentations, you must thoroughly grasp information presented thus far.

Flip jobs

The first application for secondary tool offsets is merely an extension of the way primary offsets are used. There are times when CNC turning-center users wish to machine both ends of the workpiece in one setup. By using this technique, a completed workpiece can be machined during each cycle. In this case, the operator loads the rough stock and starts the cycle. When the first side of the workpiece is complete, the programmer stops the machine with an M00. At this time, the operator turns the workpiece around and continues the cycle by pressing the cycle start button.

If concentricity is critical, this application normally requires that the work-holding jaws be double-bored. This double boring allows the first side of the workpiece being machined to be held on a different diameter of the jaw than the second side. Each jaw boring can be done to hold its appointed diameter accurately.

Figure 3.7 shows a workpiece being machined in this manner (though double-bored jaws are not shown). The drawing on the left shows the first operation, while the drawing on the right shows the second operation.

When running workpieces in this manner, you must ensure that the offsets used for the first operation do not affect those used during the second operation, and vice versa. For example, say tool 1 is a rough-

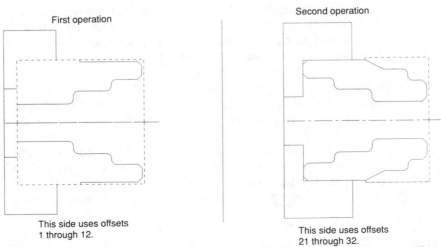

First operation

Second operation

This side uses offsets 1 through 12.

This side uses offsets 21 through 32.

Figure 3.7 Secondary offsets are used when both ends of the same workpiece are machined in one setup.

turning tool that is used during the machining of both sides of this workpiece. Say that tool 1 uses offset 1 during the first operation. If tool 1 also uses offset 1 for the second operation, any X or Z offset made to compensate for imperfections during the first operation will affect the way tool 1 machines during the second operation.

For this reason, you must use two different offsets for each single tool required in both operations. We recommend that you use a logical method for assigning tool offsets in order to avoid confusion on the operator's part. The operator must know which offsets affect each tool in each setup. If, for example, the machine has 12 turret stations and the control has at least 32 offsets (a common configuration for turning centers), you can use offsets 1 to 12 for the first operation and offsets 21 to 32 for the second operation. To come up with the secondary offset for any tool, the operator will simply add 20 to the tool station number. With this method, tool 1 would use offset 1 for the first operation and offset number 21 for the second operation, tool 2 would use offset 2 for the first operation and offset 22 for the second operation, and so on.

If the control does not allow the number of offsets you need for this technique (32 in our example), you can still add a constant number to the tool station number to come up with the offset number to be used for each tool in the second operation. For example, say the machine has 12 turret stations but the control allows only 25 tool offsets. For the first operation, offsets 1 to 12 can be used for tools 1 to 12. For the second operation, you can simply add the number 12 to the tool station number to come up with the offset number to use for each tool in the second operation. In this case, tool 1 will use offset 1 for the first operation and offset 13 for the second operation. Tool 2 will use offset 2 for the first operation and offset 14 for the second operation, and so on. Though this technique is not as easy to use as the one just given, at least the programmer and operator can stay in synchronism with regard to secondary offset numbers.

Holding size for critical diameters with secondary offsets

The programmer should always use the mean value of the dimension for each surface in order to come up with the programmed coordinate. The mean value of a dimension is perfectly in the middle of the specified tolerance. For example, 3.0005 in is the mean value for the dimension 3.000 in + 0.002, −0.001 in.

Of course, this requires that the overall tolerance must be taken into account for *every* coordinate used in the program and the mean value must be calculated and used as the programmed dimension for *every* coordinate. In most cases, when the mean value for each dimension is used for programmed coordinates, only one offset is required for the each turning or boring tool. If one diameter or face is sized properly, all diameters and faces machined by the tool will also come out to size.

However, there are times when tool pressure will affect machining in different ways on different workpiece surfaces. If substantial tool pressure exists, and if tolerances are tight, it can be difficult to hold size no matter what dimension is programmed.

Look at Fig. 3.8. Notice that this rather lengthy workpiece has two critical diameters. The 2-in nominal diameter has a $+0-$, -0.0002-in tolerance. The 4-in nominal diameter has a $+0.0002-$, -0-in tolerance. In this case, the programmer should program the value 1.9999 in for the 2-in nominal diameter and 4.0001 in for the 4-in nominal diameter.

Though the mean dimension of each tolerance is programmed, the operator may still experience difficulty holding both diameters to size. As the finish-turning tool machines the very end, notice the tailstock used for support. The workpiece will be very rigid in this area. However, as the finish-turning tool machines this workpiece and gets farther and farther from the tailstock, machining becomes less rigid. When the tool reaches the 4-in diameter, the tool pressure may be substantially different than for machining the 2-in diameter, meaning the 4-in diameter may not come out to size even though the 2-in diameter does.

One way to handle this problem is to actually change the programmed dimension for one of the diameters once the workpiece is run and the amount of tool pressure is known. However, this makes sizing the workpiece quite difficult. Also, if a workpiece must be machined in order to determine the amount of tool pressure, it is likely that at least one workpiece will be scrapped. And the deviation caused by tool pressure will change with the sharpness of the tool.

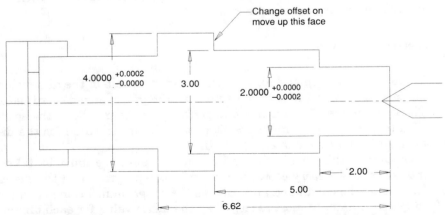

Figure 3.8 Drawing demonstrating the use of a secondary offset to hold size for two or more critical diameters.

As the tool dulls, tool pressure will increase. It would be difficult to keep changing the program to allow for this constant change in tool pressure.

This is a case when a secondary offset can be used to force both dimensions to come out correctly. In effect, one offset will be used to hold the 2-in diameter (the primary offset) and another offset will be used to hold the 4-in diameter (the secondary offset). Note that this technique can be repeated for the number of critical dimensions to be held.

Here is a program for the workpiece shown in Fig. 3.8 that uses a secondary offset for this purpose. For this example, note that only the finish-turning tool portion of the program is shown.

Program:

O0036 (Program number)
N005 G50 X _____ Z _____ (Set program zero)
N010 G00 T0101 M42 (Index to station 1, instate offset 1, select spindle power range)
N015 G96 S500 M03 (Turn spindle on CW at 500 SFM)
N020 G00 X1.999 Z.1 (Rapid up to workpiece, note X value is mean dimension)
N025 G01 Z-2. F.007 (Turn 2-in diameter)
N030 X3. (Face to 3-in diameter)
N035 Z-5. (Turn 3-in diameter)
N040 X4.0001 T0121 (Face to 4-in diameter, switch offsets on the way up the face)
N045 Z-6.75 (Turn 4-in diameter)
N050 G00 X4.25 (Rapid away from workpiece)
N055 X _____ Z _____ T0100 (Rapid back to tool change position, cancel offset)
N060 M30 (End of program)

In this case, offsets 1 and 21 are used to control tool 1. The primary offset (1) will be used to control the 2-in diameter. The secondary offset (21), instated on the facing movement up to the 4-in diameter in line N040, will be used to control the 4-in diameter.

In order to use this technique, you *must* understand the presentations made earlier in relation to what happens during an offset change in a straight-line motion command. When making offset changes for tool 1, *both* offsets (1 and 21) must be considered. First of all, the Z value *must* be the same for *both offsets* for this technique to work. If there is any difference between offset 1's Z value and offset 21's Z value, the face machined prior to the 4-in diameter will be tapered.

When it comes to the X value for each offset, there should be only a tiny difference in offset value, reflecting *only* the amount of tool pressure. If either is changed to bring the part on size, or to allow for tool wear, both should be changed by nearly the same value.

Here is a full example of how this workpiece could be sized. Say you wanted to make a trial-finishing pass allowing 0.020 in in the same way as shown earlier. The X value for *both* offsets (1 and 21) *must* be set to +0.020 in (and the Z values must be identical). Once tool 1 has machined the workpiece, both diameters can be measured. Say the 2-

in diameter was measured as 2.0215 and the 4-in diameter was measured as 4.0218 in. In this case, offset 1 will be reduced by 0.0216 in (2.0215 − 1.9999) and offset 21 will be reduced by 0.0217 in (4.0218 − 4.0001). The X value of offset 1 will end up as −0.0016 in (0.020 − 0.0216) and the X value of offset 21 will end up as −0.0017 in (0.020 − 0.0217). This tiny difference in X-axis offset values represents the difference in tool pressure from the 2-in diameter to the 4-in diameter.

As mentioned earlier, this technique can be repeated for as many critical tolerances as required. However, it must be made very clear to the operator which offsets are used to control each diameter. Also, this technique should be used only to allow for deviations caused by tool pressure for very critical dimensions when finishing. There will never be a need to use this technique during roughing operations. The tiny deviations caused by tool pressure will not be substantial enough during roughing to affect finishing operations.

Using a secondary offset to allow for unwanted taper

In similar fashion, a secondary offset can be used to rid diameters of unwanted taper caused by tool pressure. Figure 3.9 shows an example of a turned-diameter workpiece that is very stable at one end (because of tailstock support) and less stable at the other. Tool pressure may change as the 3-in diameter is being turned over its 3-in length. In this case, as the 3-in diameter is turned, the workpiece would have the tendency to push away from the tool, causing the headstock end of the 3-in diameter to be larger than the tailstock end.

As with the previous discussion, one way around this problem is to change the program, making the machine actually command a tapered motion to a smaller diameter as it turns the 3-in diameter. This programmed taper will allow for the amount of tool pressure and

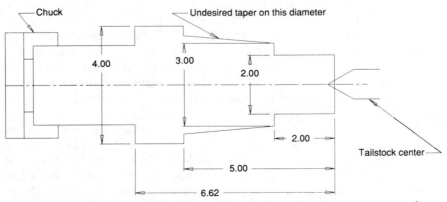

Figure 3.9 Drawing demonstrating the use of a secondary offset to remove unwanted taper.

counter the unwanted taper experienced. However, since tool pressure changes as a tool dulls, the amount of unwanted taper will also change. This means the program may have to be changed several times for each cutting edge of the tool if the diameter is critical.

A better way to handle this problem is to use a secondary offset to control how much taper is induced during the turning of the 3-in diameter. As the 3-in diameter is turned, the secondary offset can be instated. The primary offset will control the tailstock end diameter and the secondary offset will control the headstock end diameter. Here is the program to machine the workpiece shown in Fig. 3.9.

Program:

```
O0037 (Program number)
N005 G50 X _____ Z _____ (Set program zero)
N010 G00 T0101 M42 (Index to station 1, instate offset 1, select spindle power
range)
N015 G96 S500 M03 (Turn spindle on CW at 500 SFM)
N020 G00 X2. Z.1 (Rapid up close to workpiece)
N025 G01 Z-2. F.007 (Turn 2-in diameter)
N030 X3. (Face to 3-in diameter)
N035 Z-5. T0121 (Switch tool offset as 3-in diameter is turned)
N040 X4. (Face to 4-in diameter)
N045 Z-6.75 (Turn 4-in diameter)
N050 G00 X4.25 (Rapid away from workpiece)
N055 X _____ Z _____ T0100 (Rapid back to tool change position,
cancel offset)
N060 M30 (End of program)
```

In line N035, notice how the secondary tool offset is instated during the turning of the 3-in diameter. As with the previous example, it is very important that you understand how this offset change will affect machining. In this case, the Z value for both offsets (1 and 21) *must* be the same. If there is any difference, the 5-in dimension given to the face after the 3-in diameter will not be correct.

The tiny difference in the X values of offsets 1 and 21 will reflect *only* the amount of taper caused by tool pressure. In this case, since the workpiece will have the tendency to push away from the tool as the 3-in diameter is turned, offset 21 should end up slightly smaller than offset 1.

Here is an extended discussion on how trial machining can be done when you are using this technique. Say you want to trial-turn these diameters with 0.020-in excess stock as shown earlier. In this case, you would make *both* offsets' (1's and 21's) X values plus by 0.020 in (the Z offset values *must* be the same). After this preliminary machining you measure the tailstock side of the 3-in diameter and find it to be 3.021 in. However, when you measure the headstock side of the 3-in diameter, you find it to be 3.0215 in. This means you have 0.0005-in taper in the 3-in diameter. To correct the taper problem and bring the 3-in diameter to size, you will reduce offset 1 by 0.021 in (3.021 − 3.0) and reduce offset 21 by 0.0215 in (3.0215 − 3.0). The next time this tool machines the workpiece, the 3-in diameter will come out to size without taper.

Headstock alignment problems. The discussions related to unwanted taper in the previous presentation reflected a problem caused by a difference in tool pressure. Unless your company runs a great number of very flimsy setups, you should only rarely have to deal with this problem.

However, unwanted taper on each diameter more commonly will result from a headstock misalignment problem. If the headstock is not perfectly aligned with the turret, when the machine turns *every* diameter, it will be machining with taper. This kind of misalignment is usually caused by some kind of mishap. If a crash has occurred (the tool rapids into the workpiece, for example), it is possible that the force exerted during the crash pushed the headstock out of position.

It is very important that you regularly check for misalignment, especially after a mishap of any kind and regardless of severity. To check for misalignment, place a relatively rigid workpiece in the spindle. For example, a piece of mild steel, 4 in in diameter and about 6 in long, would work nicely. *Do not engage the tailstock.* When engaged, the tailstock could induce its own taper if *it* is not properly aligned.

With this test workpiece in the spindle, index the turret to a turning tool, start the spindle, and manually skim the outside diameter of the workpiece for its entire length. Then, stop the spindle and measure for taper. If there is *any* taper in the workpiece, the headstock is out of alignment with the turret and the machine *must* be repaired.

Most CNC turning-center manufacturers make it relatively easy to repair this taper problem. Knowing that the misalignment problem caused by a crash is a very common problem, they design the machine accordingly. However, it is wise to contact them to learn the proper way to realign the headstock.

The techniques given earlier for removing unwanted taper from a diameter with offsets should be used *only* to compensate for tool-pressure-related problems. While this technique may be a temporary fix for a misaligned headstock, it is *not* a permanent cure. We never recommend compensating for machine problems with programming techniques. In *all* cases, if the machine is behaving improperly, it *must* be repaired.

Using a secondary tool offset to machine long shafts

As stated, tool pressure has the tendency to push a workpiece away from the cutting tool. The weaker the workpiece, the more likely it is that the workpiece will be pushed away from the tool during machining.

Figure 3.10 shows another example of when this result of tool pressure is likely to occur. When you are machining long, skinny shafts and using the tailstock for support, the workpiece will be well-supported at both ends. However, the closer it is to the center of the workpiece, the weaker the support becomes.

When you are finish-turning this workpiece, as the tool begins machining from the tailstock end, there will be ample support, and no deflection will occur. However, as the tool comes closer to the center of the workpiece, support will become progressively worse. As this happens, tool pressure will cause deflection when the workpiece begins pushing away from the tool. When the tool is in the center of the workpiece, the deflection will be at its worst. After the tool passes center and comes closer to the headstock, support becomes progressively better and tool pressure becomes progressively less.

This kind of problem is the result of a poor setup. It normally requires a change in the method by which the workpiece is held. For example, a steady rest may have to be placed in the center of the workpiece to provide consistent support from one end to the other. However, if no such device is available, and if there is only a slight tendency for deflection, a secondary tool offset can be used to compensate for this deflection.

Here is a program for machining the workpiece in Fig. 3.10 that uses a secondary offset for this purpose.

Program:

```
O0038 (Program number)
N005 G50 X _____ Z _____ (Set program zero)
N010 G00 T0101 M42 (Index to station 1, instate offset 1)
N015 G96 S300 M03 (Start spindle CW at 300 SFM)
N020 G00 X1. Z.1 (Rapid up to workpiece)
N025 G01 Z-5. F.007 T0121 (Turn half way, instate offset 21)
N030 Z-10. T0101 (Turn the rest of the way, reinstate offset 1)
N035 X1.2 (Feed off workpiece)
N040 G00 X _____ Z _____ T0100 (Return to tool change position,
cancel offset)
N045 M30 (End of program)
```

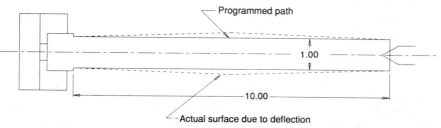

Figure 3.10 Drawing demonstrating the use of a secondary offset to remove unwanted taper from long shafts.

This program uses offsets 1 and 21 to control the size of the 1.00-in diameter as well as any unwanted deflection. As with other uses for secondary offsets, you must consider them together. The Z values of *both* offsets *must* be the same. For X, the difference in offset values will reflect the amount of deflection caused by tool pressure.

Here is the trial-machining discussion. Say you wish to trial-turn the 1-in diameter with 0.020-in excess stock. You place the value 0.020 in (plus) in offsets 1 and 21. After machining, you measure the workpiece. Say both the headstock and tailstock ends of the 1-in diameter come out to 1.022 in. But in the center, the 1-in diameter is measured to be 1.024 in. In this case, you reduce offset 1 by 0.022 in (1.022 − 1.00) and reduce offset 21 by 0.024 in (1.024 − 1.00).

The next time tool 1 machines the workpiece, as it turns to center in line N025, offset 21 is instated. The X-axis end point will become smaller in diameter (by 0.002 in) during the move to center (forming a tapered movement). In effect, this compensates for the 0.002-in difference between the center and ends of the workpiece. As the tool continues in line N030 to the final Z ending position, offset 1 is reinstated. In this case, the X axis end point will become larger in diameter (by 0.002 in).

As stated, this technique should be used only to compensate for minor tool deflection. In more severe cases, the weakness of the workpiece in the setup will cause more severe problems like vibration (chatter) during machining. If this occurs, the setup, cutting conditions or process must be changed.

Using a secondary offset to control groove width

When grooving, there are many times when the groove to be machined is wider than the grooving tool. This requires that the programmer make multiple passes, each making the groove wider. Normally, the programmer begins by plunging in the center of the groove. Then, as many passes as necessary are programmed, each widening the groove.

When considering offsets, most programmers use only one offset with a grooving tool to size the diameter plunged by the grooving tool and the position of the groove in the Z axis. For the groove to be the proper width, they depend on the grooving tool width to be perfect.

Indeed, grooving-tool carbide-insert manufacturers make their grooving tools to exacting tolerances. And in most cases, if the program is written correctly, the groove width will be machined correctly to size. However, if the width of the grooving tool is not perfect, of if there is unexpected tool pressure, the width of the groove will not come out to size.

Figure 3.11 shows a workpiece to be machined by the program to

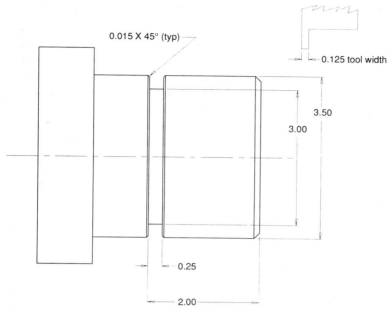

Figure 3.11   Drawing demonstrating the use of a secondary offset to control the width of a groove.

follow. Note that only the grooving tool portion of the program is shown.

Program:

O0039 (Program number)
(Grooving tool)
N005 G50 X _____ Z _____ (Set program zero)
N010 G00 T0101 M41 (Index to station 1, instate offset 1, select low spindle range)
N015 G96 S400 M03 (Turn spindle on CW at 400 SFM)
N020 G00 X3.7 Z-1.9375 (Rapid to clearance position in X and center of groove in Z)
N025 G01 X3. F.005 (Plunge groove to depth at center)
N030 G04 P500 (Pause for 0.500 second to relieve tool pressure)
N035 G00 X3.7 (Rapid out in X)
N040 Z-2.015 (Rapid to left side of left chamfer)
N045 G01 X3.5 (Feed flush to groove diameter)
N050 X3.47 Z-2. (Form left chamfer)
N055 X3. (Plunge left side of groove to size)
N060 G04 P500 (Pause for 0.500 second to relieve tool pressure)
N065 G00 X3.7 (Rapid out in X)
N070 Z-1.86 T0121 (Rapid to right side of right chamfer, instate offset 21)
N075 G01 X3.5 (Feed flush to groove diameter)
N080 X3.47 Z-1.875 (Form right chamfer)
N085 X3. (Plunge right side of groove to size)
N090 G04 P500 (Pause for 0.500 second to relieve tool pressure)
N095 G00 X3.7 (Rapid out in X)
N100 X _____ Z _____ T0100 (Rapid to tool change position, cancel offset)
N105 M30 (End of program)

In this program, tool 1 is under the influence of the primary offset (offset 1) until line N070. Once the left half of the groove is completed and, during the tool's motion over to the right side of the groove, offset 21 is instated. This allows the left side of the groove to be controlled by offset 1 and the right side of the groove to be controlled by offset 21. In this application, the X value of each offset *must* be the same for both offsets (1 and 21). If they are not identical, there will be a step along the groove bottom (the 3-in diameter in this case).

Say you wish to allow excess stock while using the above technique. You will place an identical plus value in the X position for both offsets 1 and 21. If you wish 0.020-in excess stock (in diameter), you will make the X position of both offsets 1 and 21 the value 0.020 in. In Z, you will place a *plus* value in offset 1, and a *minus* value in offset 21. This will keep the left side of the groove to the *right* of its final position and the right side of the groove to the *left* of its final position. Say you place the value 0.010 in in offset 1 and −0.010 in in offset 21.

After running the cycle, you measure the 2-in dimension and find it to be 1.992. You measure the distance from the end of the shoulder to the right side of the groove and find it to be 1.759 in (it should be 1.750 in). You find the bottom diameter of the groove to be 3.019 in. In this case, you *reduce* the Z value of offset 1 by 0.008 in (2.0 − 1.992), *increase* the Z value of offset 21 (make it less minus) by 0.009 in (1.759 − 1.750), and *reduce* the X value of both offset 1 and offset 21 by 0.019 in (3.019 − 3.0). When the tool is rerun, the groove will come out to size.

Note that using this technique even allows a grooving tool of a slightly different width than the one for which the program is written. In the above program, for example, we intended to use a 0.125-in-wide grooving tool. But say, for example, the operator has no 0.125-in grooving tool inserts left and must use a different size. Say the operator wishes to use a ³⁄₃₂-in-wide (0.0937-in) tool. In this case, the Z value of offset 21 will be increased by 0.0313 in (0.125 − 0.0937). Of course, the grooving tool must be wide enough to completely machine the groove in the same series of passes as was planned for the original grooving tool.

Using secondary offsets with form grooving tools

It can be very difficult to calculate tool motions when you are programming form tools. This problem is even more complicated when multiple passes must be made. When the tool is ground with the same basic configuration as the surface to be machined, trigonometry must be used to calculate accurate program coordinates according to the angles and radii of the form tool. This can be a difficult problem for the programmer if the form tool includes more than simple angles and incorporates a free-flowing contour.

Figure 3.12 shows a drawing that would be quite difficult to program by conventional techniques. Notice that our drawing does not even include the angles on each side of the groove, making it impossible to calculate the position to which the tool must be sent on each side before the groove can be plunged. In this case, the programmer would have to contact the design engineer to find out the values of these related angles.

Secondary offsets can make it much easier to handle this problem. Here is a program that can be used to machine the workpiece shown in Fig. 3.12. Note that if you use two secondary offsets, it is not even necessary to know the angles that form the sides of the groove. Of course this assumes that the grooving tool has been machined with the correct side angles.

Program:

```
O0040 (Program number)
N005 G50 X _____ Z _____ (Set program zero)
N010 G00 T0101 M41 (Index to station 1, instate offset 1, select low spindle range)
N015 G96 S400 M03 (Turn spindle on CW at 400 SFM)
N020 G00 X3.7 Z-1.93 (Rapid to a position somewhere in the center of the groove)
N025 G01 X3. F.005 (Feed to groove bottom)
N030 G04 P500 (Pause for 0.500 second to relieve tool pressure)
```

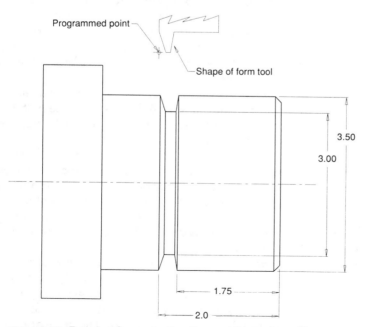

Figure 3.12 Drawing demonstrating the use of secondary offsets to easily control the width of a form groove.

N035 G00 X3.7 (Rapid out of groove)
N040 T0121 W0 (Instate offset 21, incrementally, move nothing in Z; the value in offset 21 controls move amount)
N045 G01 X3. (Feed to bottom of groove)
N050 G04 P500 (Pause for 0.500 second to relieve tool pressure)
N055 G00 X3.7 (Rapid out of groove)
N060 G00 T0141 W0 (Instate offset 41, incrementally, move nothing in Z; the value in offset 41 controls move amount)
N065 G01 X3. (Feed to bottom of groove)
N070 G04 P500 (Pause for 0.500 second to relieve tool pressure)
N075 G00 X3.7 (Rapid out of groove)
N080 G00 X _____ Z _____ T0100 (Return to tool change position, cancel offset)
N085 M30 (End of program)

This program requires further explanation. In line N020, we send the form-grooving tool to a clearance position in X and to a location somewhere in the center of the groove in Z under the influence of offset 1. Note that this Z position is not critical. As long as the grooving tool does not violate the workpiece surface when the first pass is made, any position in the center of the groove will work fine. It is this location where the first pass will be made. The Z value of offset 1 works with the program to control this first position.

At this approach Z position, the first plunging pass is made in line N025. The grooving tool pauses and then retracts from the groove. In line N040, no real motion appears to be commanded, offset 21 is simply instated. The W0 is included just in case the control requires that a motion command is given to completely instate the offset. However, if your particular control instates the offset immediately, the W0 is not required. In either case, the offset instated in line N040 *will* cause a motion equal to the difference between the Z value of offset 1 and offset 21. More on this in a moment.

Next, the second pass is made in line N045. The tool then pauses and rapids out of the groove. In a similar way to line N040, line N060 instates offset 41 (this example assumes the control has at least 41 offsets). The third and last pass is then made.

When you are sizing the first workpiece, the X values of all three offsets must be the same, and can be made to allow excess stock on the bottom of the groove. Say you set the X values of offsets 1, 21, and 41 to 0.020 in. For this first time the program is run, the Z values of offsets 1, 21, and 41 will be left at zero, and the program will machine the groove in the same Z location three times. Of course, the second and third passes will machine nothing at this time.

After machining, the groove bottom diameter can be measured. Say it comes out to 3.019 in. In this case, the X values of offsets 1, 21, and 41 *must all* be reduced by 0.019 in. At this point, the program is run again, and when it is finished, the bottom diameter will be to size.

With the bottom diameter finished, you can measure the critical dimensions from the end of the workpiece to the left and right sides of the groove. Let's say the measurement from the end of the workpiece to the left side of the groove comes out to 1.945 in (it must eventually be 2.000) and the dimension from the end of the workpiece to the right side of the groove comes out to 1.785 in (it must eventually be 1.750 in).

In this case, you will *reduce* the Z value of offset 21 by 0.055 in (2.000 − 1.945), making it −0.055 in. Then you will *increase* the Z value of offset 41 by 0.035 in (1.785 − 1.750), making it +0.035 in. By this method, the left side of the groove will be machined before the right side. If you simply reverse the offset numbers or the values within each offset discussed above, you can easily reverse the machining order.

When the program is run again, after the first pass, when line N040 is executed, the tool will move minus in Z by 0.055 in, forcing the second pass to make the groove wider and forming the left side of the groove to size. After the second pass, when line N060 is executed, the control will now move to the right side of the groove. The actual motion (in this case) will be 0.090 in (− 0.055 to +0.035 offset change). The third grooving pass is then made, forming the right side of the groove to size.

While this may sound a little complicated, this technique allows the operator to control the size of the groove nicely at the machine. It also keeps the programmer from having to come up with coordinates that are difficult (if not impossible) to calculate.

Conclusion to secondary tool offsets

As you have seen, there are numerous times when using more than one offset per tool in a turning-center program is advantageous. We have illustrated many of these times here. Keep in mind that your own ingenuity will allow you to come up with even more.

If you are faced with a difficult workpiece sizing problem on a turning center, it is likely that the use of a secondary offset will help. With your new understanding of what happens as an offset is instated, both in rapid (G00) and straight-line (G01) cutting modes, you should be able to develop your program in a way that helps the operator handle almost any sizing problem.

Tool Offset Techniques with Tool Length Compensation on a Machining Center

The tool length compensation feature on a machining center allows the programmer to forget about the length of all tools used by a program as the program is written. A command in the program tells the control to instate tool length compensation. This command points at a tool offset. In the tool offset is stored the tool length value. The program will position the tool, while executing the tool length compensation command, according to the value found in the related tool length offset value.

One popular control uses this command to instate tool length compensation:

N045 G43 H01 Z.1

In this command, the G43 tells the control to instate tool length compensation. The H word (H01 in our case) tells the machine the offset number in which is stored the tool length information (offset 1 in our case). The Z.1 tells the control the end point in the Z axis at which the *tip* of the tool must stop.

In the offset, the operator will store the tool length value as the part of the setup. On most machining centers, the operator will actually store the length of the tool (the distance from the tip of the tool to the nose of the spindle). However, depending on the machine and application, it is possible that the operator will store the distance from the tip of the tool while the Z axis is at its reference position to the program zero point in Z as the tool length value. In this case, a large negative value will be stored in each tool length compensation offset. Keep in mind that the points we make in this section will work regardless of which tool length offset method is used.

Just as the dimensional tool offsets of a turning center help with workpiece sizing, so does the tool length compensation offset of a machining center. However, for machining-center application, the tool length compensation offset can help only with Z-axis sizing. Also, the amount of sizing allowed by tool length compensation is quite small in comparison to the turning center's dimensional tool offsets (more on why a little later).

As an example, say an end mill is used to machine a rectangular pocket, and the depth of the pocket is quite critical. Say the dimension for the pocket depth is specified as 0.2500 in ±0.0005 in. It would be foolish for the operator of the machining center to simply run the program without concern for the tool offset for the end mill which machines the pocket. If the offset is not considered, the operator will have no control of the pocket depth. Luck will determine whether the pocket depth comes out correctly.

To assure that excess stock is left after the end mill is finished, the operator can *add* a small value to the tool length compensation value. If the length of the tool is stored as the tool length offset value, the operator will make this offset value bigger. If the distance from the tip of the tool to program zero is stored as the offset value (big negative number), the offset value can be made a smaller negative number (less minus) by the amount of excess stock to allow. Once the workpiece is actually machined, the operator can measure the depth of the pocket to find out exactly how much excess stock has been left and adjust the tool length offset value accordingly.

Say, for example, tool station 1 is the end mill and its length compensation value is stored in offset 1. The operator wishes to leave

0.020 in excess stock at the pocket bottom to ensure that the end mill will not machine too deep. Say the length of the end mill has been measured as 6.4533 in long, and this tool length value is currently stored in offset 1. To allow the excess stock (0.020 in), the operator will *increase* the value of offset 1 by 0.020 in. In this case, the new value of offset 1 will be 6.4733 in. Now the control will think the tool is 0.020 in longer than it really is and keep the tip of the tool 0.020 farther away from the programmed Z depth.

After machining, the operator measures the depth of the pocket and finds it to be 0.2315 in. In this case, the operator knows there is 0.0185 in of stock yet to machine at the pocket bottom. Offset 1 will be *reduced* by 0.0185 in and the value of offset 1 will be made 6.4548 (6.4733 − 0.0185).

For the sake of completeness, let's look at the same example when the distance from the tool tip to program zero is stored as the (large negative) offset. Say the operator measures the distance from the tip of the end mill to program zero and stores this value in offset 1. Say this measured distance stored in offset 1 is −14.5475 in.

To force the control to machine with 0.020-in excess stock, the operator would add 0.020 to this large minus number. Adding a plus number to a minus value reduces the actual value of the minus value. In this case, the new value to be stored in offset 1 will be −14.5275 (−14.5475 + 0.020).

After machining, the operator measures the pocket depth and finds it to be 0.2315 in deep. This means 0.0185 in is yet to be machined from the pocket bottom. Now the operator subtracts 0.0185 in from the current offset value, making it −14.546 in (−14.5275 − 0.0185). The tool is run again and machines the pocket depth to size. To remember in which direction to change the offset (plus or minus), simply think about the Z-axis direction. As the spindle nose comes closer to the workpiece, the Z axis is moving in a *minus* direction. As it moves farther away, it is moving *plus*. In order to keep the tool farther away from the workpiece (making the pocket shallower), *increase* the offset size. This, in effect, keeps the spindle farther away from the Z surface being machined. To keep the tool closer to the workpiece (making the pocket deeper), you would bring the spindle toward the workpiece by *decreasing* the offset size.

Limit to possible offset adjustment

Keep in mind that you normally position the tool to within 0.100 in from the solid surface being machined. If a mistake is made in the program, you may be deceived into making a dreadful mistake with tool offsets. For example, in the previous rectangular pocket example, after machining the pocket with excess stock, you measure the depth and find it to be 0.1245 in deep. The pocket still has 0.1255 in of stock on the bottom yet to be machined. However, if you decrease the offset value by 0.1255 in, it is likely that the tool will rapid into the work surface on its approach move. In this situation, something is very wrong. Either the tool length value was measured incorrectly or the programmed pocket depth in the Z axis is not correct.

In all cases, the amount by which you must adjust each tool's Z offset for sizing purposes should be well under 0.100 in. If you find you need more than 0.100 in, check the tool length value stored in the offset (by remeasuring the tool) and check the programmed Z positions in the program to find the mistake.

Though our discussions to this point have been related to pocket milling, these principles apply to all kinds of machining center tools.

Tooling problems versus offset problems

There is one time when you may be deceived into changing an offset value when something more basic is needed. For example, say a drill is supposed to machine a hole to a depth of 1.0 in. Yet, after machining, the hole depth is found to be 0.945 in deep. Thinking it is an offset problem, you adjust the tool offset accordingly and remachine the workpiece with the drill. But after machining, the drilled hole is still not to depth.

In this case, it is probable that the drill is slipping in its holder. Collet-style tool holders are notorious for this kind of slippage. If this is the case, your offset changes will have little if any effect on the hole depth from one workpiece to the next. Of course, the drill (or whatever tool is being used) must be tightened in its holder, its length value remeasured, and its length offset value reentered.

Tool Offset Techniques with Cutter Radius Compensation

Just as tool length compensation allows the programmer to forget about tool lengths as the program is written, cutter radius compensation allows the programmer to forget about the tool's radius during programming. Cutter radius compensation is used only with tools that have the ability to machine on the periphery of the cutter, like end mills and shell mills.

Also like tool length compensation, cutter radius compensation uses a tool offset. For most CNC machining-center controls, this tool offset is used to tell the control the tool's radius. However, there are some CNC controls that use this offset in which to specify the tool's diameter.

There are two ways to specify coordinates when using cutter radius compensation. The value stored in the tool offset depends on which method is used. Most manual programmers prefer to program the surface of the workpiece, using actual workpiece dimensions as coordinates for the program. With this method, the value stored in the offset is the actual cutter radius.

CAM system programmers will often force the system to output the tool's centerline coordinates for the program for the planned cutter size. For example, if the programmer believes that the operator should use a 1.00-in-diameter cutter, the CNC program generated by the CAM system will include the centerline coordinates for a 1.00-in-diameter cutter. In this case, the offset value will be the difference from the intended cutter size, normally in terms of radius. If a 1.00-in cutter is used, the cutter radius compensation offset value will be zero. If the cutter being used is smaller than the intended cutter size, the offset value will be minus. If bigger, the offset value will be plus.

Since most controls use cutter *radius* values as the offset with cutter radius compensation, all specific techniques in this section will show the cutter radius value. If your particular control happens to use diameter values for cutter radius compensation, all offset changes shown in this section must be doubled. However, whether diameter or radius input is needed, the same principles will apply no matter whether the CNC program is generated with work surface coordinates (offset equals cutter radius) or centerline coordinates (offset equals difference from intended cutter size to actual cutter size).

Cutter radius compensation requires the use of three G codes:

G40   Cancel

G41   Cutter left

G42   Cutter right

G41 and G42 are used to instate cutter radius compensation. To decide which one to use, look in the direction the cutter is moving and ask yourself which side of the workpiece the cutter is on. If the cutter is on the left side of the workpiece, you will use G41 to instate cutter radius compensation. If on the right, you will use G42.

If you can tell the difference between climb and conventional milling, there is an easier way to evaluate G41 versus G42. With a right-hand tool (running the spindle in the CW direction with M03), G41 is used for climb milling and G42 is used for conventional milling.

For most controls, the actual command to instate cutter radius compensation looks something like this:

    N050 G41 D31 X3.

The G41 tells the control to instate cutter radius compensation left. The D word tells the control in which offset the radius value is stored. There must also be an axis motion. In this example, the motion is to an X position of 3.0 in.

Since most controls allow you to specify any offset as the radius offset, you should choose this offset number (D word) in a logical manner.

We recommend adding a constant number to the tool station number in order to come up with the offset number in which the radius of the tool will be stored. For example, if the machine has less than 30 tool stations, add 30 to the tool station number to come up with the cutter radius compensation offset number. With this method, the tool *length* value of tool 1 will be stored in offset 1. The *radius* value of tool 1 will be stored in offset 31.

Of course, the command to instate cutter radius compensation will depend on whether cutter left (G41) or cutter right (G42) is to be used. Also, the axis motion will vary with the kind of machining to be done. Some controls will use an H word in place of the D word to point to the tool offset being used.

Once instated, cutter radius compensation will remain in effect until it is canceled. That is, the control will continue to keep the cutter positioned on the left or right side (based on G41 or G42) of the surfaces programmed until a cancellation command (G40) is given. The programmer *must* remember to cancel cutter radius compensation when finished. Otherwise cutter radius compensation will remain in effect, even for the following tools, making motions quite unpredictable. A lengthy discussion of cutter radius compensation problems is given in Chap. 2.

This short introduction to cutter radius compensation barely scratches the surface of how cutter radius compensation is used. However, it should prepare you to understand the presentations to follow. To learn more about how to apply cutter radius compensation for your particular control, you must refer to its programming manual.

Sizing the surfaces machined with cutter radius compensation

One of the most important advantages of using cutter radius compensation is that it gives you the ability to easily size the surfaces machined. As with all machining operations, *before* you allow a tool using cutter radius compensation to machine the workpiece, you *must* consider its radius offset. As with other forms of compensation we have been discussing in this chapter, you can change the radius offset in a way that forces the tool to leave excess stock, machine the workpiece, measure the surfaces machined, change the offset accordingly, and remachine the workpiece to size.

In *all* cases, to allow excess stock you *increase* the value of the cutter radius compensation offset (make it more plus). This will keep the tool farther away from the surface being machined. Once the workpiece has been machined and measured, you can decrease the cutter radius compensation offset value accordingly.

Figure 3.13 shows a workpiece to be used as an extended example.

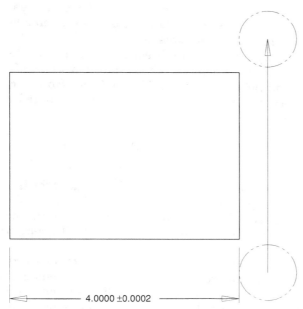

Figure 3.13 Use of a cutter radius compensation offset to size a workpiece.

Notice that the right side of this workpiece is being milled. There is a very tight tolerance for the surface to be milled. It would be foolish for the operator to run the program without considering the cutter radius compensation offset value that machines this surface.

Say the tool used to machine this surface is a 1.00-in-diameter end mill and its radius value is to be stored in offset 31. Also, the work surface has been programmed; that is, the radius of the tool is to be stored as the radius value. As the offsets are entered, the operator sets offset 31 to a value of 0.500 in. If excess stock is to be allowed, *before* running the tool, the operator *must* alter the offset (31) to force the control to allow excess stock. Say the operator wishes to allow 0.020-in excess stock. Offset 31 will be *increased* by 0.020 in, making its new value 0.520 in.

After machining, the operator measures the 4-in dimension and finds it to be 4.0185 in. Offset 31 must be *reduced* by 0.0185 in. The final value of offset 31 will be 0.5015 (0.520 − 0.0185).

Keep in mind that this example shows only one surface being machined. There will be times when the tool will machine more than one surface and the operator will be measuring an overall dimension (across two machined surfaces) machined by the same tool. For example, if the workpiece in Fig. 3.13 required that both ends be machined, when the 0.020-in value is added to offset 31, it would force 0.020-in

186   Chapter Three

excess stock to be left on *both* surfaces. When taking the overall measurement, the operator must calculate the amount of stock to be machined accordingly, dividing the overall stock left by 2.

For example, if the operator is machining both ends of the workpiece in Fig. 3.13, and the overall measurement comes out to 4.0374 in, the overall stock yet to be machined would be 0.0374. However, this value *must* be divided by 2 in order to come up with the value by which the offset must be reduced.

Using offsets during roughing to allow stock for finishing

Cutter radius compensation allows the same coordinates used for finishing to be used for roughing. This minimizes the number of coordinates the programmer must calculate, and if subprogramming or program-copy techniques are used, dramatically shortens the length of the program.

Figure 3.14 shows the workpiece to be used for the example program. For this example, we intend to use a 1.00-in-diameter end mill for roughing (in tool station 1), and another 1.00-in-diameter end mill for finishing (in tool station 2). Note that we use program copy in the

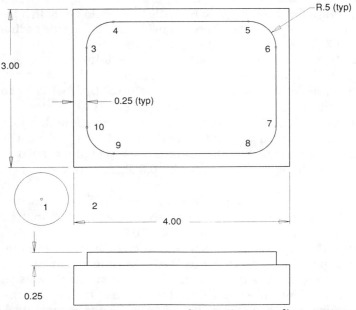

Figure 3.14   Drawing demonstrating the use of cutter radius compensation offsets to allow stock for finishing.

example, but the same thing can be accomplished with subprogramming techniques.

Offsets are

31   0.530 in (allows 0.030-in finishing stock)

32   0.500 in

Program:

```
O0041 (Program number)
(1-in roughing end mill)
N005 G54 G90 S350 M03 T02 (Select coordinate system, absolute mode, turn
spindle on CW at 350 RPM, get tool station 2 ready)
N010 G00 X-.6 Y-.6 (Rapid to point 1)
N015 G43 H01 Z.1 (Rapid down to just above workpiece)
N020 G01 Z-.245 F30. (Fast feed to work surface, note 0.005-in finishing stock)
N025 G41 D31 X.25 (Instate cutter radius compensation, move to point 2)
N030 Y2.25 F4. (Feed to point 3)
N035 G02 X.75 Y2.75 R.5 (Circular move to point 4)
N040 G01 X3.25 (Feed to point 5)
N045 G02 X3.75 Y2.25 R.5 (Circular move to point 6)
N050 G01 Y.75 (Feed to point 7)
N055 G02 X3.25 Y.25 R.5 (Circular move to point 8)
N060 G01 X.75 (Feed to point 9)
N065 G02 X.25 Y.75 R.5 (Circular move to point 10)
N070 G00 Z.1 (Rapid up to clearance position)
N075 G40 (Cancel cutter radius compensation)
N080 G91 G28 Z0 M19 (Return to reference position in Z, orient spindle for tool
change)
N085 M01 (Optional stop)
N090 T02 M06 (Change tools)
N095 G54 G90 S500 M03 T01 (Select coordinate system, absolute mode, turn
spindle on CW at 500 RPM, get tool station 1 ready)
N100 G00 X-.6 Y-.6 (Rapid to point 1)
N105 G43 H02 Z.1 (Rapid to just above workpiece)
N110 G01 Z-.25 F30. (Fast feed to work surface)
N115 G41 D32 X.25 (Instate cutter radius compensation, move to point 2)
N120 G25 P030 Q075 (Repeat lines N030 through N075)
N125 G91 G28 Z0 M19 (Return to reference position in Z, orient spindle for tool
change)
N130 M01 (Optional stop)
N135 T01 M06 (Tool change)
N140 G91 G28 X0 Y0 (Return to reference position in X and Y)
N145 M30 (End of program)
```

In line N025, cutter radius compensation is instated for the roughing end mill. Since a value of 0.030 in more than the actual cutter size is stored in offset 32, the control will keep this cutter away from the surface being machined by 0.030 in, in effect, allowing 0.030-in finishing stock.

In line N115, cutter radius compensation is instated for the finishing end mill. Since the value stored in offset 32 is the actual cutter radius, this tool will machine the surface to size. Of course, we still recommend that you use the sizing techniques shown earlier to assure that the surface milled by the finishing end mill comes out to size on the first workpiece.

Limitation related to machining inside radius. If you are machining an inside radius, of course the radius being machined *must* be larger than the cutter radius. If it is not, the cutter will not fit into the radius being machined and the control will generate an alarm. When using the technique shown above for roughing purposes, the inside radius being machined *must* also be larger than the *offset value* used with roughing. If it is not, the control will generate the same alarm.

This is important to know because there will be times when you wish to use a tool with a radius equal to an inside radius to be machined. For example, you may wish to use a 1-in-diameter end mill to machine one or more inside radii specified with a 0.500-in radius. If you actually program the circular movements around the 0.500-in inside radius, the largest offset value allowed by the control will be 0.500 in.

CNC Techniques for Specific Machining Operations

At this point, you have been exposed to numerous techniques involving CNC programming functions. While many of the techniques have been related to some kind of machining operation (milling, drilling, turning, etc.), we have primarily stressed control-related functions.

In this chapter, we will switch the emphasis from programming functions to machining operations. While certain programming functions will still be explained during each presentation, our intention is to acquaint you with numerous CNC techniques that can help when specific machining operations must be performed.

Some of the information presented in this chapter is little more than basic machining practice. If you have good experience in the machine shop, you will find these presentations easy to follow. However, you may be surprised at the number of relatively basic points we make that you may not have considered from a CNC programmer's standpoint.

When it comes to basic machining practice, there is a great deal of disagreement, even among experienced machinists. One person may prefer to climb-mill while another will only conventional-mill. One person will run only carbide tools, while another prefers high-speed steel. One person will center-drill all holes, while another seldom center-drills at all. And the list of argued points goes on, and on, and on. The machining practice points we make in this chapter are basic, and intended to help the beginner to CNC. They are simply guidelines for safe and successful operations, and *not*, by any means, the best or only way to handle the basic machining practice problem being discussed.

Keep in mind that we are just scratching the surface of basic machining practice as each presentation is made. We wish to get just deep enough into basic machining practice to show you the CNC-related techniques we are trying to explain. If you want to know more about a particular machining operation, we must refer you to one of the excellent texts on the subject.

Hole-Machining Operations

Hole machining is the most common operation performed on a CNC machining center. Almost every machining center program you write will require some form of hole-machining operation. For this reason, most CNC machining-center control manufacturers give you a series of canned cycles to help with these basic operations. In Chap. 2, we discussed several of the advanced implications of canned cycles (plane selection, incremental canned cycles, subprogramming techniques, etc.). If you have been working with CNC machining centers for any length of time, it is likely that you are familiar with the series of canned cycles your machine uses.

In this section, we intend to acquaint you with the many basic machining practice points related to hole-machining operations and how the various CNC programming functions can help. Note that most of the points we make in this section can be applied to both machining centers and turning centers. However, hole-machining operations are much more common on machining centers. That is, the typical machining-center program will perform many more hole-machining operations than the typical turning-center program. For this reason, most of the specific examples we will show are related to machining-center applications. Also note that most turning-center controls have limited (if any) canned-cycle commands with which to program hole-machining operations.

Center drilling

Center drilling is done to assure that the subsequent drilling operation gets off to a good start. Note that center drilling is necessary only for drills that have a drill point, like twist drills and spade drills. For carbide-insert drills and flat-bottom drills, center drilling is not required.

If the hole's position is critical, it is *always* best to center-drill (for drills with a drill point). Figure 4.1 shows a plain-type center drill as well as specifications for its most common sizes.

When a hole has been center-drilled, there will be clearance for the point of the drill to follow. And since the drill will come into contact

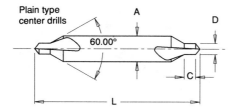

Plain type
center drills

60.00°

Size	A	D	C	L
00	1/8	0.025	0.030	1-1/8
0	1/8	1/32	0.038	1-1/8
1	1/8	3/64	3/64	1-1/4
2	3/16	5/64	5/64	1-7/8
3	1/4	7/64	7/64	2
4	5/16	1/8	1/8	2-1/8
5	7/16	3/16	3/16	2-3/4
6	1/2	7/32	7/32	3
7	5/8	1/4	1/4	3-1/4
8	3/4	5/16	5/16	3-1/2

Figure 4.1 Plain-type center drill.

with the workpiece at a very small diameter, the drill will get started into the hole correctly. Figure 4.2 shows this.

Generally speaking, if the hole has *not* been center-drilled, it will have the tendency to wander from its desired path. With larger, rigid drills (over 0.500-in in diameter), the drill may be able to overcome this tendency to wander, and will machine the hole correctly. But, as

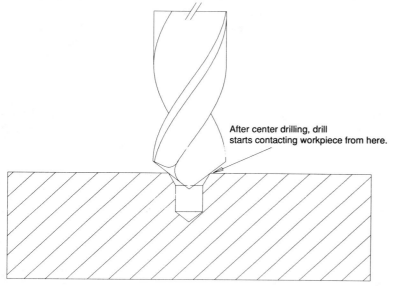

After center drilling, drill
starts contacting workpiece from here.

Figure 4.2   How center-drilled hole assists with the subsequent drilling operation.

stated, if the hole is critical, and for smaller diameter drill sizes, it is always best to center-drill. Note that, as the center drill plunges deeper into the hole, the diameter of the hole at the top becomes larger. To attain the best results from center drilling, the diameter of the center-drilled hole should be just large enough to allow clearance for the subsequent drill point. That is, you should *not* attempt to center drill the hole to a diameter that would form a chamfer after drilling. If you attempt this, the drill will still be prone to wander (more on why during our discussion of spot drilling a little later).

There are times when the hole location is not critical and a certain amount of wandering is acceptable. If you wish to chamfer the hole as the hole is center-drilled, we recommend that you use a spot drill (discussed next) instead of a center drill. As you will see, the spot drill will form a 45° chamfer for the drilled hole.

Programming suggestions for center drilling.   When center drilling, it is best to simply feed the center drill to its desired depth and then retract it. For machining-center applications, this is best handled with a G81 canned-cycle command. For turning centers that do not have canned cycles for hole-machining operations, you must use G01 to plunge the center drill into the hole and G00 to retract.

If holes of different sizes must be machined, it is wise to center-drill *all* holes *before* any drilling operation. This gives two benefits. First, cycle time will be reduced, since the number of tool changes required can be minimized. Second, after the center drill has machined all holes, the hole locations can be easily checked *before* the holes are drilled. If a center-drilled hole is out of position, it is likely that the drilled hole will be too, especially if program-copy or subprogramming techniques are used. Using this technique gives the programmer a chance to change the program *before* the workpiece is scrapped.

Spot drilling

Another way of premachining a hole before drilling is spot drilling. Figure 4.3 shows a picture of a common spot drill. Notice that the spot drill has a 90° point angle which can easily form a 45° chamfer for the hole being machined.

The depth of the spot-drilled hole determines the chamfer size, and it is very easy to calculate. Simply divide the desired chamfer diameter by 2 to come up with the depth. Figure 4.4 shows this.

For example, say you are going to drill the hole to a diameter of 0.250 in. And say you want a 0.015-in by 45° chamfer around the top of the hole. In this case, the chamfer diameter desired is 0.280 in (0.25 + 0.015 + 0.015). The depth required for the spot drill in this case is 0.140 in (0.280 ÷ 2).

There is one problem with spot drilling. When the drill comes into

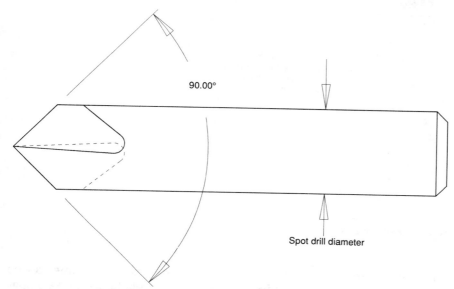

90.00°

Spot drill diameter

Figure 4.3 Popular style of 90° spot drill.

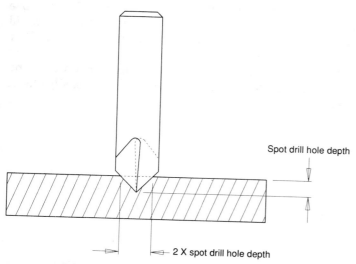

Spot drill hole depth

2 X spot drill hole depth

Figure 4.4 Calculating spot drill depth to generate the desired chamfer size.

contact with the spot-drilled hole, the first surface of the drill to contact the workpiece will be the outside diameter of the drill, not the drill's point. Figure 4.5 shows this. Most experienced machinists would agree that this will cause a tendency for the drill to wander. As stated earlier, it is always better to center-drill if hole location is crit-

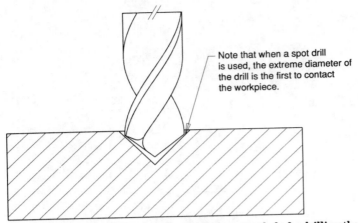

Figure 4.5 Why center drilling allows a better start hole for drilling than spot drilling.

ical. However, if the hole's location is not critical, cycle time can be saved, if a chamfer is required at the top of the hole, by using a spot drill instead of a center drill.

Programming suggestions for spot drilling. As with center drilling, use a G81 on machining centers to simply feed to the bottom and rapid out. On turning centers, use G01 and G00 if the control does not allow canned cycles for hole machining.

Also as with center drilling, machine with the spot drill for all the holes *first* to minimize cycle time and allow the ability to easily check the hole locations.

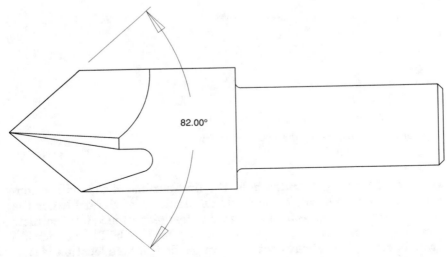

Figure 4.6 Common style of countersink.

Countersinking

The purpose of countersinking is to chamfer a *previously machined* hole. That is, a countersink is used only in an existing hole to form a chamfer around the rim. It does not have the ability to start a hole from solid stock. Figure 4.6 shows a countersink.

Notice the point angle of 82°. Though this tool does not have the ability to form a true 45° chamfer, most machinists still use it to chamfer holes. However, if this tool is used in a program, you must use trigonometry to calculate the desired depth for the diameter you will be chamfering and the 82° point angle.

Since this tool is used only after the hole has been machined, it is possible to rapid the point into the hole and close to the surface to chamfer. Doing so minimizes cycle time. This way the feed motion can be kept very short (just enough to form the chamfer). In Fig. 4.7, notice how far the point of the tool has traveled into the hole when chamfering begins. Of course, like the final depth, this clearance position must be calculated by trigonometry.

Since the depth and clearance position are harder to calculate, since the angle of chamfer is not truly 45°, and since spot drills allow two functions with one tool (spotting the hole as well as chamfering), most programmers prefer to use spot drills for smaller holes (up to 1.00 in in diameter), if chamfering is to be performed. Only when the hole becomes too large to spot-drill, or if no centering tool is required, is it necessary to use a countersink to chamfer the hole.

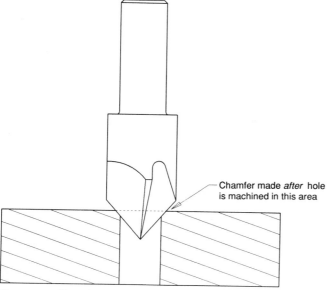

Chamfer made *after* hole is machined in this area

Figure 4.7 Use of countersink in previously machined hole to form chamfer.

Programming suggestions for countersinking. As with center drilling, use a G81 on machining centers to simply feed to the bottom and rapid out. On turning centers, use G01 and G00 if the control does not allow canned cycles for hole machining.

If you are trying to minimize cycle time, you will want to rapid the countersink into the hole to a position in Z just above where machining starts. If there are several holes to countersink, keep in mind that most current controls allow obstructions between holes to be avoided. This means you will be able to easily rapid the tool completely out of each hole prior to moving over to the next hole from within the canned-cycle command. Though you will have to check your programming manual to find the exact format, most controls that have this ability use a G98 and G99 for this purpose.

One popular control that has this feature allows the programmer to set two clearance positions in the Z axis, one just above the work surface and one just above the clamps. The clearance position just above the work surface is called the R *plane* and is set in the canned-cycle command itself. The clearance position above the obstruction is called the *initial plane* and is the Z position just prior to the canned cycle command.

Figure 4.8 shows a workpiece requiring countersinking in several holes. Here is a program that performs only the countersinking operation.

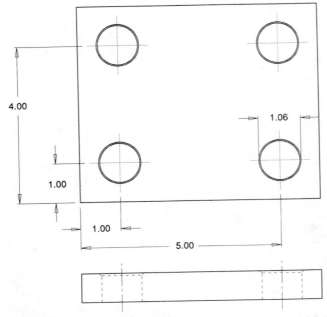

Figure 4.8 Countersinking techniques.

Program:

O0041 (Program number)
N005 G54 G90 S300 M03 (Select coordinate system, absolute mode, turn spindle on CW at 300 RPM)
N010 G00 X1. Y1. (Rapid to lower left hole location)
N015 G43 H01 Z.1 (Rapid tip of tool down just above work surface, note that this position sets initial plane)
N020 G81 X1. Y1. R-.45 Z-.592 F3. G98 (Countersink lower left hole, rapid out to initial plane)
N025 Y4. (Countersink upper left hole)
N030 X5. (Countersink upper right hole)
N035 Y1. (Countersink lower right hole)
N040 G80 (Cancel canned cycle)
N045 G91 G28 Z0 (Return to Z reference position)
N050 M30 (End of program)

In line N015 the Z.1 position sets the initial plane, since this is the last Z position prior to the canned cycle. In line N020, even though the rapid plane (set by R) is below the work surface, the G98 word in this command tells the control to retract the tool to the initial plane, which is 0.100 in above the work surface. Remember that each control will have its own specific programming commands to allow this function. Our example has shown only one possible way. Your control's programming manual will show you more about this feature.

Drilling with twist drills

There are many different styles of drilling tools. We begin our discussion with twist drills. Figure 4.9 shows the major parts of a twist drill.

For standard drilling purposes, the drill is plunged to its programmed depth in one pass. The tool is then retracted from the hole at rapid. For machining-center application, a G81 is used for this purpose. On turning centers that do not allow canned cycles for drilling, you must use G01 and G00 to accomplish this motion.

Allowing for the drill point. When most design engineers specify the depth of a hole, they mean for the hole to be machined with the specified diameter to the depth given. This means if a twist drill (or any drill with a point angle) is used, the programmer *must add* the drill point amount (called the *lead* of the drill) to the depth of the hole programmed. While there are times when the design engineer will specify the hole depth to the very point of the drill, the drill point must usually be taken into consideration when a hole is machined.

A hole which does *not* pass completely through the surface being machined is called a *blind hole*. A hole which passes completely through the surface being machined is called a *through hole*.

For a standard 118° point angle twist drill, the amount of drill lead

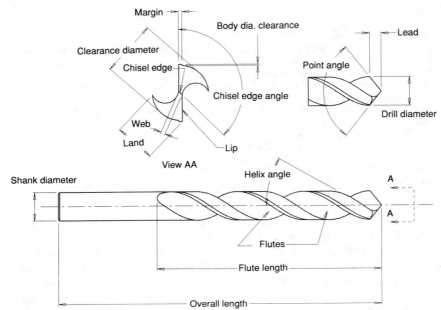

Figure 4.9 Common twist drill.

is easy to calculate. Simply multiply the diameter of the drill by the value 0.30 to come up with the drill lead. For example, a 0.50-in-diameter twist drill has a 0.15-in lead (0.3 × 0.5). In this case, the value 0.15 must be added to the hole depth specified on the drawing to come up with the hole depth for the program.

Calculating the depth of through holes. If you are machining a hole through a surface with a twist drill, of course the drill lead must be added to the workpiece thickness. Additionally, you must add a small amount of clearance which forces the drill to truly break through the surface. Normally 0.030 in is sufficient. If you do not add this small amount to your hole depth, it is likely that the hole will not be completely machined through the surface. This is especially likely if the material is gummy, having the tendency to push away from the cutting edges of the drill. For example, if machining through a 1.0-in-thick workpiece with a 0.500-in-diameter drill, you should program the depth of the hole as at least 1.180 in (1.0 + 0.15 + 0.030).

Peck drilling to break chips. In some materials, the motions described above (feed in, rapid out) for drilling will cause a long, stringy chip to be formed as the drill plunges the hole to its final depth. This long chip will be whipped around the drill, and grow longer and longer. If left to grow, the chip will eventually break and be thrown away from the drill. If the protective guarding around the machine is inadequate, it is quite possible that this chip will be thrown into the operator, causing injury.

Generally speaking, gummy materials like steel and aluminum are most prone to this kind of stringy chip when a hole is drilled. On the other hand, more powdery materials like cast iron will never form a stringy chip.

One way to solve the stringy chip problem is to force the chip to break at manageable lengths as the hole is being drilled. In this case, peck drilling can be done to break chips. For example, the drill can be plunged into the hole a short distance (say 0.100 in). Then the drill can be retracted a very small amount (about 0.005 in). It is during this small retraction motion that the chip is forced to break. This plunge and small retraction can be repeated for the entire hole depth.

Since this kind of motion would be somewhat difficult (and quite lengthy) to program with G01 and G00, most control manufacturers offer a peck-drilling cycle for the purpose of breaking chips. Most use a G73 for this cycle. One popular control uses a Q word to specify the depth of each peck before the chip is forced to break.

Deep hole drilling.   The flutes of a twist drill limit the drill's maximum drilling depth (see Fig. 4.9). However, you must know that most twist drills cannot machine to this maximum depth in one pass. If this is attempted, the flutes of the twist drill will pack with chips, and these chips will eventually bind up between the drill and the workpiece. If drilling continues after this binding, the drill may break. For this reason, when deep holes must be machined, the tool must peck into the hole a specified depth, then retract to clear chips. Then, if the hole must be machined deeper, the drill can be sent back into the hole at rapid to within a small clearance distance from where it left off. The hole can then be machined to a greater depth.

For most materials, this maximum peck depth can be calculated by multiplying the diameter of the drill by 3. That is, a twist drill has the ability to machine to a depth 3 times its diameter without danger of the chips packing up. If the required depth of hole is deeper than 3 times the drill depth, you should use peck-drilling techniques to clear chips.

For example, say you must machine a 0.500-in-diameter hole to a depth of 2.5 in. Three times 0.500 in is 1.5 in. In this case, you will first peck to a 1.5-in depth, then retract the drill to clear chips. You will then send the drill back into the hole (at rapid) to a clearance position just above where the drill left off (into the hole by 1.4 in will work nicely for this example). Finally, you will command that the balance of the hole be drilled.

Since deep-hole peck drilling is often necessary, most machining-center controls have a peck-drilling cycle for clearing chips in this manner. On most controls that allow this feature, a G83 command is used for this purpose. On one popular control, a Q word is used to specify the peck depth per pass (3 times the drill diameter).

When an extremely deep hole must be drilled, the shear length of the drill will weaken its own rigidity. In this case, if the drill is allowed to start from solid material, it may bend and/or break before the hole even gets started (even if the hole has been center-drilled). At the very best, the drill will wander as the hole is started and the hole will not be straight.

For this reason, extremely deep holes (over about 6 times the drill diameter) should be pilot-drilled. Pilot drilling means using a shorter drill of the same diameter to start the hole and machine it to a reasonable depth. Then, the long drill which is capable of machining to the required depth can continue machining to the final depth. We recommend that you make the pilot drill machine to at least 4 times the drill diameter before the long drill is used.

Drilling with spade drills

For larger-diameter holes, spade drills offer many of the features of twist drills for a fraction of the cost. Since one spade drill holder can be used to hold a variety of blade sizes, the spade drill is quite versatile and cost-effective. A 2.00-in-diameter blade for a spade-drill holder will sell for a fraction of the cost of a 2.00-in-diameter twist drill. And the same holder used to hold a 2.00-in-diameter blade can also hold a whole range of blade sizes. Figure 4.10 shows a drawing of a common spade drill.

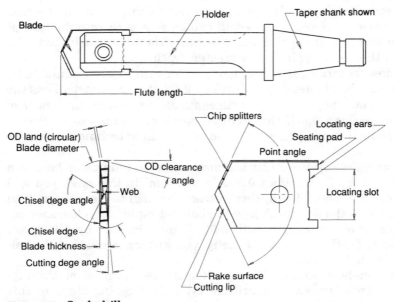

Figure 4.10   Spade drill.

Most spade-drill blades are made from high-speed steel (HSS) and therefore run at low spindle speeds. For this reason, large spade drills require a great deal of thrust from the CNC machine's Z-axis servo drive system in order to apply the pressure required to plunge the hole. This means the CNC machine must possess a very strong servo drive system if you are to use large spade drills. And even so, the extreme pressure generated during spade drilling may tax even a large CNC machine to its limit. You will find that even relatively large CNC machines, possessing as much as 30 or 40 horsepower for the *spindle* drive motor, do not have axis drives capable of pushing a 2-in-diameter spade drill at optimum feed rates.

One way to minimize the thrust required for drilling large holes with HSS drills is to machine the hole to a smaller diameter first. Using this technique allows you to machine the hole in steps, each to a larger diameter. However, this requires substantially more cycle time than plunging the hole to its final diameter with one tool.

Since this kind of tool is so taxing to the machine's servo drive system, and since carbide-insert drills offer another cost-effective means of large-hole machining, many companies prefer *not* to use spade drills (or extremely large twist drills) for CNC applications when cycle time is critical.

For programming purposes, the spade drill can be programmed in much the same way as a twist drill. The G81, G83, or G73 canned cycles can be applied as discussed earlier, depending on the workpiece material and the depth of the hole to be drilled.

Drilling with carbide-insert drills

This style of drill transfers the power required for machining a large-diameter hole from the servo drive motor, which pushes the drill into the hole to the spindle drive motor, which rotates the drill. Since the cutting edges of this drill are made of carbide, its cutting speeds are *much* faster than those of HSS twist drills and spade drills (at least 4 times faster for most materials). This means the servo drive motor of the CNC machine does not have to apply nearly the thrust required for other styles of drills. On the other hand, the *spindle* drive motor must have the horsepower required to rotate the carbide-insert drill to allow optimum machining.

Figure 4.11 shows one kind of carbide-insert drill. Keep in mind that the insert configuration and even the drill itself will vary dramatically from one tooling manufacturer to the next. However, *all* carbide-insert drills share one thing. *All* carbide-insert drills require coolant to be fed through the drill itself. The coolant flows out the end of the drill close to the inserts.

Notice the coolant holes in the drill shown in Fig. 4.11. The coolant flow serves two purposes. First, it enhances the cutting action as coolant would for any machining operation. Second, its use is *mandatory*

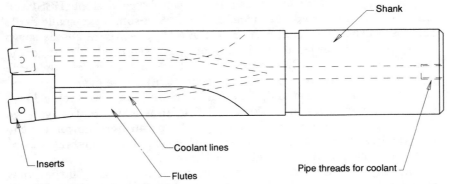

Figure 4.11   Carbide-insert drill.

to force the chips out of the hole and away from the machining area as the drill gets deeper into the hole.

Generally speaking, you will find that carbide-insert drills are not designed to machine deep holes. Though there are exceptions, normally a carbide-insert drill can machine only to a depth of about twice the drill diameter.

When it comes to programming technique, the carbide-insert drill requires that a hole be machined in only one pass (as a G81 cycle on a machining center would allow). *Never* try peck drilling with a carbide-insert drill unless the technical information included with the drill from the drill's manufacturer says it is acceptable to do so.

Carbide-insert drills are intended to begin machining from solid stock. That is, a smooth, flat, solid surface is required for this kind of drill. The carbide-insert drill is not designed to continue machining a hole, opening it up to a larger diameter, as a twist drill or spade drill can. Also, no center drilling can be done prior to machining a hole with a carbide-insert drill.

As mentioned earlier, flood coolant (M08) must be flowing at maximum pressure *before* the carbide-insert drill begins machining. In fact, some carbide-insert drills require special high-pressure coolant pumps in order to attain the needed flow pressure.

If the machine has a poor coolant system that does not come on instantaneously, remember that you can program a dwell command (G04) as shown in Chap. 2 to allow sufficient time for the coolant to come on and flow at maximum pressure.

Counterboring

Counterboring is performed *after* a hole has been machined (usually by drilling) to open the hole to a larger diameter. The bottom of the hole machined by the counterboring tool is flat. The purpose of counterboring is usually to relieve a surface for the head of a bolt. Figure 4.12 shows an application requiring a counterbored hole.

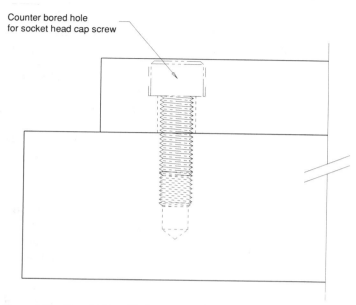

Counter bored hole
for socket head cap screw

Figure 4.12   Counterbored hole.

A true counterbore has a pilot that locates in the previously machined hole and keeps the counterbore from wandering as the hole is
machined. Figure 4.13 shows a counterbore.

If a true counterbore tool is used for the counterboring operation,
the pilot is actually sent into the hole (at rapid) until the cutting edge
is within the clearance position (R plane) of the work surface. As we
indicated earlier (during the discussion of countersinking), you can
use the control's obstruction clearing techniques (usually G98 and G99)
to ensure that the pilot is clear of the work surface before a movement in
X-Y to another hole location is made. Most machining-center controls
use a G82 canned-cycle command for counterboring. At the bottom of the
hole, a short pause is usually specified to take up tool pressure. One popular control uses a P word to specify the pause time.

Keep in mind that most companies use an end mill for counter-

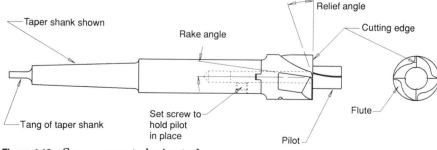

Taper shank shown

Rake angle

Relief angle

Cutting edge

Tang of taper shank

Set screw to
hold pilot
in place

Pilot

Flute

Figure 4.13   Common counterboring tool.

boring purposes to minimize the number of tools required. (In fact, there are experienced programmers that have never used a true counterboring tool.) All end mills allow machining in a plunging direction. However, if the end mill is not a center-cutting end mill, you must be careful that the previously machined hole is larger than the small hole in the center of the end mill.

An end mill does not require a pilot, so there is no need to clear the pilot between holes. The G82 command is still used with an end mill, and a short pause is still required to relieve tool pressure, but there will be no need to make clearance motions (with G98 and G99) to clear a pilot.

Reaming

Reaming is done to improve the surface finish and size of a previously machined hole. Normally the hole is machined very close to the finish size by some other tool (usually a drill) prior to reaming. A reamer is not intended to machine a great deal of stock. Figure 4.14 shows a common reamer.

The surface finish and diameter accuracy machined by the reamer will be much better than that machined by a drill. However, the reamer will follow the previously machined hole. If the drill wandered as it machined the hole, so will the reamer.

Holes under 0.500 in in diameter are usually drilled about 1/64 in undersize prior to reaming. Holes over 0.500 in in diameter are usually drilled about 1/32 in undersize prior to reaming. Note that this assumes a straight hole is to be reamed.

Figure 4.15 shows another style of reamer. This reamer has the ability to ream a tapered hole. With this kind of reamer, it is best to machine the hole with a matching taper prior to reaming (if possible).

When it comes to programming technique, reaming is quite simple. The reamer is fed into the hole to the final depth and then retracted. This is easily accomplished with a G81 canned cycle. Note that most machining-center controls have another canned cycle designated for reaming (normally a G85). However, the reaming canned cycle will feed the reamer in both directions (into and out of the hole). Most experienced

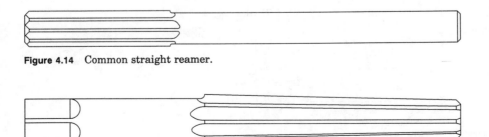

Figure 4.14 Common straight reamer.

Figure 4.15 Common tapered reamer.

machinists would agree that, since there is no machining action as the reamer is being fed out of the hole, this motion is a waste of cycle time.

Boring

Boring, like reaming, is done to improve the quality of size and finish of a previously machined hole. Just as for reaming, the hole must be machined before boring to a diameter very close to the size of the hole to be bored. But unlike reaming, the boring operation does not have the tendency to follow the previously machined hole. If cutting conditions are correct, the boring bar will make its own path.

Figure 4.16 shows a boring bar. As you can see, the size to be machined by the boring bar can be precisely adjusted by an adjustment scale (usually turned by a set screw). In Chap. 2, we showed how the hole size can be easily adjusted by trial boring.

Depending on the precision required of the hole to be machined, any of three recommended methods can be used for boring. If the hole requires no critical size or finish (as would be the case in rough boring), a simple G81 (feed in, rapid out) cycle can be used. In this case, a witness mark in the form of a spiraling circle will be left in the hole by the boring bar's tip as it retracts from the hole. If the hole is more critical (as would be the case in semifinish or finish boring), a G86 canned cycle can be used. This cycle will feed the boring bar to the hole bottom, then stop the spindle and retract the tool from the hole. This cycle will also leave a witness mark in the hole. This time the witness mark will be in the form of a drag line as the tool tip retracts directly from the hole.

If the hole is extremely critical and absolutely no witness mark is allowed, programming becomes slightly more difficult. Most CNC machining center controls have a canned cycle called the *fine-boring cy-*

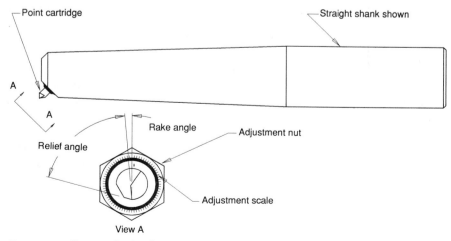

Figure 4.16 Common boring bar.

cle. It is usually specified by G76. This command will feed the boring bar to the hole bottom and stop the spindle. Then the spindle will rotate to the orient position (just like M19). Next the tool will move in a direction that takes the boring bar tip away from the surface of the hole. Finally, the tool will retract from the hole and the spindle will restart. Since the tool's cutting edge is no longer in contact with the hole surface, no witness mark is left in the hole when this cycle is used.

This cycle requires the programmer to know which direction the boring bar tip will be pointing when the orient position of the spindle (M19) is reached. This can be somewhat difficult to know when programming, especially with straight-shank boring bars (like the one shown in Fig. 4.16) that are held in collet-style tool holders. The tip of this kind of boring bar can be pointing in any direction. The programmer must make it very clear to the operator or setup person how to load the tool into position.

Some programmers wait until the job is being set up on the machine to determine the direction and amount of movement at the hole bottom. With the boring bar already set up, they load it into the spindle (manually) and command an M19 (spindle orientation) by manual data input (MDI) techniques. At the completion of the M19, the tip of the boring bar will be pointing in a specific direction, showing the programmer which way the boring bar must move at the hole bottom in order to keep from leaving a drag line.

For example, say the boring bar is in the spindle when an M19 command is given. At the completion of the M19, say the boring bar's tip is pointing in the X plus direction. In this case, the boring bar must be moved in the X minus direction at the hole's bottom to keep from leaving a drag line.

The G76 fine-boring command incorporates an I and/or J word to control the distance and direction of movement at the hole bottom. I is related to X, J is related to Y. For the above example, the movement at the hole bottom is to occur in the X minus direction. In this case, an I minus value must be included in the G76 command.

We recommend that you keep the value of the movement at the hole bottom very small, just enough to clear the tool pressure (about 0.0005 in is sufficient). With this small amount, the worst that can happen if the operator loads the boring bar incorrectly is that a 0.0005-in-deep line will be drawn in the hole.

It is possible to use this technique for fine boring even if the control does not have a G76 fine-boring cycle, but each hole must be programmed longhand. Here is a sequence of commands that will machine one hole and yield the same results as the G76 command:

```
...
N045 G00 X3.5 Y2.5 (Rapid to hole position)
N050 G43 H01 Z.1 (Rapid to just above work surface)
```

N055 G01 Z-1. F2. (Feed to hole bottom)
N060 M19 (Orient spindle)
N065 G00 X3.4995 (Move away from hole surface, assume boring bar tip is pointing *X* plus)
N070 Z.1 (Rapid out of hole)
N075 M03 (Restart spindle)
...

Though this technique requires the same series of commands to be repeated for each hole, at least the fine-boring technique can be incorporated without the fine-boring cycle (G76). If a large number of holes must be bored with this technique, remember that a subprogram can be used for the actual hole machining. Here is another series of commands that incorporates subprogramming techniques to finish-bore four holes:

Main program:

...
N065 G00 X2. Y2. (Rapid to first hole)
N070 G43 H01 Z.1 (Rapid to just above work surface)
N075 M98 P1000 (Bore first hole)
N080 G00 Y4. (Rapid to second location)
N085 M98 P1000 (Bore second hole)
N090 X4. (Rapid to third location)
N095 M98 P1000 (Bore third hole)
N100 Y2. (Rapid to fourth location)
N105 M98 P1000 (Bore fourth hole)
...

Subprogram:

O1000 (Program number)
N001 G01 Z-1. F2. (Feed to hole bottom)
N002 M19 (Orient spindle)
N003 G00 G91 X-.0005 (Move away from hole surface, assume boring bar tip is pointing *X* plus)
N004 G90 Z.1 (Rapid out of hole)
N005 G91 X.0005 M03 (Move back to hole center, restart spindle)
N006 G90 (Reselect absolute mode)
N007 M99 (End of subprogram)

Note how incremental techniques were used in the subprogram to make a more general-purpose series of commands. No matter where the hole is bored in *X-Y*, the movement at the hole bottom will be correct. Also note that the subprogram repositions the tool back on center after the hole is machined. The tool is left back at its starting position in *X-Y* at the completion of the subprogram. This makes positioning movements in the main program very easy, even after a hole is bored.

Tapping

Tapping is done to machine threads on the inside of hole that has been previously machined (normally by drilling). Prior to tapping, the hole is machined smaller than the major diameter of the thread to be tapped. This amount smaller than the thread's major diameter determines the fit of the thread as well as how difficult the thread will be to tap. The smaller the hole, the better (tighter) the fit, but the more difficult the hole will be to tap. The hole prior to tapping *must* be larger than the thread's minor diameter.

One very common class of fit uses 75 percent of the thread depth. In this case, the hole, prior to tapping, is machined to a diameter equal to the major diameter of the thread minus 2 times 75 percent of the thread depth. Every reference handbook related to tapping will show you a tap drilling chart which recommends drill sizes based on the class and size of thread to be tapped.

The hole prior to tapping must also be deep enough to allow tapping. Some taps have lengthy leads (imperfect threads or chamfer length). This requires that the hole be machined much deeper than the tapping depth. Other taps have very short leads (like bottoming taps), and require very little extra hole depth. The lead of any tap can be calculated by multiplying the pitch of the thread (1 ÷ number of threads per inch) by the number of imperfect threads. The tap's lead must, of course, be added to the depth required of the tapped hole. This in turn, means the tap drill depth must be increased accordingly.

As with drilling, a hole that passes through the work surface is called a *through hole* and a hole that does not is called a *blind hole*. The type of hole will help you determine which style of tap to use.

Generally speaking, through holes are best machined with plug taps. Figure 4.17 shows a drawing of a plug tap. As the thread is tapped, the plug tap will push the chips machined by the tap farther into the hole. Since a through hole is being machined, these chips will be sent though the hole and not interfere with the machining action.

Since the chip produced by a plug tap is pushed further into the hole, a plug tap makes a poor choice for blind-hole tapping. If the chip

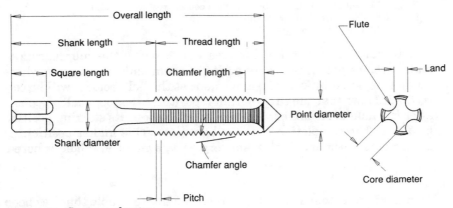

Figure 4.17   Common plug tap.

is pushed farther into a blind hole, it will have nowhere to go, and eventually interfere with the machining action. In this case, a spiral-flute tap should be used. The spiral-flute tap (shown in Fig. 4.18) is designed to pull the chip out of the hole along the flutes of the tap.

Tool holders for taps used on CNC machines.   The actual motions required during tapping are as follows. With the spindle running, the tap is fed into the hole to the hole bottom. At the hole bottom, the spindle direction is reversed and the tap feeds back out of the hole. Once the tap is out of the hole, the spindle reverses again to get ready for the next hole to tap.

During the tapping feed motion, it is mandatory that the feed rate and spindle speed be perfectly synchronized (you will see how a little later). If there is any deviation in speed of feed rate during tapping, the tool will have the tendency to rise or fall relative to the spindle. Also, as the spindle slows down and speeds up during its change in direction, the tapping feed rate must be kept perfectly coordinated with these changes. Most CNC machines do not have the ability to keep the motion synchronized with regard to speed, feed, and change in direction. With these machines, special provisions must be made, otherwise the tap will surely break during the tapping cycle.

However, newer CNC machines offer a feature called *rigid tapping*. This feature gives the ability to perfectly align spindle speed and feed rate, even during the spindle reversal, at remarkably high speeds. If this feature is used, the tap can be held in a rigid tool holder; that is, the tap can be clamped firmly into the holder.

Though actual programming techniques vary from one machine-tool builder to the next, rigid tapping uses a special programming word (usually an M code or G code) to place the machine in the rigid-tapping mode. Once rigid tapping is instated, an ordinary canned cycle for tapping (usually G84) is used to perform the tapping operation.

As stated, rigid tapping is a relatively new feature. Though it is becoming more popular, most CNC machines in use today do not possess the rigid-tapping feature; as noted, they cannot perfectly synchronize the speed and feed with motion, especially during the spindle and axis reversal. If the tool is held in a rigid tool holder and not allowed to float, the tap will break as the spindle is reversed.

For this reason, most CNC machines require that taps be held in a special tool holder that allows the tool to float in a direction parallel to

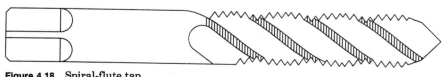

Figure 4.18   Spiral-flute tap.

the spindle. These tapping tool holders are spring-loaded. The neutral position of the tap holder is in the center of the float travel. The tool can be compressed or pulled out from this neutral position. When this pushing or pulling pressure is released, the tap will spring back to its neutral position. This style of tapping-tool holder is called a *tension/compression tap holder*.

With this style of holder, if there is any deviation in synchronization related to speed, feed, and/or motion reversal, the tap will simply float (up or down) in the tension/compression holder. It will be under no stress during the entire tapping cycle.

Rapid plane position when tapping with a tension/compression holder.
Since the tool can float in a tension/compression holder as a hole is tapped, it is possible that the tap will actually pull out (away from the spindle) as the hole is being tapped. When the spindle reverses, it is likely that the feed motion will not be able to keep up with the spindle reversal, compounding this problem. If the tool is sent to a clearance plane (the R plane of the G84 canned cycle) very close to the workpiece, as would be the case for drilling, it is possible that the tap will not truly be out of the hole when the tapping cycle is finished. The greater the pitch, the more the tap's tendency to float in the holder.

For example, say you rapid tap to 0.100 in above the surface to be tapped as you would for drilling. Say you are machining with a relatively course-pitched tap, like a ¾-10 tap, having 10 threads per inch tap. The pitch of this tap is 0.100 in (1 ÷ 10). If there is any deviation in speed and feed synchronization, 0.100-in float will occur *per spindle revolution* of deviation. In this case, it is quite possible that more than 0.100-in float will occur. If the deviation occurs in a way that pulls the tap in the direction away from the spindle, the tap will *not* be out of the hole at the completion of the tapping cycle. When the next motion occurs in X, Y, and/or Z, the tap will break, also causing damage to the workpiece.

For this reason, we recommend keeping all taps at least 0.250 in away from the work surface prior to tapping unless your machine allows rigid tapping (R.25 in the canned cycle G84). This will allow for a great deal of float and will assure that the tap is truly out of the hole after the tapping cycle.

Speed and feed considerations while tapping.   As mentioned, the spindle speed and feed rate must be synchronized during the tapping cycle. The RPM for any tap can be calculated for any tool with the following formula:

$$RPM = 3.82 \times SFM \div \text{tap diameter}$$

The SFM for tapping can be found in reference books related to cutting conditions and is based on the material to be machined and the material of the tap. Also note that the technical information supplied by the tap's manufacturer will also give the recommended speed in SFM.

Once the RPM is determined, the feed rate must be made to synchronize with calculated RPM. If the machine can be commanded for feed rate in inches per revolution (as most turning centers can), this is as simple as programming the pitch of the thread as the feed rate. In the inch system, the pitch is equal to 1 divided by the number of threads per inch. In the metric system, the pitch is specified directly as part of the thread designation.

For example, a ⅜-16 (inch) thread has 16 threads per inch. The pitch is 1/16, or 0.0625 in. If the machine can be programmed in inches per revolution, F.0625 would be the proper feed rate. No matter what speed in RPM was commanded, the machine would move at the proper feed rate.

Unfortunately, most machining centers cannot be programmed in inches per revolution. These machines *must* be programmed in inches per minute. This means the inches per minute feed rate must be calculated. If you simply multiply the tap's RPM times the pitch, you will come up with the feed rate in inches per minute.

For example, consider the ⅜-16 tap again. Say you look in your reference book on cutting conditions and find that, for the material you are machining and the style of tap, the book recommends 30 SFM for tapping. According to the RPM formula given earlier, the proper speed for this tap is 305 RPM (3.82 × 30 ÷ 0.375).

As stated earlier, the pitch for 16 threads per inch is 0.0625 in (1/16). To come up with the feed rate for this operation, you multiply 0.0625 in by 305 RPM. The result is 19.06 inches per minute. F19.06 is the proper feed rate for this tap in the inches per minute mode.

Disabled control panel functions. Since tapping requires synchronization between feed and speed, certain operation panel controls are disabled during tapping. Feed-rate override, spindle-speed override, and feed hold are features that have no effect during tapping. Even if any of these controls is manipulated during tapping, the control will ignore it. The programmed feed rate and spindle speed will be used no matter what the condition of the feed-rate override and spindle-speed override switches. And, if the feed hold button is pressed during tapping, it will be ignored.

If the control were to do otherwise, your manipulation of these functions would cause the tap to break. Think of what would happen if the tap were in the middle of tapping a hole when you pressed feed hold. If the control *did* stop the feed motion with the spindle still running, the tap could not withstand the stress. The same is true for feed-rate override and spindle-speed override. If not at 100 percent, the speed and feed would not be synchronized during the tapping cycle.

Note that the control knows that it should not allow these control panel functions *only* if the tapping cycle is commanded by a true tapping command (like G84). If for some reason, you are tapping with G01, reversing the spindle, and pulling back out with another G01, the control *will* allow the control panel functions to operate as usual.

The only reason you would tap with G01 is if your machine does not have a tapping canned cycle (some turning-center controls do not have a canned cycle for tapping). In this case, the operator *must* be sure that the feed-rate override and spindle-speed override switches are set to 100 percent, and the feed hold button must *not* be pressed during tapping.

When to tap.   Most experienced CNC operators would agree that tapping is among the most troublesome operations to perform with CNC equipment. When a tap dulls, or if cutting conditions are not correct, it is likely to break as a hole is being tapped, leaving the broken tap in the hole. Any tap is under a great deal of stress as a hole is tapped, and especially so when the tap is quite small or the hole to be tapped is quite deep.

Tapping compound (a kind of machining oil especially designed for tapping) can be used to help with the tapping action. Tapping compound works *much* better than the machine's normal flood coolant to aid with the tap's machining action. Since most CNC machines do not have a way of applying tapping compound automatically, it must be applied manually, by the operator.

Since tapping can be so troublesome, and since a prior manual application of tapping compound must usually be done, we recommend that you do *all* tapping at the very end of the program's cycle. Just prior to the first tapping operation, include an M00 program stop command to stop the program. This gives the operator the time to apply the tapping compound. Here's an example:

N255 M00 (Apply tapping compound)

Note that you can even place a message in parentheses that tells the operator exactly what is expected when the M00 command stops the machine.

When the cycle is reactivated after the program stop command, the operator will be present to check for problems during tapping. If a tap breaks, the operator will know it and be available to stop the cycle.

Controlling the depth of tapered pipe taps.   Most taps have a constant outside diameter. The hole they machine is straight. Calculating and controlling the depth of straight tapped holes is relatively easy. It is easy to measure and determine whether a tapped hole has been tapped to the proper depth. If the tapped hole must be deeper, the program can easily be changed and rerun. In most cases, if the tapped

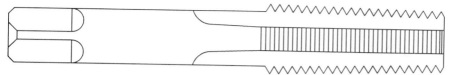

Figure 4.19   Tapered pipe tap.

hole is too deep, it will present no major problems in the quality of the workpiece (of course the program can still be changed for future workpieces).

However, there is a style of tap with which the depth is very critical, the tapered pipe tap. Figure 4.19 shows one. As a tapered pipe tap machines a hole, the diameter at the top surface being machined by the tap grows. The deeper the tap goes into the hole, the larger the top diameter becomes. The hole formed by tapered pipe tapping must match its mating part. If the tapped hole is not deep enough, the mating part will not fit into the hole. If the tapped hole is too deep, the mating part will not form a seal with the tapped hole. Since pipe tapping is often required for plumbing fittings requiring a good seal to prevent leakage of liquid or gas, if the tapped hole is too deep, the joint will not be acceptable.

It is much more difficult to measure the depth of the tapered pipe tapped hole. A special gauge is usually required. The gauge is rotated into the hole until it contacts the hole bottom. At this point, if the thread is not deep enough, the gauge will show the operator how much deeper the hole should be.

When no gauge is available, the operator can use the mating part (usually a fitting of some kind) to check the hole depth. Unfortunately, the mating part will not even fit into the hole until the tapped hole is very close to its required depth. This means the operator must cautiously sneak up on the hole depth, trying to fit the tapered mating part with each new depth. This can be tedious, time-consuming, and error-prone, since the operator must guess at how much deeper the tapped hole must be, change the program accordingly, and rerun the tool.

There is a way to confirm that the tapered tap will machine to the correct depth on the very first try. It requires the use of a special setup gauge that is easy to make. Figure 4.20 shows this gauge. Of course, a gauge is necessary for each tapered tap size.

Simply machine a piece of round stock to a precise overall length (our example is precisely 1 in long). In the center of this round part, machine the tapped hole to its required depth (manually). Use the thread gauge or mating part to determine the thread's correct depth.

Once this gauge is made, it is fitted to the end of the tap during the tool's length measurement. Figure 4.21 shows how.

The gauge is then removed for machining. In the program, the programmed depth of the thread will simply be the length of the setup

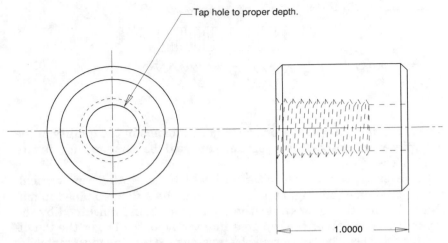

Tap hole to proper depth.

1.0000

Taper tap setup gauge

Figure 4.20   Tapered pipe tape gauge that can be used during setup to help hold tap depth.

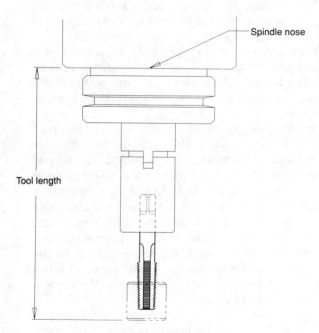

Spindle nose

Tool length

Figure 4.21   Tapered pipe tap length is taken from end of gauge to nose of spindle.

gauge (1 in in our case). Here is an example command using G84 to tap the hole to the correct depth:

N055 G84 X2. Y3. R0 Z-1. F16.4

Since there was plenty of clearance from the tip of the tap to the bottom of the thread gauge, you can use an R plane of R0 in the canned-cycle command. Also, note that the depth of the hole is precisely 1 in. This assumes, of course, that the program zero point in Z is the surface of the workpiece being tapped and that the setup gauge is precisely 1 in long.

While it will take some time to machine the setup gauge, remember you can use it during every setup from that point. In the long run, this will save you hours of frustration while confirming the thread's depth.

Milling Operations

Until only recently, CNC controls did very little to help with milling operations. The G00 (rapid motion), G01 (straight-line motion), and G02/G03 (circular motion) commands have been the only commands available to make milling motions. Of course, cutter radius compensation can be used to allow several milling advantages (a variety of cutter sizes, easy sizing, easy roughing, etc.), but milling motions themselves require many tedious calculations of the manual programmer.

In Chap. 2 we discussed several CNC techniques that help with milling operations. We showed how to make arc-in and arc-out motions for approaching and retracting from the surface being milled. You saw how to spiral-mill a circular pocket. Techniques were given to take up tool pressure as an end mill plunges into solid stock to begin machining a pocket. We even discussed how the plane selection commands affect circular motion and cutter radius compensation as it relates to milling.

The techniques we have shown so far require many tedious and error-prone calculations to be made to come up with the actual cutter path end points. The end point for each motion was needed, and the programmer commands every movement the machine makes during milling independently.

As stated, even most current CNC controls require this kind of programming when milling must be done. However, there are some controls that have special features designed to help with milling.

Round pocket and circle milling commands

A few popular machining-center controls have commands to help with milling round pockets or counterbores. These commands allow the programmer to specify that an entire circular pocket be milled with only one command. The number of motions this command generates is based on the variables in the round-pocket-milling command itself.

While we will show a specific example, note that this kind of feature varies dramatically from one control builder to the next. One control may allow only a simple circle to be milled; therefore only one pass is made around the circle. Others allow a large round pocket to be milled from solid stock with a small end mill, meaning the control will make as many passes as necessary to generate the round pocket to the specified size. You must check with your control's programming manual first to see if this command is available. If it is, you must study to understand the specific use of the command as it applies to your particular control, and it will be well worth the time it takes to do so.

Figure 4.22 shows a workpiece and the tool path to be generated by the circle pocket command in the example program to follow. As stated, this is only an example of how this kind of command is applied to one particular control.

This particular CNC machining-center control uses G12 to specify a circular pocket to be milled in a clockwise direction while G13 mills in a counterclockwise direction. In the case of the tool motions shown in Fig. 4.22, the motion is clockwise, and G12 will be used.

The words to be included in the G12 or G13 command tell the control how the circular pocket is to be milled. These variables make the control behave differently, depending on their values. Here is a list of words that can be included in the G12 or G13 command and their meanings as applied to one CNC machining center control:

Word	Description
K	Diameter of pocket to be milled
Q	Depth of cut in X-Y for milling
D	Offset number where the radius of the tool is stored
F	Feed rate for milling

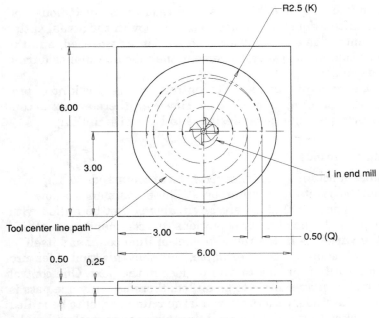

Figure 4.22 Drawing for round pocket example.

As you can see from these variables, if the G12 or G13 command is given correctly, the control will know everything it needs to know to mill the pocket. It will internally calculate the number of passes needed and machine the pocket according the variables it sees in the G12 or G13 command. The K word tells the control the final diameter of the pocket. The D word tells the control in which offset to find the tool's radius, so motions will be based on the tool diameter actually being used. The Q word tells the control how deep to make each X-Y pass and must be kept smaller than the cutter diameter. This value is the amount of overlap from one X-Y pass to the next.

Here is an example program that uses a 1-in end mill to mill the workpiece in Fig. 4.22. Note that the value 0.500 in must be stored in offset 31 when this program is run.

Program:

```
O0042 (Program number)
N005 G54 G90 S600 M03 (Select coordinate system, absolute mode, turn spindle on
CW at 600 RPM)
N010 G00 X3. Y3. (Move to pocket center in X-Y)
N015 G43 H01 Z.1 (Rapid down to just above work surface)
N020 G01 Z-.25 F2. (Feed to pocket bottom surface)
N025 G12 K2.5 Q.5 D31 F3. (Mill pocket)
N030 G00 Z.1 (Rapid out of pocket)
N035 G91 G28 Z0 (Return to reference position in Z)
N040 G28 X0 Y0 (Return to reference position in X-Y)
N045 M30 (End of program)
```

Limitations of special milling cycles

In similar fashion, some (but not many) CNC controls also allow other standard patterns to be milled. Square and rectangular pockets can be done in much the same way as the round pocket example shown above. However, note again that these commands vary dramatically from one control to the next.

Whenever *any* special milling function is used (round pocket, circle milling, square pocket, rectangular pocket, etc.), the actual motions made will be left to the control. While programming becomes *much* simpler, there are those experienced machinists who will not agree with the specific motions any one control will make during these cycles. When any special milling cycle is used, the programmer is, in effect, allowing the control to figure out how the shape should be milled. In some cases, you will not agree with how the control makes the motions.

For example, say a pocket has 0.510 in of stock to be machined in X-Y. The programmer specifies a 0.250-in depth of cut in X-Y for the machining of the pocket. Most controls that have the pocketing feature will make two passes of 0.250 in and one pass of 0.010 in. The experienced machinist would think this is silly. Of course two equal passes of 0.255 in would be acceptable. While the programmer using the pocket-milling command can easily change the depth of cut to force the control to make the desired number of passes, most CNC controls have absolutely no intelligence in this regard. They simply do as they are told.

This is but one example of when an experienced machinist may not agree with how pocket milling takes place. Whether the pocket is finished in *X-Y* before *Z*, how much stock is left for finishing, whether the same tool must be used for rough and finish milling, and the physical order of motions during roughing are among other things experienced machinists may take exception with when special milling cycles are used.

For this reason, these special milling commands may not be totally accepted within a company. If you do not agree with the way your control generates the motions needed for milling these standard shapes, you must probably revert to the older method of programming, using only G00, G01, G02, and G03 to specify tool motions in a longhand manner.

One exception to this statement has to do with something called *parametric programming*. Parametric programming will be discussed at length in Chap. 5. With parametric programming, a programmer has the means available to create the kinds of milling cycles discussed in this section (and many more). In this case, the programmer can generate cutter motions in the method desired.

Thread milling

Thread milling can be very useful on a machining center for holes that are too large to tap and for machining male threads on an outside diameter. Here we present many of the basic considerations you must be concerned with when thread milling.

The first point to make is that there are actually two types of thread-milling cutters. One resembles a Woodruff cutter and requires several passes around the workpiece to form the complete thread. This kind of tool has the form of the thread ground on its outside diameter and is best used when there are a limited number of workpieces to machine.

When production quantities grow to the point that the previously mentioned tool is not economical to use (because of the length the tool must travel during cutting), there is a second type of thread-milling cutter which actually forms the entire thread in one pass around the workpiece diameter to be threaded. This tool resembles a combination of a hog- (rough-) milling cutter and a tap. With this type of tool, the total length of cut required to machine the thread is greatly reduced.

Most current CNC controls have a standard feature called *helical interpolation*. This feature is used to make a circular movement in two axes while making a linear movement in the third axis. When thread milling, you will cause the thread-milling cutter to form a circular motion in *X-Y* while making a linear motion in the *Z* axis. The result is a spiraling movement during which the radius remains constant.

The *X* and *Y* circular motion will form the diameter to be thread-milled. The *Z*-axis linear motion will form the actual pitch (or lead) of the thread.

The most important thing to remember with helical motion is that any *Z* motion during a circular *X-Y* motion *must* reflect the pitch of the thread to be thread-milled. If you are making a circular motion all the way around the diameter in one command, the *Z* departure of the command will be equal to the pitch of the thread. Also, any arc-in or arc-out motions used to minimize witness marks must reflect the thread's pitch.

Figure 4.23 shows a workpiece requiring thread milling in a hole. Notice we even show the arc-in and arc-out motions required of the thread-milling cutter. Note that both the arc-in and arc-out motions are 90° of a circle. In these movements, the *Z*-axis departure must equal one quarter of the pitch (since we are making one quarter of a circle).

Here is an example program to machine the workpiece shown in Fig. 4.23. This example assumes that the hole has previously been machined (to the thread's minor diameter) and that a thread-milling cutter capable of machining the thread in one pass around the diameter is used.

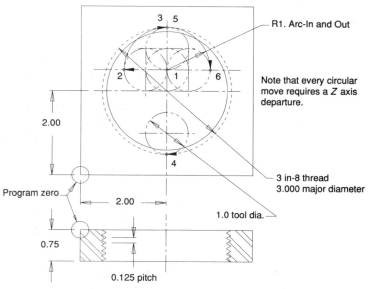

Figure 4.23 Drawing for thread milling example program.

Program:

O0044 (Program number)
N005 G54 G90 S400 M03 (Select coordinate system, absolute mode, turn spindle on CW at 400 RPM)
N010 G00 X2. Y2.5 (Rapid to point 1)
N015 G43 H01 Z.1 (Rapid to just above work surface)
N020 G01 Z-.85 F30. (Fast-feed through workpiece)
N025 G42 D31 X1. (Instate cutter radius compensation, move to point 2)
N030 G02 X2. Y3.5 Z-.8812 I1. F3. (Helical move to point 3)
N035 X2. Y.5 Z-.9437 J-1.5 (Helical move to point 4)
N040 X2. Y3.5 Z-1.0062 J1.5 (Helical move to point 5)
N045 X3. Y2.5 Z-1.0374 J-1. (Helical move to point 6)
N050 G00 G40 X2. (Rapid to point 7, cancel cutter radius compensation)
N055 G00 Z.1 (Rapid out of the hole)
N060 G91 G28 Z0 (Return to the reference position in Z)
N065 G28 X0 Y0 (Return to the reference position in X-Y)
N070 M30 (End of program)

Most CNC machining-center controls use a G02 and G03 to command helical motions. The only difference to making helical motion is the addition of the Z departure in the circular command.

The Z departures in the above helical motions may take some study. Remember that each helical motion takes into consideration the pitch of the thread. For example, in line N030, since the helical motion makes a quarter circle, the amount of Z departure must be one quarter of the pitch (0.125 ÷ 4 = 0.0312). Since the previous position of the tool is −0.85 in, the first helical command ends at −0.8812 (−0.85 − 0.0312). In line N035, half a circle is made. This means the Z departure must be half the pitch (or 0.0625 in). And so on for each helical motion.

Turning Operations

We will now discuss those machining operations that are performed only by turning centers. Rough and finish turning, rough and finish boring, grooving, and threading are among the topics to be discussed. Note that our intention is to acquaint you with the most important things a CNC turning-center programmer *must* know in order to prepare CNC programs for turning centers.

One of the most important things a CNC turning-center programmer must know is how to correctly and efficiently apply tooling. For this reason, as we discuss each type of turning operation, we will show the tools used for machining.

Beginning CNC programmers seem to have problems understanding just what can be done with the various tools applied to turning centers. We will attempt to show the kinds of operations possible with a variety of tool types. Note that we will *not* address specific cutting condition factors like tool material, workpiece material, speed, and feed. Recommendations for this kind of information can be found in the tooling manufacturer's technical documentation.

We *will* discuss each tool's machining capability with regard to tool geometry and motion, showing beginners to CNC turning-center programming just what each tool is intended to do. Experienced turning-center programmers will find much of this to be quite basic, and can consider this information as review.

As with all forms of machining practice, there are differing viewpoints on how turning-center tooling should be applied. While our discussions will be limited to proven and safe methods, we readily concede that there are *many* ways other than what we show.

As we discuss each type of operation, we will also give suggestions on how the operation can be simplified by making the most of the control's programming features. You will find that even difficult programming tasks are simplified by these high-level manual programming features.

Turning (outside-diameter machining)

In this section we will discuss both rough and finish turning. The tooling used for both operations is identical. Only the cutting conditions will be different (speed, feed rate, depth of cut, tool material, etc.).

Figure 4.24 shows a typical turning tool. Of primary importance to our discussions will be lead angle, nose angle, clearance angle, and nose radius. These basic factors determine the kind of work that a tool is capable of machining.

The insert of the tool in Fig. 4.24 is in the shape of a diamond. The nose angle of the tool and the shape of the insert give this tool its most basic classification. There are other styles of turning-tool inserts (round, triangular, and square). However, the diamond-shaped insert is, by far, the most popular. For this reason, we will limit our discussions in this text to the diamond-shaped insert. Most of what we will discuss regarding the diamond-shaped insert will apply to other insert shapes as well.

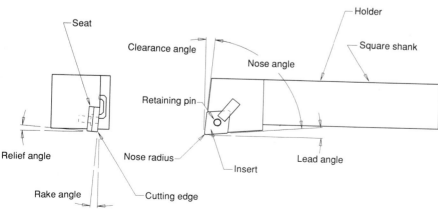

Figure 4.24   Common rough-turning tool.

There are three standard insert nose angles for diamond-shaped inserts: 80, 55, and 35°. Generally speaking, the larger the nose angle, the more rigid or rugged the tool and the longer it will last. The programmer must choose a tool with the largest nose angle that allows the workpiece to be machined.

Figure 4.25 shows a series of very common insert configurations. Note from this drawing that the same insert style can be applied in a variety of ways, depending on how it is held in the tool holder. For instance, the 80° diamond insert is shown in five different attitudes.

Figure 4.26 shows the most basic cutting directions allowed by the various 80° diamond-tool holders. Figure 4.27 shows the same for 55° diamond-style tool holders. Figure 4.28 shows cutting directions for 35° diamond-tool holders.

As stated, the nose angle determines how strong the tool is. An 80° diamond is much stronger than a 55 or 35° diamond. For this reason, the 80° diamond makes a much better choice for roughing operations than a 55 or 35° diamond tool. However, the tool's clearance angle determines whether recesses can be machined. The greater the tool's clearance angle, the more flexible the tool in this regard. Figure 4.29 shows a comparison of each diamond-shaped insert tool's capability to machine a recess.

These extremely basic points must be well-understood by the CNC turning-center programmer. Without an understanding of each tool's machining capabilities, the programmer will have the tendency to try

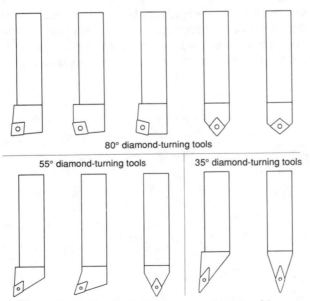

Figure 4.25   Common diamond-style tool holders used in turning operations.

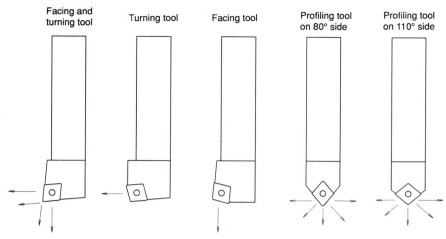

Figure 4.26 Common cutting directions for 80° diamond tool holders.

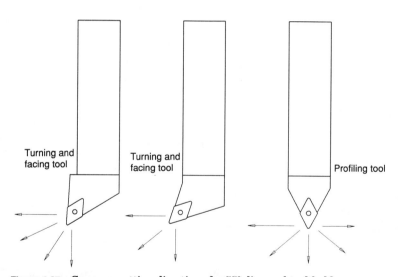

Figure 4.27 Common cutting directions for 55° diamond tool holders.

to make the tool do more than is physically possible. In this case, it is possible that the programmer commands the tool to move in a way that gouges or rubs on the tool's clearance angle side. This will cause damage to the tool and workpiece.

To help beginners understand these points, Figs. 4.30 through 4.40 show more examples of specific tool motions, illustrating each tool's capabilities.

These drawings should help you to see what is possible with each kind of tool. For more information on each tool's capabilities, we must

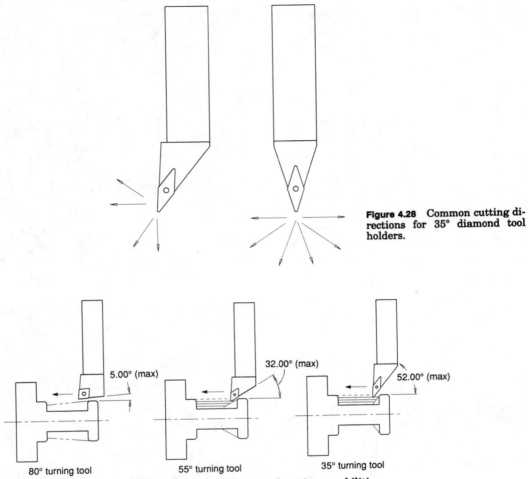

Figure 4.28 Common cutting directions for 35° diamond tool holders.

5.00° (max)

32.00° (max)

52.00° (max)

80° turning tool

55° turning tool

35° turning tool

Figure 4.29 Comparison of 80, 55, and 35° diamond tool cutting capabilities.

refer you to the technical information supplied by the tooling manufacturer. In any event, you *must* understand these basic points before you attempt to apply tooling for turning-center applications.

Programming tips for rough turning. It can be very tedious and error-prone for the manual programmer to command roughing operations. If the manual programmer elects to use only G00 rapid motion, G01 straight-line cutting motion, and G02/G03 circular motion, *every* movement the machine makes during roughing must be programmed independently.

This means each roughing pass will require at least four commands. Figure 4.41 shows these four most basic commands.

Note also that, if more that one roughing pass is needed and if the

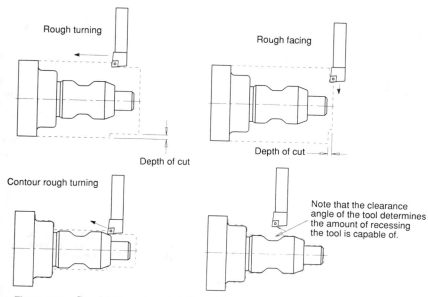

Rough turning

Rough facing

Depth of cut

Depth of cut

Contour rough turning

Note that the clearance angle of the tool determines the amount of recessing the tool is capable of.

Figure 4.30 Capabilities of an 80° diamond turning tool used during roughing.

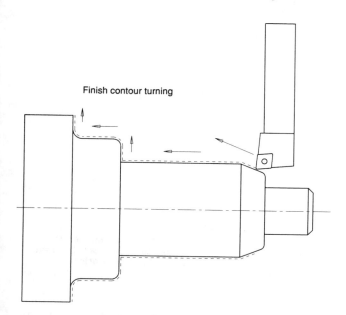

Finish contour turning

Figure 4.31 An 80° diamond turning tool used for finishing.

finished workpiece includes several tapers, radii, and chamfers, programming roughing commands longhand can be extremely difficult. Figure 4.42 shows an example requiring a rough-turning operation that would be quite difficult to program longhand.

By the way, this is one of the most basic reasons turning-center programmers elect to use CAM systems to prepare programs. A good

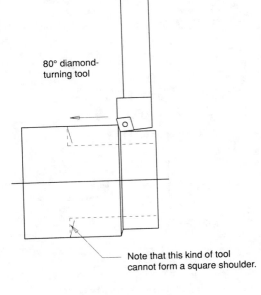

80° diamond-
turning tool

Note that this kind of tool
cannot form a square shoulder.

Figure 4.32 An 80° diamond turning tool that can be used only for turning operations.

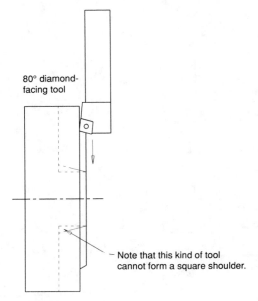

80° diamond-
facing tool

Note that this kind of tool
cannot form a square shoulder.

Figure 4.33 An 80° diamond turning tool that can be used only for facing operations.

turning-center CAM system makes it easy to command rough-turning operations.

Because the programming of roughing commands is so tedious with only basic motion types, most current CNC turning-center controls offer some very nice features to help with rough turning and rough boring. While we will give one specific example, we must point out that

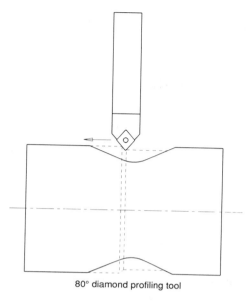

80° diamond profiling tool

Figure 4.34 An 80° diamond turning tool used for profiling operations.

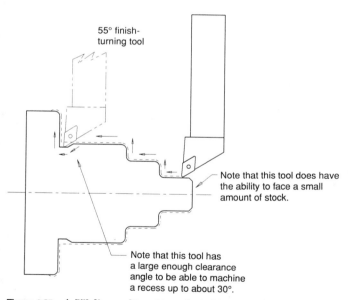

55° finish-turning tool

Note that this tool does have the ability to face a small amount of stock.

Note that this tool has a large enough clearance angle to be able to machine a recess up to about 30°.

Figure 4.35 A 55° diamond turning tool used for finishing operations.

these commands vary from one control builder to the next. You will have to check your control's particular programming manual to learn more about how they are programmed.

Some manufacturers call these commands *multiple repetitive cycles.* Others call them *lapping cycles.* Yet others call them simply *canned*

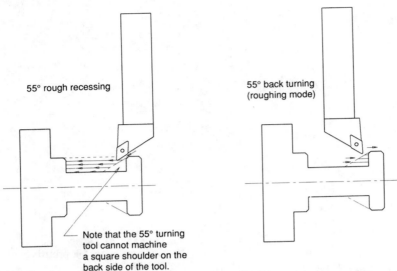

55° rough recessing

55° back turning
(roughing mode)

Note that the 55° turning
tool cannot machine
a square shoulder on the
back side of the tool.

Figure 4.36 Shown here are 55° diamond turning tools used for recessing and
back turning.

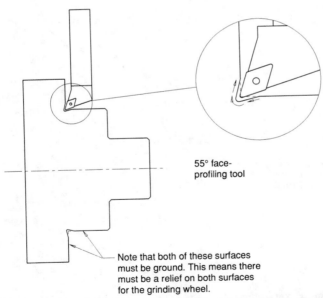

55° face-
profiling tool

Note that both of these surfaces
must be ground. This means there
must be a relief on both surfaces
for the grinding wheel.

Figure 4.37 Drawing illustrates a 55° diamond turning tool used
for face and diameter necking.

cycles. No matter what they are called, these cycles will dramatically
reduce the number of commands required for rough-turning operations.

With most controls that have these features, the programmer specifies how rough turning is to take place with only one command. This

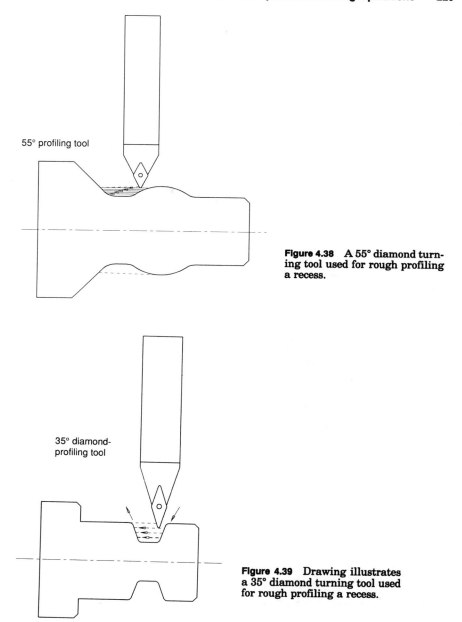

Figure 4.38 A 55° diamond turning tool used for rough profiling a recess.

35° diamond-profiling tool

Figure 4.39 Drawing illustrates a 35° diamond turning tool used for rough profiling a recess.

command gives the control information like the desired depth of cut for each roughing pass, how much stock is to be left for finishing on each diameter and each face, and the feed rate for the rough-turning operation. The rough-turning command also points to the commands that include the finish-pass definition for the workpiece to be machined.

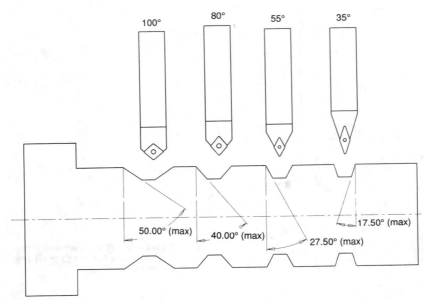

Figure 4.40 Comparison of the uses of profiling tool styles.

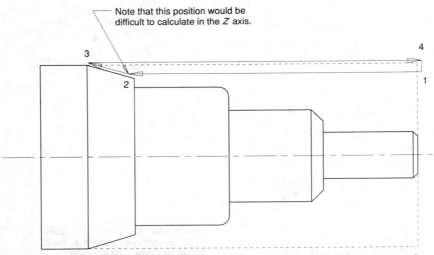

Figure 4.41 Illustration of the difficulty related to calculating and programming each motion during rough turning.

Although we have not gone into details, this rough-turning example should show you much of what is involved. Your control's programming manual will include precise information on how to use the rough-turning command. As you will see, it will be well worth the time it takes to learn this command completely, since it will save you

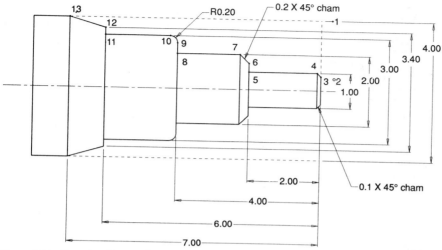

Figure 4.42 Drawing for rough-turning example program.

hours of programming time for each complicated rough-turning operation you must perform.

A popular control is used for our example program. For this particular control, a G71 command is used for rough turning and a G70 is used for finishing. Here are the word meanings for these two commands as they apply to the control used for our example.

For G71 roughing:

P Sequence number where finish-pass definition begins (always the next command in the program)

Q Sequence number where finish-pass definition ends

U Amount of stock to be left on all diameters for finishing

W Amount of stock to be left on all faces for finishing

D Depth of cut for rough-turning cycle

F Feed rate for rough-turning cycle

For G70 finishing:

P Sequence number where finish-pass definition begins

Q Sequence number where finish-pass definition ends

F Feed rate for finish-turning pass

Though it may be a little difficult to follow at this point, here is the program for the workpiece shown in Fig. 4.42.

Program:

O0044 (Program number)

(Rough-turning tool)
N005 G50 X _____ Z _____ (Assign program zero)
N010 G00 T0101 M41 (Index to station 1, instate offset 1, select low spindle range)
N015 G96 S400 M03 (Turn spindle on CW at 400 SFM)
N020 G00 X4. Z.1 (Rapid to point 1)
N025 G71 P030 Q085 U.040 W.005 D.200 F.015 (Rough-turn the workpiece, see above for word meanings)
N030 G00 X.8 (First block of finish-pass definition, rapid to point 2)
N035 G01 Z0 (Feed to point 3)
N040 X1. Z-.1 (Feed to point 4)
N045 Z-2. (Feed to point 5)
N050 X1.6 (Feed to point 6)
N055 X2. Z-2.2 (Feed to point 7)
N060 Z-4. (Feed to point 8)
N065 X2.6 (Feed to point 9)
N070 G03 X3. Z-4.2 R.2 (Circular move to point 10)
N075 G01 Z-6. (Feed to point 11)
N080 X3.4 (Feed to point 12)
N085 X4. Z-7. (Last block of finish-pass definition, feed to point 13)
N090 G00 X _____ Z _____ T0100 (Return to tool change position, cancel offset)
N095 M01 (Optional stop)
(Finish-turning tool)
N100 G50 X _____ Z _____ (Assign program zero)
N105 G00 T0202 M42 (Index to station 2, instate offset 2, select high spindle range)
N110 G96 S600 M03 (Turn spindle on CW at 600 SFM)
N115 G00 X4. Z.1 (Rapid to point 1, note that this is the same position as the approach for a rough-turning operation)
N120 G70 P030 Q085 F.007 (Make finish pass; the control will execute the commands from line N030 through N085)
N125 G00 X _____ Z _____ T0200 (Return to tool change position, cancel offset)
N130 M30 (End of program)

Believe it or not, line N025 specifies that the entire rough-turning cycle be done. It tells the control to look between lines N030 and N085 to find the finish-pass definition (specified by P030 and Q085). Note that at the time this command is written, the programmer will not know the last block number of the finish-pass definition. It is only *after* the finish-pass definition has been made that you will know this last block's sequence number.

The U and W in our example program specify that 0.040 in of stock be left on all diameters and 0.005 in of stock be left on all faces for finishing. The D word specifies that 0.200-in depth of cut be used for each pass of the roughing cycle. And the F0.015 specifies the feed rate to be used for the entire roughing cycle.

Line N025 causes the entire rough-turning cycle to be done. The control will reduce the diameter being turned by 0.200 in (the depth of cut) for each new rough-turning pass. It will machine across that diameter until a face is encountered. Then it will return to make the next pass.

At the completion of line N025, the workpiece will have been entirely roughed, and the control will continue execution at line N090.

At this time the program tells the control to return to the tool change position to index to the finish-turning tool.

In line N120, the G70 command tells the control to make the finish-turning pass. In essence, this command tells the control to go back to line N030 and go through line N085. These are the line numbers where the finish-pass definition is made, so the control truly finishes the workpiece at this point. When line N120 is completed, the workpiece will have been finished and the control will continue with line N125.

The G71 command also allows easy optimizing at the machine when the workpiece is being run. If the programmer determines that the depth of cut must be changed to make deeper passes, one simple word can be changed (the D word). The control will then generate a whole new series of roughing passes based on the new D word in the G71 command.

Note that each control will have many rules as to what is allowed during the finish-pass definition. For example, one popular control does not allow a reduction in diameter once the finish-pass definition is started. As stated, you must check your particular control's programming manual to find out more about this very helpful series of rough- and finish-turning commands.

Programming tips for rough and finish facing. Most CNC turning-center controls also have a special cycle to help with rough facing. Figure 4.43 shows an example workpiece. In this workpiece's case, it would be

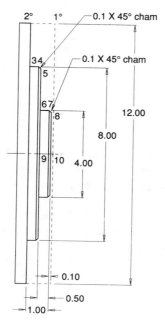

Figure 4.43 Drawing for rough-facing example program.

better if roughing occurs in a facing mode, rather than a turning mode. This will minimize the number of passes required. Note that the command for rough facing (G72 for our example) is very similar to that for rough turning. In essence, the only real difference is the mode of machining (facing mode instead of turning mode).

Here is the example program to machine the workpiece in Fig. 4.43:

Program:

O0045 (Program number)
(Rough-facing tool)
N005 G50 X _____ Z _____ (Assign program zero)
N010 G00 T0101 M41 (Index to station 1, instate offset 1, switch to low spindle range)
N015 G96 S500 M03 (Turn spindle on CW at 500 SFM)
N020 G00 X12.4 Z.1 (Rapid to point 1)
N025 G72 P030 Q070 U.040 W.005 D.125 F.015 (Rough-face the entire workpiece; see above for word meanings)
N030 G00 Z-1. (Rapid to point 2)
N035 G01 X8. (Feed to point 3)
N040 Z-.6 (Feed to point 4)
N045 X7.8 Z-.5 (Feed to point 5)
N050 X4. (Feed to point 6)
N055 Z-.1 (Feed to point 7)
N060 X3.8 Z0 (Feed to point 8)
N065 X0 (Feed to point 9)
N070 Z.1 (Feed to point 10, end of finish-pass definition)
N075 G00 X _____ Z _____ T0100 (Return to tool change position, cancel offset)
N080 M01 (Optional stop)
(Finish-facing tool)
N085 G50 X _____ Z _____ (Assign program zero)
N090 G00 T0202 M42 (Index to station 2, instate offset 2, select high spindle range)
N095 G96 S600 M03 (Turn spindle on CW at 600 SFM)
N100 G00 X12.4 Z.1 (Rapid to point 1, same approach position as for rough facing)
N100 G70 P030 Q070 F.010 (Finish-face workpiece)
N105 G00 X _____ Z _____ T0200 (Return to tool change position, cancel offset)
N110 M30 (End of program)

As you can see, this program is very similar to the rough-turning example. There are only three differences. First, the approach movement for rough facing is above the workpiece in X (instead of flush with the stock diameter). Second the G72 command is used instead of G71. Third, in the first command of the finish-pass definition (in line N030), the direction of motion is in Z rather than in X and the motions during the finish-pass definition are in the facing mode.

Note how G70 is still used for finishing, and finishing motions will now occur in the facing mode.

Again, specific techniques required for rough facing will vary from one CNC turning-center control to the next. You must check in your control's programming manual for more information.

Internal turning operations (boring)

Though there are many specific terms that refer to various machining operations, most machinists refer to machining done on outside diameters of a workpiece as *turning operations*. Machining done on inside diameters of a workpiece is referred to as *boring*. Here we begin our discussion of operations performed on inside diameters.

You will find *many* similarities between tool configurations for boring tools and those for turning tools. In fact, many times the same tool inserts used in outside-diameter turning tools can be used in inside-diameter boring bars. This means the same basic tool geometry discussed earlier for turning tools also applies to boring bars. Figure 4.44 shows a boring bar held in a typical boring-bar holder for a turning center.

While all of the cutting direction discussions still apply, generally speaking, boring bars are not nearly as rigid as turning tools. That is, you must be more cautious with a boring bar's cutting conditions, since it is not as strong as a turning tool. Also, most boring bars are designed to machine best when cutting in only one direction. Figure 4.45 shows this.

As you can see, a boring bar can machine much better when the strength of the boring bar is behind the cut. If machining at 90° to the boring bar, the machining tool will have the tendency to bend the boring bar. The smaller the boring bar, the greater this tendency.

As with outside-diameter turning tools, boring bars are used for roughing and finishing operations. Before a boring bar can be used, a hole must exist in the workpiece that is large enough to allow the boring bar to enter. While there are boring bars that have drilling capabilities, most cannot machine a hole from solid material. Another hole-machining tool must be used for this purpose (see the section "Hole-Machining Operations" earlier in this chapter for more information).

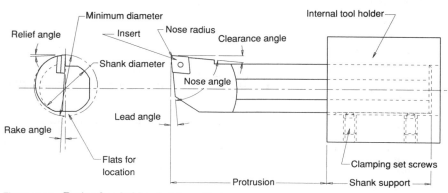

Figure 4.44 Boring bar held in holder with terms.

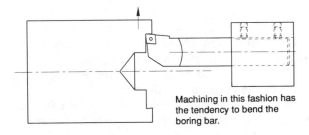

Machining in this fashion has
the tendency to bend the
boring bar.

Note that the boring bar is much more
stable and rigid when machining in
this direction.

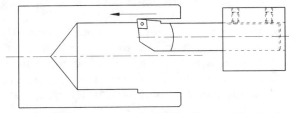

Figure 4.45 Drawing compares boring bar used in a boring
mode versus a facing mode.

Figure 4.46 shows the motions a boring bar makes during rough
boring. Note the similarity to rough turning. Also note the current
hole size when rough boring begins.

Programming tips for rough and finish boring. Most CNC controls use
the same commands for rough and finish boring that are used for
rough and finish turning (G71 and G70 for one popular control). In
fact, the same basic logic used to develop programs for outside-
diameter roughing and finishing is used for inside-diameter roughing
and finishing. Figure 4.47 shows the drawing we will use for our example program.

Program:

```
O0046 (Program number)
(Rough-boring bar)
N005 G50 X _____ Z _____ (Assign program zero)
N010 G00 T0101 M41 (Index to station 1, instate offset 1, select low spindle range)
N015 G96 S500 M03 (Turn spindle on CW at 500 SFM)
N020 G00 X2. Z.1 (Rapid to point 1)
N025 G71 P030 Q070 U-.040 W.005 D.125 F.010 (Rough-bore entire workpiece)
N030 G00 X4.2 (Rapid to point 2)
N035 G01 Z0 (Feed to point 3)
N040 X4.0 Z-.1 (Feed to point 4)
N045 Z-1. (Feed to point 5)
N050 X3.4 (Feed to point 6)
```

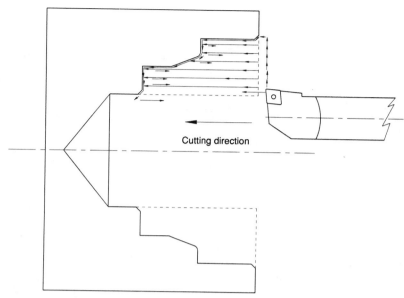

Figure 4.46 Drawing of common motions made by boring bar in rough boring cycle.

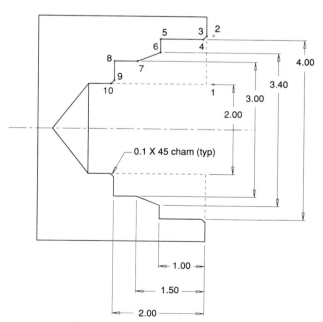

Figure 4.47 Drawing for example program, demonstrating rough and finish boring.

N055 X3. Z-1.5 (Feed to point 7)
N060 Z-2. (Feed to point 8)
N065 X2.2 (Feed to point 9)
N070 X2. Z-2.1 (Feed to point 10, last block of finish-pass definition)
N075 G00 X _____ Z _____ T0100 (Return to tool change position, cancel offset)
N080 M01 (Optional stop)
(Finish boring bar)
N085 G50 X _____ Z _____ (Assign program zero)
N090 G00 T0202 M42 (Index to station 2, instate offset 2, select high spindle range)
N095 G96 S600 M03 (Turn spindle on CW at 600 SFM)
N100 G00 X2. Z.1 (Rapid to point 1)
N105 G70 P030 Q070 F.007 (Finish-bore workpiece)
N110 G00 X _____ Z _____ T0200 (Return to tool change position, cancel offset)
N115 M30 (End of program)

Note how similar this program is to the example showing rough and finish turning. There are very few differences.

Note the minus value of the U word in line N025. This particular control requires that the programmer point the direction in which the rough stock is to be left. In the case of rough boring, the rough stock is to be left in the minus X direction. Also notice how the tool is positioned first flush with the hole diameter prior to the G71 command. In both cases (rough turning and rough boring), the tool is positioned to the current stock diameter from which roughing begins.

The G70 command is still used to finish (bore, in this case) the workpiece. This command tells the control to go back to the first block of the finish-pass definition and go through the last block of the finish-pass definition.

Threading

Turning centers allow threads to be machined on outside and inside diameters. Threads come in a variety of shapes and specifications. These early threading discussions will relate specifically to National Standard threads (later we will discuss other thread forms). A National Standard thread is a V thread with a 60° included angle. Figure 4.48 shows an external National Standard thread, as well as many terms involved with a thread's designation.

Threading is done in a chasing manner. By chasing, we mean the threading tool makes multiple passes over the thread. During each pass, the threading tool goes deeper, but follows the same motion as its last pass. The number of passes required for threading depends on the pitch of the thread. Generally speaking, the coarser the thread, the more passes required.

As each threading pass is made, most experienced machinists would agree that the threading tool should machine only on the front side of the threading tool. On manual engine lathes, this is accomplished by

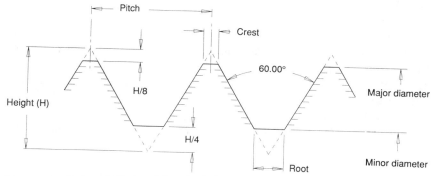

Figure 4.48 External National Standard thread form.

adjusting the compound rest to an angle of 29.5° before any infeed is made. This same principle applies to threading on CNC turning centers. While there are exceptions, most tooling manufacturers specify that the threading tool should machine only on the front side of the thread. Figure 4.49 shows this angular infeed.

The feed rate during threading is equal to the pitch of the thread. As stated earlier (during tapping), the pitch of a thread designated in the inch system is equal to 1 divided by the number of threads per

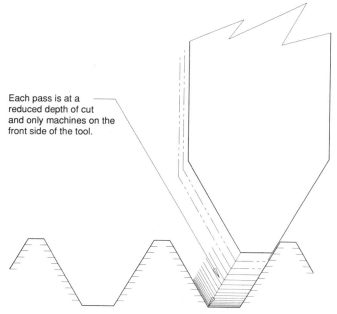

Figure 4.49 How threading tool forms compound angle with reduced depths of cut during threading.

inch. For example, the pitch of a 16 thread per inch thread is ¹⁄₁₆ or 0.0625 in.

Though they vary dramatically from one tooling manufacturer to another, National Standard threading tools have similarities to other turning tools. For machining outside-diameter threads, the threading tool resembles a turning tool. Figure 4.50 shows a drawing of this kind of threading tool.

Internal threading tools resemble boring bars. Figure 4.51 shows an internal-threading tool. Older CNC controls required a command sim-

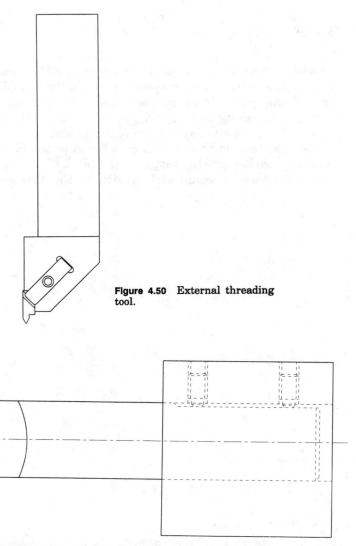

Figure 4.50 External threading tool.

Figure 4.51 Drawing shows internal threading tool.

ilar to G01 (straight-line motion) to make the actual threading pass. One common command for this purpose is a G32. The G32 works just like a G01, except the G32 allows chasing motions to occur (the tool will follow the same path for every pass). G00 rapid motion commands were used to position the tool to its starting position for each pass. With this older technique, four commands were required for each pass. Each new depth position was difficult to calculate since the depth of cut must be reduced for each pass. Also, if you were trying to incorporate an angular infeed (as shown in Fig. 4.49), the starting position for the threading tool would have to be changed (in Z) for each pass.

All of this made thread programming *very* difficult. Fortunately, current CNC controls allow an entire thread to be machined by one very simple command. As with the rough-turning, rough-boring, and rough-facing commands, the actual command used for threading varies dramatically from control to control. Here we will show how one popular control allows threading to be specified.

Our example control uses a G76 with which to specify threading. As with G71, the G76 command requires a list of words (or variables) to be included in the threading command. Here is a list of words needed for threading.

Word	Description
X	Major (for inside threads) or minor (for outside threads) diameter of the thread
Z	End point of the thread along the Z axis
K	Thread depth (major diameter − minor diameter ÷ 2, for outside threads)
D	Depth of the first threading pass (all subsequent passes will be at a reduced depth)
A	Tool angle (60° for National Standard threads)
F	Pitch of the thread (1 ÷ number of threads per inch)
I	For tapered threads only, this value specifies the distance and direction in X (on the side) from the end point of the thread to the starting point of the thread

Figure 4.52 shows a drawing to be used for the example program. Notice that both an outside-diameter and inside-diameter thread will be machined, and in fact, this is all the example program will do (no other machining is done by the example program).

Program:

```
O0047 (Program number)
(Outside-diameter threading tool)
N005 G50 X _____ Z _____ (Assign program zero)
N010 G00 T0101 M41 (Index to station number 1, instate offset 1, select low
spindle range)
N015 G97 S400 M03 (Turn spindle on CW at 400 RPM)
N020 G00 X5.7 Z-.8 (Rapid up to clearance position)
N025 G76 X5.392 Z-1.88 K.054 D.015 A60. F.0625 (Machine entire thread)
N030 G00 X _____ Z _____ T0100 (Return to tool change position)
```

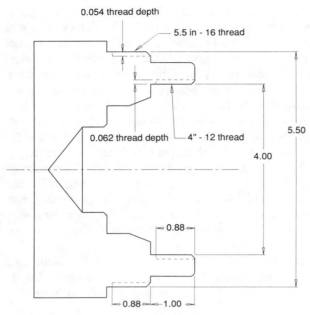

Figure 4.52   Drawing for threading example program.

N035 M01 (Optional stop)
(Internal threading tool)
N035 G50 X _____ Z _____ (Assign program zero)
N040 G00 T0202 M41 (Index to station number 2, instate offset 2, select low spindle range)
N045 G97 S500 M03 (Turn spindle on CW at 500 RPM)
N050 G00 X3.8 Z.2 (Rapid up to clearance position)
N055 G76 X4.124 Z-.88 K.062 D.012 A60. F.0833 (Machine entire internal thread)
N060 G00 X _____ Z _____ T0200 (Return to tool change position, cancel offset)
N065 M30 (End of program)

In line N025, the entire outside diameter thread is machined. For this thread, the X value represents the minor diameter of the thread. The K represents the thread depth. D specifies the depth of the first pass. A gives the threading tool angle. From these four numbers, the control can determine how to machine the thread.

In the same way, line N055 machines the inside-diameter thread. This time, the X represents the *major* diameter of the thread.

In some cases, the workpiece print will not provide all information needed for the program, especially with regard to thread depth. You may have to consult a reference book on threading to determine some of these values based on the class of thread being machined.

The depth of the first pass (D word) helps the control to calculate the number of passes desired. If you want more passes to be made, reduce this word's value. If you want fewer passes, increase this word.

Exactly how many passes will be made for any one thread will be difficult to determine on the basis of the program only. You can find how the control determines this number within the programming manual for your particular control. In reality, however, you should not be overly concerned with this number as the program is written. We recommend that you pick a small number (about 20 percent of the thread depth) to start. This forces the control to make more passes than necessary. Once you see the thread being machined, you can manipulate the D word to optimize production.

In the example program, note the approach distance from the tool's position in Z when the threading command is given to the surface of the workpiece to be machined. In the example program's case, the approach distance is 0.200 in. It is during this distance of motion that the control must accelerate the tool to a very precise motion rate. Of course, this motion rate (feed rate) determines the pitch of the thread. No CNC turning center is capable of instantaneously accelerating from a stopped condition to the proper feed rate. The response capabilities of the machine's servo drive system, the pitch of the thread, and the spindle RPM are all factors which determine how quickly the machine can reach the required feed rate.

We recommend that this approach distance be at least 3 times the pitch *or* 0.200 in, which ever is *smaller*. Most relatively small, current CNC machines can respond in this short motion. However, with older, or extremely large machines, this value may have to be increased.

With regard to the infeed angle, the A word tells the control the tool's included angle. And, if specified, this angle will cause the tool to machine on only the tool's leading edge. If for some reason, you wish no infeed angle, the A word can be left out, or a value of A0 can be specified. This will cause the tool to plunge straight into the thread in each pass, cutting equally on both sides of the threading tool. Note that some form tools designed for threading require this kind of motion.

Tapered threads. Most CNC turning-center controls allow tapered threads to be machined with the same ease as straight threads. Of course, the surface to be taper-threaded must also be in the form of a taper. With taper threading, only one more word is required in the threading command to specify the amount of taper. One popular control uses the I word for this purpose. Figure 4.53 shows how the I word is related to tapered threads and how the functions of other threading words change when taper threading is done.

For this popular control, the I word is the distance and direction in X (on the side) *from* the end point of the thread *to* the start point of the thread. Though this technique may vary from one control to the next, this is a common way to designate tapered threads.

Note that the I word also requires the *direction* (plus or minus) from

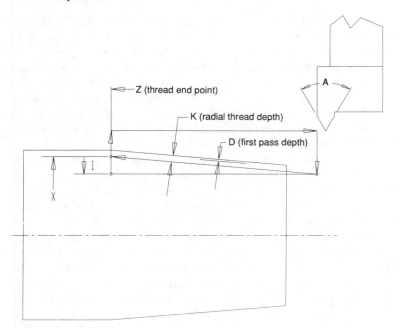

Figure 4.53 Values used when taper threading is required.

the end point to the start point in *X*. As long as the thread is machined toward the headstock end, outside-diameter threads require a minus value for I and inside-diameter threads require a plus value for I.

As you can see from Fig. 4.53, determining the I word requires trigonometry. This value must also take into consideration the approach distance from the tool's starting position to the threaded surface. To calculate the value of I, multiply the tangent of the taper angle (on the side) by the overall threading length (approach plus thread length). The workpiece print should include the taper angle (normally 1.789° on the side).

Multiple-start threads.   Here is another variation of thread that can be machined by a CNC turning center. A multiple-start thread allows the fast linear motion per revolution of a very coarse thread and the smooth, close fit of a fine thread. Figure 4.54 shows how a multiple-start thread is formed. This figure shows a four-start thread. As you can see from the drawing on the left, one of the starts has a 0.500-in lead. The drawing on the right shows the rest of the starts in place, 0.125 in apart.

As shown in Fig. 4.54, each thread start can be thought of as an independent thread. In fact, many CNC controls actually require that you program each thread start independently. One start is machined in its entirety, then the next. And so on for all thread starts.

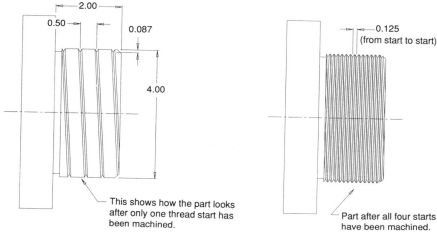

Figure 4.54   How a multiple-start thread is formed.

There is one disadvantage to machining multiple threads in this manner. If the workpiece material being threaded is gummy, it will have the tendency to push away from the cutting edge. If one thread start is completely machined before the next, as the adjacent thread start is being machined, the threading tool will have the tendency to push the material over into the previously machined thread start, damaging the thread.

The best way to avoid this problem is to rough-machine *all* thread starts before any one start is finished. The smaller the depth of cut for finishing, the better chance there will be that the material will not push over into the next start. In fact, many machinists will make free passes, machining absolutely no stock. These passes, called *spring passes,* will remove excess stock pushed over from the finishing of the adjacent thread start.

We must point out that design engineers do not use completely standard procedures when designating multiple-start threads. In some cases, it can be difficult to determine from the drawing that a thread *is* a multiple-start thread, let alone its specifications per start.

While CNC controls vary with regard to how multiple-start threads are specified, *you must* understand what is intended from the workpiece drawing before you can write your program for any control.

Several CNC controls allow you to specify that the entire number of thread starts be machined in one command. With this type of control, the F word of the threading command specifies the overall pitch internal to one start (the 0.500 value in Fig. 4.54). Another word (like Q) specifies the number of starts. The control will automatically divide the overall pitch (F word) by the number of starts to determine the pitch between each adjacent start. Here are two commands that would completely machine the thread shown in Fig. 4.54 using this method:

```
...
N060 G00 X4.2 Z.2 (Rapid into position)
N065 G76 X3.826 Z-1.9 K.087 D.015 A60. F.500 Q4.
(Machine entire thread including four starts)
...
```

Other CNC turning-center controls are not so helpful. They require that you program each thread start independently. Some force you to actually move the tool to a new starting position for each start to force the thread to be cross-threaded in a controlled manner. For the workpiece shown in Fig. 4.54, this means moving over in Z a value of 0.125 in between starts. Here is a series of commands that machines the thread with this technique:

```
...
N055 G00 X4.2 Z.2 (Rapid to starting position)
N060 G76 X3.826 Z-1.9 K.087 D.015 A60. F.500 (Machine first start)
N065 G00 Z.325 (Move over ¼ pitch)
N070 G76 X3.826 Z-1.9 K.087 D.015 A60. F.500 (Machine second start)
N075 G00 Z.450 (Move over ¼ pitch)
N080 G76 X3.826 Z-1.9 K.087 D.015 A60. F.500 (Machine third start)
N085 G00 Z.575 (Move over ¼ pitch)
N090 G76 X3.826 Z-1.9 K.087 D.015 A60. F.500 (Machine fourth start)
...
```

As you can see, this series of commands is not nearly as easy to work with as the commands given earlier. Also, this series of commands requires a longer movement with each thread lead machined (increasing cycle time). This is not to mention the problems that would occur if there were an obstruction (like a tailstock) in the way to prevent plus movement from the original starting position.

Yet another version of the threading command available from CNC turning-center control manufacturers allows each thread start to be specified in angular position. With this technique on one popular control, a Q word within the threading command specifies the angular position of the thread start. Here is a series of commands using this technique to machine the thread shown in Fig. 4.54:

```
...
N055 G00 X4.2 Z.2 (Rapid to starting position)
N060 G76 X3.826 Z-1.9 K.087 D.015 A60. F.500 Q0. (Machine first start)
N065 G76 X3.826 Z-1.9 K.087 D.015 A60. F.500 Q90.
(Machine second start)
N070 G76 X3.826 Z-1.9 K.087 D.015 A60. F.500 Q180.
(Machine third start)
N075 G76 X3.826 Z-1.9 K.087 D.015 A60. F.500 Q270.
(Machine fourth start)
```

While these commands still require one command per thread start, at least the starting position need not be altered. This minimizes cycle time and allows multiple-start threads to be machined even if an obstruction exists on the plus side of the thread's starting position.

Your control's programming manual will tell you which of these techniques to use (or may recommend yet another technique).

Specifying accurate thread pitch. Though this discussion is also presented in Chap. 2, it is repeated here because of its relevance to threading. As stated, most CNC turning-center controls allow the specification of thread pitch by an F word. However, with most controls, the F word is limited to a 4-digit format in the inch system. That is, pitch can be specified to only 4 digits of accuracy with the F word. There are times when this 4-digit limitation may cause problems with workpiece accuracy.

For example, if machining a 16 thread per inch thread, the pitch is $1 \div 16$, or 0.0625 in. In this case, the thread pitch happens to come out to precisely a 4-digit number. On the other hand, a 12 thread per inch thread has a pitch of $1 \div 12$, or 0.08333333333333 in. If you designate this pitch with an F word, it will be limited to four places of accuracy. In this case, only the 4 digits F.0833 could be used.

In most cases, this cutoff of accuracy will not affect the quality of the workpiece. For example, if you are simply making mating workpieces, as long as the same pitch is used for both mating threads, the workpieces will fit together nicely. However, there is one time when 4 digits of accuracy may not be good enough.

When the pitch accuracy affects the use of the workpiece, as would be the case with a lead screw, it would be helpful to be able to specify more than 4 digits of accuracy. Some controls allow this by the use of an E word in place of the F word in the threading command. If the E word can be used, most controls allow 2 more digits of accuracy to be specified. With the previous 12 thread-per-inch example, a pitch of E.083333 could be programmed to specify 6 digits of pitch accuracy.

Other thread forms. To this point, we have been discussing only National Standard threads. By far, this is the most common form of thread. However, you must be prepared to work with other thread forms. Here we will introduce two other common threads.

You will find dramatic similarities with regard to how these other thread forms are handled on CNC equipment. For this reason, we will limit our discussions to only those additional points we wish to make for these other threads.

Acme threads. An Acme thread has a 29° included angle instead of the 60° included angle of the National Standard thread. Also, generally speaking, Acme threads are much wider at the top and bottom than National Standard threads, which almost come to a point at the crest and root of the thread. For these two reasons, an Acme threading tool resembles a grooving tool more than a threading tool.

Acme threads can still be easily machined by the G76 multiple repetitive cycle. If you wish to force the tool to machine only on the tool's leading edge, you can include the word A29. in the threading command (instead of A60.). However, there are those experienced machinists who say it is unnecessary to plunge the thread at the compound angle because of the severe, almost square sides of the threading tool. If you wish *not* to plunge at the compound angle, either leave the A word out of the threading command or program A0.

Since the Acme threading tool is much stronger than the National Standard threading tool, as long as the setup is relatively rigid, you can program a much deeper first-pass depth. This is helpful since Acme threads are usually deeper (for the same pitch) than National Standard threads.

Buttress threads. Buttress threads can also be easily programmed on a CNC turning center by using the threading command. However, a Buttress thread does not have equal side angles in the thread form. Most Buttress threads have a 7° front angle and 45° back angle. For this reason, most programmers will allow the Buttress threading tool to plunge straight into the thread by leaving the A word out of the threading command or by specifying the tool angle in the threading command as A0. All other information about the threading operation remains basically the same as for National Standard threads.

Parametric Programming
Techniques

What Is Parametric Programming?

Parametric programming is the best kept secret of CNC. Throughout the industry, we have found that few people even know what parametric programming is, let alone understand its possible applications and how to use its features. This is understandable, since the original intention of parametric programming was to give machine-tool builders a way to access special devices (like probes, postprocess gauges, and tool management systems) that require more than basic CNC programming. It was not the control manufacturers' primary intention that parametric programming be used as a programming tool. However, parametric programming does make a very powerful and useful programming tool when it is understood.

In this chapter, we will take a good look at this powerful feature. You will see how it applies to both machining centers and turning centers. We will begin by introducing possible applications for parametric programming. In this section you will be able to easily determine whether parametric programming techniques can help in your particular situation. Next we will describe parametric programming, showing you how it can be related to subprogramming techniques as well as computer languages like BASIC and C. Finally, we will introduce many of the features of parametric programming and show you examples of each feature's use.

We must point out that parametric programming is sometimes considered an optional feature that must be purchased at extra charge. On other controls, it is always equipped as a standard feature. As mentioned, parametric programming is almost always required when certain optional devices are equipped on the CNC machine. You may have this feature on your control and not even know it.

To find out whether your particular machine has this feature, or to add this feature to your machine, you must contact your control manufacturer or machine-tool builder. When you ask whether your machine has this feature, keep in mind that parametric programming comes in many forms. Some control manufacturers call it *macro version A, macro version B,* or *custom macro.* Others call it *Q routine programming.* Yet others refer to it as simply *parametric programming.* Since this term works best to describe the feature, this chapter will call it parametric programming.

While this text will show one version of parametric programming that works with controls made by at least three popular control manufacturers, you must be prepared for variations. The basic function and reasoning for each parametric programming feature remains remarkably similar from one control to the next. However, specific techniques and actual commands will vary dramatically when considering the various CNC controls available today. We sincerely believe that if you can understand the reasoning behind and basic features of parametric programming, and if you have been exposed to one particular version as we show in this chapter, you should be able to adapt to any specific version of parametric programming with relative ease.

Applications for Parametric Programming

Parametric programming applications fall into three distinct categories. Understanding these applications will improve your ability to judge whether parametric programming will help you in your particular situation.

Families of parts

For the CNC user, this is the category that shows the most potential. If you find yourself constantly modifying one program to create another, you probably have a good application for parametric programming. If you have programs that include similar commands from other programs (as would be the case when using subprogramming techniques), parametric programming can help. Things like bolt-hole patterns, pockets, thread milling, grooving on lathes, peck drilling on lathes, and machining a series of holes along a line are among the most common applications for parametric programming. Along the same lines, many companies use parametric programming techniques to actually fine-tune the programming for their product line. Here are some examples.

A hand-tool manufacturer uses parametric programming techniques to machine a hex shape in its entire series of large sockets. The operator simply changes a few variables from one setup to another and is ready to run the next socket size. Programming time is less than 3 minutes!

A forging-die shop uses parametric programming techniques to remachine the shank ends of dies. If the die shank cracks, the shop uses a parametric program to reduce the programming time for a 3- to 4-hour machining cycle time to about 5 minutes. The operator simply fills in the blanks, telling the control the size of the die shank currently being remachined. The parametric program does the rest.

For this application, the forging die shop could not have justified the CNC machine if conventional programming techniques were to be used. By using conventional programming methods (either manual programming or a CAM system), it is conceivable that programming time would equal or exceed machining time!

A screw machine cam manufacturer uses parametric programming techniques to describe the rises and falls in a circular cam. The parametric program calculates all motions required to make the cam and does so automatically. Again, programming time is reduced to about 5 minutes per cam!

A piston ring manufacturer uses parametric programming techniques to describe and machine its various ring configurations.

The list of potential applications could go on and on. In each of the above applications, there was a remarkable consistency in the product being manufactured. This consistency justified the extra time it took to develop the parametric program. Once this variable-purpose parametric program was developed, programming time for each new workpiece was reduced to almost nothing.

Since almost all companies have some kind of workpiece family, or at least some consistency from one part to another, it is this application for parametric programming for families of parts that our text will primarily address. As each feature of parametric programming is introduced and discussed, you will see how easy it becomes to handle each workpiece in a family.

Complex geometric shapes

Parametric programming techniques can also be used to generate extremely complicated shapes. (The circular screw machine cam example given earlier fits into this category as well as into the family-of-parts category). Since parametric programs allow complex arithmetic calculations to be done from within a program, there is almost no limit to the geometric shapes that can be machined. Spheres, pyramids, and cones are among common shapes in this category. However, any shape that can be mathematically defined can be described and machined by a parametric program.

This application for parametric programming is the most difficult to program. Usually, if a company has a CAM system, it would be much easier to program workpieces falling into this category with the CAM system than to use parametric programming techniques. However, parametric programming does have one advantage even over a good CAM system. This advantage has to do with program length.

Say, for example, a parametric program has been developed to machine a spherical shape with a ball end mill on a machining center. The typical parametric program for this application would be about 50 commands. The equivalent CNC program generated by the CAM system could conceivably be thousands of commands. In some cases, lengthy CAM-system-generated programs may not even fit into the CNC control's memory.

As stated, just about any definable shape can be programmed with parametric programming techniques. However, programming difficulty increases in direct proportion to the complexity of the job.

Driving machine-option devices

This application for parametric programming is usually taken care of by the machine-tool builder or by the supplier of the option device. Probes, in-process gauging equipment, postprocess gauging equipment, and tool management systems are among the types of applications that fall into this category.

Parametric programming techniques allow a means to drive these option devices from within a program. You can think of the option device itself as the hardware and the parametric program as the software that tells the option device what to do. Since parametric programming techniques allow access to tool offsets and other machine functions, as well as allow CNC commands to be executed, parametric programming makes an excellent way (if not the only way) to interface option devices to the control.

When an option device (such as a touch probe) is equipped on the CNC machine, it will come with a series of parametric programs and documentation related to their use. While special-purpose parametric programs can be prepared for the option device, the typical end user will simply use the previously prepared parametric programs.

Becoming Familiar with Parametric Programming

Whenever you are learning anything new, it is always best to work from known to unknown. Drawing from some previous knowledge or experience makes learning much easier. Here we will draw on concepts you may already be familiar with in order to develop your understanding of parametric programming.

**Parametric programming versus
subprogramming**

One way to help you understand parametric programming is to compare it to subprogramming. Almost all CNC controls have the subprogramming feature to minimize redundant commands. In Chap. 2 we gave several examples of how subprogramming techniques can help.

As you know, subprograms must be totally redundant. If *anything* changes from one job to the next, subprogramming techniques cannot be used. For example, if a subprogram is generated to machine a 0.25-in-wide by 0.25-in-deep groove for a turning center (as shown in Chap. 2), the subprogram will only machine a groove with these specifications. If a 0.187-in-wide by 0.125-in-deep groove must be machined, this subprogram *cannot* be used. Of course, another similar subprogram could be written, but it would also only machine one groove size. The same is true for *every* subprogramming application. If anything changes from one time to the next, the subprogramming technique will not help.

You can think of parametric programming as having the ability to generate general-purpose subprograms. With parametric programming, one of the main benefits is the ability to pass variables from the main program to the parametric program. The parametric program will make the machine behave differently, depending on the values of the variables passed from the main program.

With the grooving application, for example, a general-purpose parametric program can be written that will machine a groove of *any* width to *any* depth. Many other variables can also be passed from the main program to the parametric program, informing the parametric program of other important application-related values. Continuing with the grooving application, variables representing the tool width, groove diameter, groove depth, and chamfer or radius values to be machined in the corners of the groove can also be passed from the main program to the parametric program.

As we begin introducing the features of parametric programming, variables will be discussed in much more detail. You will see that variables can also be used for many purposes, not the least of which is passing information from the main program to the parametric program.

As discussed in Chap. 2, most controls use an M98 with a P word to call a subprogram. The command

N050 M98 P1000

calls program 1000. An M99 is commanded at the completion of the subprogram (O1000 in this case) to return the control to the command in the main program after the calling M98 command.

The most basic command to call a parametric program is very similar to the command that calls a subprogram. One popular command to call a parametric program is G65 and will be used throughout this text. The command

N050 G65 P1000

calls program 1000, just as the previous M98 command does. Also, the parametric program O1000 must end just like a subprogram, with an M99.

To this point, there is absolutely no difference in how the control will execute these two commands. In both cases, the control will jump to program O1000 and continue from there. When the M99 is executed at the end of program O1000, the control will return to the main program to the command after the calling command.

However, the G65 command allows an argument list of variables to be included in the command. The variables in the argument list are simple letters like A, B, C, D, and so on. Each of these letters will represent a variable to be passed to the parametric program. Each letter will be followed by a numeric value which specifies the value of the variable.

Here is a more extended example. Say you were developing a parametric program for the grooving application. One of the first steps to developing any parametric program is to come up with your wish list call statement. Here is an example call statement that includes an argument list of variables to be passed to the parametric program:

N050 G65 P1000 W.25 T.125 A2.5 D.25 C.015

The programmer determines the meaning of each variable to be used in the argument list. In our case, W represents the width of the groove, T represents the tool width, A is the large diameter (current stock diameter), D is the depth of the groove, and C specifies the chamfer size to be made on each outside diameter corner.

Wouldn't it be nice if this was all you had to do to machine any groove of any size with any tool width? Just fill in the blanks! Of course, writing the parametric program will require more work than programming one specific groove, but once written, the parametric program can be used *any* time you need to machine a groove. You should be beginning to see the benefit of parametric programming. Before you finish this chapter, you will have been exposed to all techniques needed to write this parametric program for grooving.

Parametric programming versus computer programming

Another way to become familiar with parametric programming is to compare it to computer programming languages like BASIC or C.

Many features of computer programming languages are also available in parametric programming. If you know BASIC (or any computer language) as it applies to computer software programming, you are well on your way to understanding parametric programming. If you are not familiar with BASIC, we recommend that you buy a beginner's book about the language BASIC. It will truly help you to understand the implications of each feature used in parametric programming.

The basic structure of a parametric program is also remarkably similar to a software program written in BASIC. How loops are created, how arithmetic is done, the use of variables, and unconditional branching are almost identical. If you have written programs in BASIC, we think you will be surprised when you see the first example parametric program, since it will resemble a BASIC program very closely.

Along with these computer-programming-related features, most versions of parametric programming allow many CNC control-related features. For example, most versions of parametric programming allow access to tool offsets, current axis position, current state of all modes, and much, much, more. This combination of computer-related features and CNC-control-related features blend parametric programming into an extremely powerful CNC programming tool.

The Features of Parametric Programming

Generally speaking, parametric programming features can be divided into two basic categories, computer-related features and CNC-control-related features. The computer-related features of parametric programming remain remarkably consistent from one control type to the next. For this reason, we can be reasonably specific about the use of features in this category.

However, the CNC-control-related features vary dramatically from one manufacturer to the next. While we will give a general idea as to what kinds of features are in this category and even give several general examples, this text cannot be very specific about their use.

Computer-related features

As stated, if you have experience with any computer programming language, you will find these features to be quite familiar. Though the specific format for each command used with these features may be somewhat different from what you are used to, the basic reasoning behind the feature is quite the same. Also, what we will show in this section relates specifically to how at least three popular CNC controls apply parametric programming. But, as stated earlier, you must be prepared for variations.

Variable techniques. Variables are storage locations in which values are placed. You can think of variables as like tool offsets in this regard. With a tool offset, a value (a tool length, tool radius, etc.) is permanently stored within the offset (until changed). The control will use the tool offset in different ways, depending on how the program is written. If instated by a G43 and an H word on a machining center, the offset will be taken as the tool length value. If instated with a G42 and a D word on a machining center, the offset will be taken as a cutter radius compensation value. Truly, most CNC controls will not know the meaning of the value stored in a tool offset until the program is executed.

Like offsets, variables are storage locations. Like offsets, a value (sometimes the result of a calculation) will be stored within a variable. Like offsets, the meaning or use of the variable will not be known until it is referenced in some way during the parametric program. Like offsets, most controls allow you to see their current values on the display screen. However, some variables cannot be entered or changed through the display screen as offsets can.

The use of variables is much more flexible than tool offsets. In almost all cases, a tool offset is used only with a form of compensation. On the other hand, a variable can be used to represent almost anything, depending on the application. Among the things a variable can be used to represent are an axis position, an arc radius, a chamfer size, a spindle speed, a feed rate, and a tool diameter, just to name a few. Actually, your imagination and application are the only things that limit what variables can be used to represent.

Variables can also be used as storage locations in which the results of arithmetic calculations can be held. These variables can be used later in the parametric program as axis positions, circular radii, or whatever you wish them to represent. A variable which is the result of a calculation can also be used to help with the parametric program's logic. Counters and flags are examples of variables used in this manner (more on these applications for variables a little later).

For the version of parametric programming we are presenting, variables are always designated in the body of the parametric program with a pound sign (#). For example, #101 is variable 101, #102 is variable 102, and so on. Keep in mind, however, that not all versions of parametric programming use this technique. You must be prepared for variations. If you can understand our presentations related to variables, you should be able to easily adapt to the variations. Truly, the reasoning related to why variables are used remains constant for *all* versions of parametric programming. Only the way they are referenced in the parametric program will vary.

Generally speaking, there are four types of variables used in parametric programming. Here is a discussion of each type.

Arguments from the call statement. You were briefly exposed to this form of variable earlier, as we began to acquaint you with the parametric programming feature. This kind of variable is placed in the call statement and passed to the parametric program. These variables are actually letter addresses (A, B, C, etc.) followed by a numerical value with a decimal point.

Variables (arguments) from the call statement tell the parametric program how to behave. They fill in the blanks for the current time the parametric program is to be executed. For example, if the letter R is to represent the radius of a bolt-hole pattern in a parametric program, the word R3.25 in the call statement will inform the parametric program that the radius of the current bolt-hole pattern to be machined is 3.25 in.

Keep in mind that there are some letters that cannot be used as arguments in the call statement. Certain letters, like N, O, G, P, and L are not allowed, since they conflict with letters which are used for other purposes in the call statement. Here is a list of letter addresses allowed as arguments in the call statement:

A, B, C, D, E, F, H, I, J, K, M, Q, R, S, T, U, V, W, X, Y, and Z

The parametric programmer determines the meanings of each these variables in the call statement. The programmer must choose them wisely, trying to come up with a logical meaning for each letter. For example, T may represent the tool width or diameter, D may represent the depth of cut, F may represent feed rate, R may represent a radius, and so on. This wise selection of letter addresses in the call statement makes it easy for everyone using the parametric program to remember the variable names.

For even the simplest applications, the parametric programmer should clearly document the arguments used in the call statement. Everyone who uses the parametric program *must* have a clear understanding of which variables (letters) must be placed in the call statement as well as what each one represents. One way to accomplish this is to make a drawing or sketch, showing graphically what each argument represents. The actual letters used in the call statement can be easily referenced on such a sketch. As you see example parametric programs in this chapter, notice how clearly the example drawings illustrate the meanings of each argument.

Local variables. When passed to a parametric program, the arguments from the call statement *cannot* be represented as letter addresses. This is because the control would confuse them with the actual letter addresses used for normal CNC commands (X, Y, and Z for axis position, F for feed rate, H for tool offset number, and so on).

For this reason, arguments coming from the call statement must be represented in the parametric program by local variables. For the most popular form of argument assignment, local variables range from #1 through #26. Here is a conversion table that shows the local variable number that corresponds to each letter address allowed in the call statement.

A #1	B #2	C #3	D #7	E #8	F #9
H #11	I #4	J #5	K #6	M #13	Q #17
R #18	S #19	T #20	U #21	V #22	W #23
X #24	Y #25	Z #26			

Though these local variable numbers follow no logical order, this is the way variables coming from the call statement *must* be represented within the parametric program.

For example, consider the call statement given earlier for the grooving example:

N050 G65 P1000 W.25 T.125 A2.5 D.25 C.015

In program number O1000, you cannot use the letter W, T, A, D, or C to represent values of arguments coming from the call statement. They *must* be converted to their local variable equivalents. W in the parametric program must be represented by #23, T by #20, A by #1, D by #7, and C by #3. Though this may not make much sense yet, when you see an example a little later, things should clear up nicely.

Because there is no logical order to the local variable numbers, most parametric programmers will use the letter addresses to represent variables coming from the call statement as the parametric program is written. They will write them, knowing that they must be eventually converted to their local variable equivalents. (It is also helpful to circle them as they are written.) On completing the parametric program, they go back and convert them *before* the parametric program is loaded into the CNC control's memory. This makes writing (and understanding) the parametric much easier.

Local variables are the most temporary variables. They are only remembered during the execution of the parametric program specified by the *current* call statement. As soon as the M99 is executed, *all* local variables are forgotten. That is, they are set back to vacant (having no value).

Common variables. Common variables are used for two basic purposes. One is as a place in which to store the results of arithmetic calculations. Variables used in this manner can be referenced later in the parametric program and can be used to represent almost anything.

Common variables can also be used to represent the value included after a letter address, in place of an actual number, such as the value of *any* CNC command. For example, #100 is variable 100. Say its current value is 3.500 (calculated earlier in another command). If the control reads the command

N040 G00 X#100

it will move to an *X* position of the current value of variable #100. In this case, it will be just as if this command were given:

N040 G00 X3.5

The number of common variables available within parametric programming varies from one control to the next. Normally the minimum number available is 50, and the variables range from #100 through #149. However, many controls offer more common variables (sometimes as an option that must be purchased at extra cost).

Common variables are slightly more permanent than local variables. On most controls, common variables are remembered until the control's power is turned off. Then they are set back to vacant (having no value).

Permanent common variables.   With most controls, there is a style of common variable that will be remembered even after the power is turned off (just like tool offsets). Everything else about this variable type is identical to common variables. There are usually at least 10 permanent common variables and they will range from at least #500 through #509.

These variables are helpful for applications when a continuation of the parametric program is required from day to day (after power-up). One example of this kind of application is a tool-life management system. With a tool-life management system, the parametric program must be able to keep track of each tool's current elapsed cutting time in order to make decisions as to when tools should be changed. In many cases, this will require the parametric program to remember a tool's elapsed time from day to day. In this application, permanent common variables make an excellent location in which to store each tool's elapsed time.

System variables.   System variables allow access to many CNC-control-related functions. Tool offsets, axis positions, and current modes (absolute versus incremental, inch versus metric, etc.) are among the accessible features. These variables and their corresponding numbers vary greatly from one control to the next.

They normally range from #1000 through #7000, though as stated, the numbers may vary. One popular control uses the #2000 series with which to access tool offsets. For example, #2001 contains the value of offset 1, #2002 contains the value of offset 2, and so on.

We will continue the discussion of system variables quite a bit later.

Arithmetic calculations.   Parametric programming allows arithmetic to be done from within the parametric program. Almost anything that can be done on an electronic scientific calculator can be done from within a parametric program. In most cases, common variables (#100 through #149) are used as locations in which to store the results of a calculation (though calculations can also be done within a CNC command).

Most arithmetic functions are very easy to understand, and the symbol representing the arithmetic operation is quite familiar. Equality is represented by the equal sign (=); addition, by the plus sign (+); subtraction, by the minus sign (−); multiplication, by an asterisk (*); and division, by a slash (/). Here are examples of commands with these most basic arithmetic operators:

Equality:

    #101 = 3 (Result: #101 is set equal to 3)

Addition:

    #101 = 3 + 1 (Result: #101 is set equal to 4)

Subtraction:

    #101 = 5 − 2 (Result: #101 is set equal to 3)

Multiplication:

    #101 = 3 * 3 (Result: #101 is set equal to 9)

Division:

    #101 = 9 / 3 (Result: #101 is set equal to 3)

Combining operations. As with any computer language, parametric programming allows you to combine operations. The priority of operations (order by which operations are executed) in a combined arithmetic expression follows that of any computer. For the four operations discussed so far, multiplication has the highest priority. Then comes division. Then addition. Then subtraction. Knowing this, consider the following command:

    #101 = 3 + 4 * 3

What will be the result of this calculation? Since *multiplication* has the highest priority, it will be done first. In this case, 4 will be multiplied by 3, and the result will be added to 3. The value stored in variable #101 will be 15.

This can become quite confusing. For this reason, squared brackets can be used to force the desired order of execution. Squared brackets ([]), *not* parentheses, can be placed around an operation to gain the highest level of priority. Consider this command:

    #101 = [3 + 4] * 3

This time, 3 will be added to 4 (because of the squared brackets), and *then* the result is multiplied by 3. Variable #101 will now be set to 21.

Whenever you are in doubt as to how the control will execute an arithmetic expression, you can use brackets to clarify the situation. Squared brackets will not hurt the calculation if they are placed in a calculation in which they are not required. Consider this command:

#101 = 3 + [4 * 3]

In this case, the programmer is simply forcing the control to execute the arithmetic calculation in the same way it would have done without squared brackets. This will have no detrimental effect on the calculation. The result of this command will still be that the value 15 will be stored in variable #101.

Referencing previously calculated variables. Previously calculated variables can be referenced in other calculations. In this case, the current value of a variable will be used as if it were an actual number. Consider the following series of commands:

#101 = 3
#102 = 4
#103 = #101 + #102

In this case, #103 will be set to 7. In the last command in this sequence, it will be as if the command read as follows:

#103 = 3 + 4

Consider another series of commands:

#101 = 1
...
#101 = #101 + 1

In the first command, #101 is set to the value 1. Later in the parametric program, #101 is being set equal to its current value (1) plus 1. This time variable #101 will be set to 2. If this last command is repeated, the next result for #101 is 3. This example shows how a variable (variable #101 in this case) can be used as a counter (more on counters a little later).

Advanced arithmetic calculations. Along with simple equality, addition, subtraction, multiplication, and division, most versions of parametric programming allow much more complicated arithmetic operations to be done. Here is a list of these more advanced operations as well as brief examples of their usage.

Sine:

#101 = SIN[30.] (Result: sets #101 to the sine of 30°)

Cosine:

#101 = COS[30.] (Result: sets #101 to the cosine of 30°)

Tangent:

#101 = TAN[30.] (Result: sets #101 to the tangent of 30°)

Arc tangent:

#101 = ATAN[#102]/[#103] (Result: sets #101 to the arc tangent of the result of dividing #102 by #103)

Square root:

#101 = SQRT[9] (Result: sets #101 to the square root of 9)

Absolute value:

#101 = ABS[−5] (Result: sets #101 to the plus value of −5)

Rounding:

#101 = ROUND[3.4] (Result: sets #101 to the nearest integer, in this case 3)

Round down:

#101 = FIX[3.8] (Result: sets #101 to the next lower integer, in this case 3)

Round up:

#101 = FUP[3.2] (Result: sets #101 to the next higher integer, in this case 4)

Depending on your control's version of parametric programming, you may find there are even more arithmetic functions available. You must check with your programming manual to find out what is available with regard to arithmetic functions.

When it comes to the priority of arithmetic operations, all of these functions have a higher priority than multiplication. As discussed earlier, squared brackets can be used to force the desired order of arithmetic operations. Once again, here is the priority of arithmetic operations that will occur when multiple operations are done in one command:

1. Squared brackets from left to right
2. Functions (sine, cos, tan, etc.) from left to right
3. Multiplication, then division from left to right
4. Addition, then subtraction from left to right

Knowing this about combined operations, you should be able to determine what will happen in this more complicated series of commands:

```
#100 = 360 / 8
#101 = 2 + SIN[#100] * [ 4 + .5]
```

In this case, #100 will result in the value 45. In the second command, first 4 will be added to 0.5 (because of the squared brackets). Then the sin of 45° will be calculated (0.70710). This value will be multiplied by 4.5 (result: 3.18195). Finally this value will be added to 2. The final result will be 5.1815 stored in variable #101.

A good rule of thumb related to priority of arithmetic operations is this: if you are in doubt as to what order the control will execute arithmetic operations, use squared brackets to force the desired order. As stated, brackets will never hurt in the combined operation. For example, the second command of the above example could have been written like this, and still yield the same result:

#101 = [2 +[SIN[#100] * [4 + .5]]]

In this case, the extra squared brackets simply force the control to do the operations in the order it would have followed anyway without the extra squared brackets.

Example parametric program showing call statement, variables, and arithmetic

With what you know so far about the call statement, variables, and arithmetic calculations, you should be ready to look at an example. Though it is simple, it stresses all key points made thus far.

Look at Fig. 5.1. Say the outside milled square shape of this

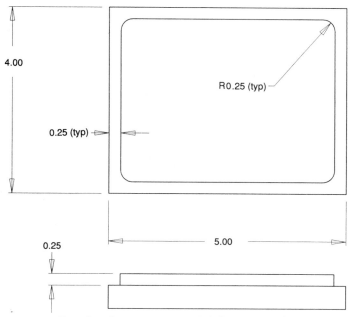

Figure 5.1 Drawing for parametric example program for call statement, variable, and arithmetic techniques.

workpiece represents but one workpiece in a family. Your company must machine this configuration in many different workpieces. However, other workpieces in the family are of different sizes. For example, some are longer or wider, while some have more or less stock to be removed. Some have a larger or smaller radius in the corner. Some must be machined to a deeper depth. In this case, *everything* about this milled configuration will be a variable.

Part of preparing to write a parametric program is to mark up the drawing or make a sketch showing what variables will be used in the call statement to tell the parametric program how to make the workpiece currently being machined. Figure 5.2 shows another drawing with all variables to be used in the call statement.

Keep in mind that *you,* as the programmer, will choose the letters representing variable names. You may or may not agree with our chosen names. As you develop your own parametric programs, you can choose any letter you wish from the list given earlier.

As you can see, there are more variables than were on the original drawing. The desired tool size and the machining feed rate are given. Here is a main program which will use the parametric program. Believe it or not, when the parametric program is finished, this main program will correctly machine the workpiece to your specifications.

Main program:

```
O0048 (Program number)
(1-in end mill)
N005 G54 S350 M03 (Turn spindle on at 350 RPM)
```

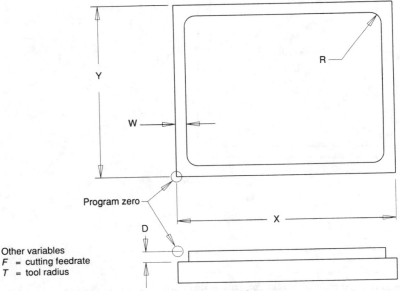

Other variables
F = cutting feedrate
T = tool radius

Figure 5.2 Variable names for parametric example program.

N010 G00 X-.6 Y-.6 (Rapid over to workpiece)
N015 G43 H01 Z.1 (Rapid down to just above workpiece)
N020 G65 P1000 X5. Y4. D.25 W.25 R.25 F5. T.5 (Machine entire outside shape)
N025 G91 G28 Z0 (Return to reference position in *Z*)
N030 G28 X0 Y0 (Return to reference position in *X-Y*)
N035 M30 (End of program)

Line N020 is the call statement and tells the parametric program the size of our current workpiece with filled-in variables. Remember that these variable letters cannot be stated in the parametric program as letters. They *must* be converted to local variable numbers to avoid confusion with true CNC letter addresses. Here is a list of the letter variables used in our call statement along with their corresponding local variable numbers:

X #25	Y #25	D #7	W #23
R #18	F #9	T #20	

Every time the parametric program references a variable coming from the call statement it *must* be in the form of a local variable. For example, if you wish to reference the length of the workpiece (*X* from the call statement), you *must* use the local variable #24.

Knowing this, you should be ready to look at your first parametric program. Though this program happens to machine the part starting from the lower left corner and mills in a conventional milling manner, motion could be generated in any method desired.

Parametric program:

O1000 (program number)
(Calculations)
#101 = #20 + .1 (Used for clearance position)
#102 = #24 − #23 − #18 (Sets *X* position at right side arc tangency)
#103 = #23 + #18 (Sets *X* position at left side arc tangency)
#104 = #23 − #20 (Sets *X* and *Y* at lower left corner)
#105 = #23 + #18 (Sets lower arc tangency in *Y*)
#106 = #25 − #23 − #18 (Sets upper arc tangency in *Y*)
#107 = #24 − #23 + #20 (Sets right side position)
#108 = #20 + #18 (Sets arc radius)
#109 = #25 − #23 + #20 (Sets to surface in *Y*)
(Cutting motions)
G00 X − #101 Y − #104 (Move to lower left position)
G01 Z − #7 F30. (Fast feed to work surface)
G01 X#102 F#9 (Move to beginning of lower right arc)
G03 X#107 Y#105 R#108 (Form lower right arc)
G01 Y#106 (Move to beginning of upper right arc)
G03 X#102 Y#109 R#108 (Form upper right arc)
G01 X#103 (Move to beginning of upper left arc)
G03 X#104 Y#106 R#108 (Form upper left arc)
G01 Y#105 (Move to beginning of lower left arc)
G03 X#103 Y#104 R#108 (Form lower left arc)
G00 Z.1 (Rapid away from workpiece in *Z*)
M99 (End of parametric program)

Notice first that the parametric program has no sequence numbers (N words). While they are allowed within parametric programs, you should reserve them for use as statement labels. (More on statement labels a little later.)

If you study the series of calculation commands, you should be able to see how the end point of each motion command is being calculated. For example, the command

#102 = #24 − #23 − #18

calculates the *X* position at the lower right tangency. This will be the *X* position referenced during cutting movements when the end mill is to come tangent with the radius at the lower right corner of this workpiece. In this case, with the current values in the call statement, #102 will be set to 4.5 (5 − 0.25 − 0.25). This is the *same number* you would have had to calculate manually if making the program to machine the workpiece without parametric programming techniques!

Once calculated, each common variable is used as if it were a constant number in the motion command. As you can see, the parametric program will behave differently, calculating different end points, as the call statement variables (arguments) change.

Notice also that *all* calculations are done *before* any cutting movements, allowing the control to flow easily from one motion command to the next. This is advantageous since arithmetic calculations do take some time to perform. If they are done during motion commands, it is possible that the tool will actually pause at the end of each motion while the next position is calculated.

We recommend that, whenever possible, you perform all calculations before you begin making cutting motions. While this is not always possible, it will keep the control from pausing during motions.

This brings up a good point related to cycle time. Since the calculations do take time, it would be foolish to allow the CNC control to make these calculations for every workpiece to be machined. Since most CNC controls remember the value of common variables until the power is turned off, you can place an optional block skip code (/) before each calculation command. For the first workpiece you run after powering up, leave the optional block skip switch off. The calculations will be made and the results stored in common variables. After the first workpiece, turn on the optional block skip switch. From this point all calculations will be skipped, saving the calculation time.

While this parametric program could be written in many different ways and still yield the same results, our intention was to give you a relatively simple example of what you can use parametric programming to do. Please study this information until you thoroughly understand the example before continuing.

Statement labels. Statement labels are key points within the parametric program to which you want execution to branch. They are commanded by sequence numbers (N words) on most CNC controls that allow parametric programming techniques. Because statement labels identify branching locations, we recommend that you use N words *only* as statement labels. Do not use sequence numbers in the manner you would in a normal CNC program, placing a sequence number at the beginning of each command.

Also, it is wise to use some logic with regard to choosing statement label numbers. First of all, they *cannot* repeat in a parametric program. Second, we recommend setting each statement label to a number from 1 to 100, on the basis of its position in the parametric program. Statement labels close to the beginning of a parametric program will be set to a low number (under 10). Statement labels in the middle of the parametric program will be around 50. Toward the end of the parametric program, statement labels will be just under 100. Using this technique in a lengthy parametric program helps you to determine where the branching locations are located within the parametric program.

Statement labels *always* work in conjunction with another command. This command will be either a conditional branching statement (the IF statement), or an unconditional branching statement (the GOTO statement).

Unconditional branching (GOTO). There will be times when you will have the control jump within the parametric program to another location, specified by a statement label. The most basic command for this purpose is the GOTO statement. Here is an example showing a portion of a parametric program:

```
...
GOTO 50
N45 G00 X2. Y1.
G01 Z-1. F5.
G00 Z.1
N50
...
```

In this case, when the GOTO 50 command is read, the control will jump to line N50 and continue from there. In this case, the motion commands will *not* be executed.

The GOTO statement is usually used in conjunction with a conditional branching statement (IF).

Conditional branching (IF) and logical expressions. This computer-related feature gives the parametric program decision-making capabilities. Based on the outcome of a choice between two (and only two) possible conditions, the parametric program will branch (jump) to one of two locations within the parametric program.

The condition set up in the conditional branching statement is called a *logical expression*. The logical expression does a comparison of two variables (or the result of two arithmetic calculations), and determines whether the statement being made in the logical expression is true or false. If the condition is true, the IF statement will cause a branch to a statement label. If the condition is false, the very next command after the IF statement in the parametric program will be executed.

There are six logical operators to help you set up your condition in the most logical way. Each is a two-letter abbreviation. Here is a list of the logical operators and their meanings:

EQ   Equal to

NE   Not equal to

LT   Less than

LE   Less than or equal to

GT   Greater than

GE   Greater than or equal to

Here is a simple example application for a conditional branch statement. One application for the IF statement is to test flags from the call statement. Say you wish to allow for either right-hand or left-hand tools to be used with a turning-center parametric program. Of course, if a right-hand tool is used, the spindle must be running forward or clockwise (M03). If a left-hand tool is used, the spindle must be run counterclockwise (M04).

In your call statement, you elect to use the letter H to specify the hand of tooling (right or left hand). You wish to set up the condition such that if H is set to 1, a right-hand tool is being used, and if H is set to 0, a left-hand tool is being used. Here is a series of commands within the parametric that will automatically run the spindle in the correct direction. (H is specified in the parametric program as local variable #11.)

```
...
IF [#11 EQ 0] GOTO 5
M03
GOTO 6
N5 M04
N6
...
```

If H is currently set to the value 1, representing a right-hand tool and clockwise spindle direction, the condition set up by the IF statement will be *false*. In this case, the very next command after the IF statement (M03) will be executed. Then the control will read the command GOTO 6, jumping over the M04 command.

On the other hand, if H is currently set to 0, representing a left-hand tool and counterclockwise spindle direction, the condition set up by the IF statement will be *true*. In this case, the unconditional branch at the right of the IF statement will be executed (GOTO 5). This time, the control will branch to line N5, and only the command M04 will be read.

Using the IF statement with flags. The above example of conditional branching is but one example of how you can pass a flag from the main program to the parametric program to specify how you wish the parametric program to behave. There are numerous other occasions when this is helpful. Here are some examples with a small portion of a parametric program to stress the point.

To control coolant. You can use a flag in the call statement to specify whether you wish coolant to come on. Say you use the letter C (#3) in the call statement for this purpose. If it is set to 1, you wish coolant to come on. If it is set to 0, you do not want coolant to come on.

```
...
IF [#3 EQ 0] GOTO 7
M08
GOTO 8
N7 M09
N8
...
```

To climb-mill versus conventional-mill. In a machining-center parametric programming application, you can allow for either climb or conventional milling. Of course, two series of motions must be included within the parametric program: one for climb milling and one for conventional milling.

Say you use the variable M (#13) to specify the style of milling in the call statement. If M is set to 1, you wish to use climb-milling techniques. If M is set to 0, you wish to use conventional-milling techniques. Here is the structure of a parametric program that would accomplish this:

```
...
IF [#13 EQ 1] GOTO 9
(Conventional milling motions)
...
GOTO 10
N9 (Climb milling motions)
...
N10
...
```

If M is set to 1, the logical expression in the IF statement will be *true*. The unconditional branch (GOTO 9) will be executed. After line N9, movements will be commanded in the climb-milling style. If M is set to 0, the logical expression will be *false,* meaning the next line following the IF statement will be executed. Here, movements will be made for conventional milling. At the completion of the conventional-milling movements, the command GOTO 10 is executed, which causes the climb-milling movements to be skipped.

Allowing stock for finishing.   You can use a flag within your call statement to specify the amount of stock to be left for finishing operations. Using this technique makes the same parametric program useful for both roughing and finishing.

Say, for example, you use the letter S (#19) in your call statement to specify the stock amount. If set to 0, no stock will be left, and the finish pass is being made. Within the parametric program, all calculations for motion commands can be based on the amount of stock to be left. In this case, the flag actually has two meanings. First, it tells the parametric program whether stock is to be left for finishing or not. Second, if stock is to be left, the S word tells the parametric program the amount of stock to be left.

```
...
IF [#19 GT 0] GOTO 12
(Calculations for motions without stock to be left for finishing)
...
GOTO 13
N12 (Calculations for motion with stock for finishing)
...
N13 (Motions)
...
```

If S is set to zero, the condition of the logical expression will be *false* (zero is not greater than zero) In this case, the next command after the IF statement will be executed, beginning a series of calculation commands for motions that do not allow stock for finishing. At the completion of these calculation commands, the unconditional branch (GOTO 13) causes the control to skip the calculation commands for allowing finishing stock.

If stock is to be allowed, the S word represents the amount of stock. Say it is set to 0.030 in. In this case, S is greater than zero, and the logical expression will be *true*. The unconditional branch will take place to line N12 and the calculations to follow allow the finishing stock.

Using the IF statement to preset variables.   It can be very helpful to configure the parametric program in a way that allows it to assume certain things if arguments are not included in the call statement.

When the value of any variable has not been set (including local variables), it is assumed by the control to be vacant. By *vacant,* we mean it has *no value.* Note that this does *not* mean it has a value of zero. Zero *is* a value.

The variable representation for vacant is #0. You can test for vacancy within a parametric program to determine whether a call statement variable has been set. If the variable is *not equal* to vacant, it has been set in the call statement.

Knowing this is helpful for presetting variables within the parametric program. This technique minimizes the length of the call statement. The person using the parametric program will not have to assign those variables to be left at the preset value.

For example, say you are using the variable letter D to represent the depth of cut for the machining operation. Say that, in almost all cases, the depth of cut (D word) will be 0.25 in. Yet you want to make the depth of cut a variable, just in case the programmer needs to change the depth of cut.

Here is a series of commands within the parametric program that will automatically set the depth of cut to 0.25 if the D word (#7) is not assigned in the call statement.

```
...
IF [#7 NE #0] GOTO 5
#7 = .25
N5
...
```

In this case, if D (#7) is included in the call statement, it will have a value. The result of the IF statement will be *true* (since #7 is not currently equal to vacant). The control will branch to line N5.

However, if the D word is left out of the call statement, the IF statement will be *false* (since #7 is currently vacant). In this case, the next command will be executed, and the value of #7 will be 0.25 in.

This technique can be used for all variables in the call statement which will have a common value, and keep the length of the call statement much shorter.

Note that this technique should be used only for those variables which have little impact on the safety or performance of the parametric program. This technique should *not* be used for variables which change often and could cause dangerous results if incorrectly set.

For example, say you are developing a parametric program to machine a groove on a turning center. Say you have grooves to machine on a wide variety of diameters. In this case, it would be dangerous to preset the grooving diameter within the parametric program. If this is done, and if the programmer forgets to include the groove diameter in the call statement, the diameter being grooved would be that of the preset value.

Obviously, this could cause very serious problems at the machine. In this case, it would actually be wiser to test (with an IF statement) to assure that this variable *has* been included in the call statement rather than to preset it.

Testing for erroneous input from the call statement. A well-written parametric program will test to see that all key call statement variables are included in the call statement, and that they make sense. For example, with the previously given grooving example, two key variables were the groove width and the tool width. In this application, the tool width *must* be smaller than or equal to the groove width. If the tool is wider than the groove, the programmer using the parametric program has made a mistake.

This kind of problem can actually be detected from within a parametric program. When detected, the parametric program can (at least) be told to stop the machine with M00. A message in parentheses can be included next to the M00, telling the operator what is wrong. Here is an example using tool width versus groove width. In this case, T (#20) represents the tool width and W (#23) represents the groove width.

```
...
IF [#20 LE #23] GOTO 5
M00 (TOOL TOO WIDE)
N5
...
```

In this case, if the test made by the IF statement is true (tool width is less than or equal to groove width), everything is all right. The GOTO statement makes the parametric program skip the M00 command. If the IF statement test is false, the programmer made a mistake. In this case, the next command (M00) is executed, stopping the machine.

Some versions of parametric programming even allow the parametric programmer to generate machine alarms from within a parametric program. One popular version of parametric programming uses a system variable for this purpose. In this version of parametric programming, a command including system variable #3000 (if read) will generate the alarm. Here is the same tool width versus groove width example, but instead of simply using an M00 to stop the machine, the program now generates an actual machine alarm:

```
...
IF [#20 LE #23] GOTO 5
#3000 = 101 (TOOL TOO WIDE)
N5
...
```

If the command including the #3000 system variable is read (the logical expression is false and the tool is too wide), the machine will be placed into an alarm state. The alarm number (101 in this case) will be shown on the display screen along with the message TOOL TOO WIDE. With this technique, the control will not let the program continue without the operator resetting the alarm.

Generating loops.   All versions of parametric programming allow looping. This technique allows commands within the parametric program to be repeated a specified number of times. Generally speaking, something about how the commands are executed will change during each pass through the loop.

The way we will show to generate loops incorporates the IF statement. However, many versions of parametric programming allow other ways to generate loops as well. (Some use a WHILE and/or DO statement for this purpose.) In its most basic form, a loop uses a simple counter with which to count up to a number of repetitions. This counter is originally set to 1 (or some beginning number) at the beginning of the loop. Each time the control goes through the loop, the counter is stepped. Eventually the desired number of repetitions will be reached, and the control will break out of the loop.

Here is a relatively simple loop that counts to 10. No actual machining is taking place; only the basic structure of a loop is being shown.

Parametric program:

```
O1001 (Parametric program to count to 10)
#101 = 1 (Initialize counter)
N1 IF [#101 GT 10] GOTO 99 (Test if finished)
(Motion calculations usually take place here)
(Cutting motions usually take place here)
#101 = #101 + 1 (Step counter)
GOTO 1 (Go back to test)
N99 M99
```

When this parametric program is activated, variable number #101 (the counter) starts with a value of 1. When the test is made, the current value of #101 (1) is compared to the value 10. If #101 is greater than 10, the control will branch to the end of the parametric program (GOTO 99). However, this first time through the loop, #101 is not greater than 10 (1 is not greater than 10). In this case, the next command after the IF statement is executed.

The control continues executing the program in the normal order. When the command

```
#101 = #101 + 1
```

is eventually executed, the new value of #101 becomes 2. The unconditional branch (GOTO 1) then sends the control back to the test (in N1). The current value of #101 (2) is compared to 10. The test will still be false, so the next line of the parametric program is executed.

The loop is repeated until the current value of #101 eventually becomes 11. When the IF statement is read in this case, the result will be a TRUE condition. Finally, the GOTO 99 command will be executed, ending the loop.

Though the application for loops changes from one parametric program to the next, this basic structure remains remarkably similar from one loop to the next. Expressed in step-by-step form, here is the structure we recommend that you use whenever developing loops within a parametric program:

1. Initialize all variables

2. Test if finished

3. Make calculations needed for current pass through the loop

4. Make cutting motion commands for current pass through the loop

5. Step counter and all changing variables

6. Go back to test

Though there are many other ways to structure loops, this is the easiest for beginners to comprehend and use. Now let's look at an example that shows a good application for looping.

Bolt-hole circle looping example.   One common parametric program that stresses the use of looping techniques is used for machining a series of holes on a bolt-hole circle. Figure 5.3 shows a drawing of a workpiece requiring a bolt-hole pattern of holes to be machined.

If programmed manually (without a parametric program), this workpiece would require that trigonometry be done to calculate four of the hole locations. Wouldn't it be nice if no trig were required, and the programmer could specify print dimensions to command that all of the holes on the bolt-hole circle be machined?

That is exactly what the parametric program we will show will do. Figure 5.4 shows a marked-up drawing which specifies the variables to be used. Note that the desired feed rate, number of holes, hole

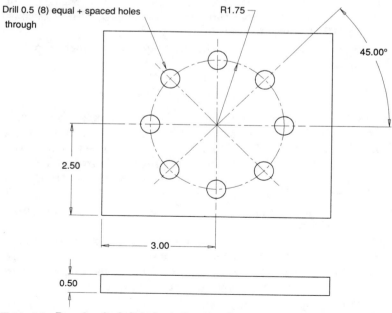

Figure 5.3   Drawing for bolt-hole circle example parametric program.

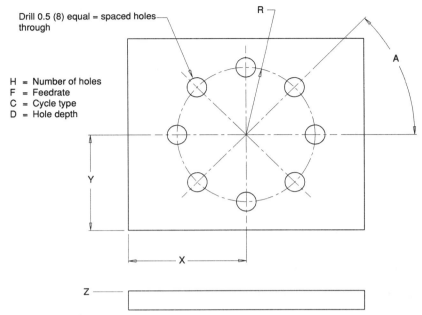

Drill 0.5 (8) equal = spaced holes through

H = Number of holes
F = Feedrate
C = Cycle type
D = Hole depth

R

A

Y

X

Z

Figure 5.4 Marked-up drawing showing variables used for bolt-hole circle example parametric program.

depth, and even the the cycle type (G81, G82, etc.) will also be specified as variables.

Before this parametric program can be written, the programmer must have a clear understanding as to how mathematics will apply to this problem. Figure 5.5 shows how the calculation will be made for each hole location in X and Y.

If you were to calculate the X and Y location of each hole, you would have to apply the formulas given in Fig. 5.5 for *every* hole location that was not along a quadrant line. Our parametric program will use these same formulas and do so automatically, no matter how many holes are on the bolt-hole circle.

This brings up a good point. As stated, the programmer must have a clear understanding of how to solve *all* problems addressed by the parametric program *before* the program can be started. In many cases, this is as simple as coming up with an arithmetic formula. In other, more complicated cases, the programmer may have to spend several hours visualizing all possible conditions under which the parametric program must behave.

This is truly the hardest part of preparing a parametric program and can be compared to any form of puzzle. When you know the solution to a puzzle, solving the puzzle is easy. But until the solution comes to you, solving the puzzle may seem impossible. The better you

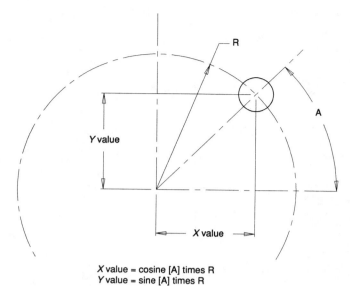

X value = cosine [A] times R
Y value = sine [A] times R

Figure 5.5 How the hole position for each hole on the bolt-hole pattern can be calculated.

are at solving the problem related to the parametric program's application, the easier it will be to prepare for it.

When confronted with a seemingly impossible problem, always try to break it into smaller pieces. In our bolt-hole example, to solve the problem of machining many holes, we looked at how only one hole would be programmed manually. In many cases, if you look at only one facet at a time, the overall task will be easier.

Here is the main program to machine the bolt-hole pattern shown in Fig. 5.3, assuming the parametric program is properly prepared.

Main program:

```
O0049 (Main Program)
(0.500-in drill)
N005 G54 G90 S800 M03 (Select coordinate system, absolute mode, turn spindle on
CW at 800 RPM)
N010 G00 X0 Y0 (Rapid over to workpiece in X and Y)
N015 G43 H01 Z.1 (Rapid down to just above workpiece)
N020 G65 P1001 X3. Y2.5 Z0. R1.75 D.75 A45. H8. C81. F5.
(Machine entire bolt-hole pattern)
N025 G91 G28 Z0 (Return to reference position in Z)
N030 G28 X0 Y0 (Return to reference position in X-Y)
N035 M30 (End of program)
```

Here is a list of the call statement arguments and their local variable conversions:

X #24	Y #25	Z #26	R #18	D #7
A #1	H #11	C #3	F #9	

Here is the parametric program to machine bolt-hole patterns:

Parametric program:

```
O1001 (Parametric program number)
#101 = 1 (Initialize counter)
#102 = #1 (Initialize current angle to the value of A)
#103 = 360 / #11 (Initialize incremental angle between holes by dividing 360 by
the number of holes)
#104 = #26 + .1 (Initialize R plane for canned cycle)
#105 = #26 - #7 (Initialize Z position for canned cycle)
N1 IF [#101 GT #11 ] GOTO 99 (If the current hole number is greater than the
number of holes, end the loop)
#110 = #24 + [COS[#102] * #18] (X position of current hole)
#111 = #25 + [SIN[#102] * #18] (Y position of current hole)
G[#3] X#110 Y#111 R[#104] Z - [#105] F[#9] (Machine holes with current
values)
G80 (Cancel cycle)
#101 = #101 + 1 (Step hole counter)
#102 = #102 + #103 (Step current angle)
GOTO 1 (Go back to test)
N99 M99 (End of loop and subprogram)
```

The two key things to look for in this loop are variables #101 (the counter) and #102 (the current angle). The test in this loop is made against the counter. When the loop is started, the current value of the hole counter is 1. The value of the current angle will be the value of A (45 in our example). As the calculations are made to calculate the X and Y locations of the current hole, the current angle is used.

Based on the results of the X-Y calculations, a hole is machined with the cycle specified in the call statement. The counter is then stepped by 1, and the current angle is stepped by the angular distance between holes. The GOTO statement then sends the parametric program back to the test.

For the second time through the loop, the counter is at 2 and the incremental angle is 90°. The test will still be false, and the calculations will be based on the 90° angle. Another hole is machined, the counters are stepped, and the loop is repeated.

Eventually, the counter (#101) will be greater than the number of holes (the eleventh time the IF statement is executed). When it is, the IF statement will be true, and the loop will be terminated.

Determining how many times the loop must be executed can sometimes be more difficult. In the case of the bolt-hole circle, knowing the number of holes to be machined makes this task rather easy. Coming up is an example of when calculations may have to be made in order to determine how many times the loop must be executed.

Grooving example. Figure 5.6 shows a drawing of the grooving example discussed earlier. This drawing already has the variables needed for the parametric program filled in.

In this case, the parametric program will be written in a way that allows a grooving tool to make the number of passes necessary to ma-

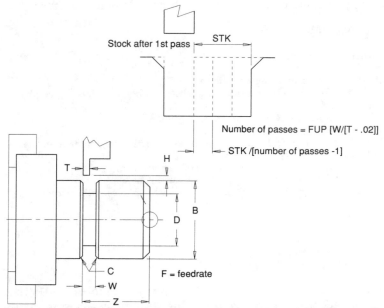

Stock after 1st pass

STK

Number of passes = FUP [W/[T - .02]]

STK /[number of passes -1]

T

H

B

D

C

W

Z

F = feedrate

Figure 5.6 Marked-up drawing showing workpiece and variables for grooving example parametric program.

chine the groove to the required width. Since they are both **variables**, the T (tool width) and the W (groove width) work together to determine the required number of passes.

But the grooving example provides more of a challenge related to number of repetitions for the loop. If multiple passes are made in the groove, there must be some overlap between passes. If there is not, there will be witness marks left in the bottom of the groove. Also, it is quite likely that an even number of passes will be difficult to calculate. For example, if the groove width is 0.349 in and the tool width is 0.125 in, how much stock will each pass take? This application truly requires a great deal of thought.

It is this kind of problem which leads some programmers to develop the loop in a way that tests against axis position instead of number of passes. While this kind of testing will work just fine, the simplicity of developing the loop in this manner can be deceiving. In almost *all* cases, it is better to (somehow) determine the number of passes and test against this number for looping purposes. One way to solve our particular repetition problem related to number of passes and incremental move-over amount is shown at the top of Fig. 5.6. The number of passes can be calculated by this formula:

$$\text{Number of passes} = \text{FUP}[W/(T - 0.02)]$$

In this case, we are rounding up (with FUP) the result of the division of $W/(T - 0.02)$. The 0.02 value provides a sure overlap from one pass to the next. If, for example the width of the groove W is set to 0.375 in and the width of the tool T is set to 0.125, the parametric program will generate four passes (0.375 ÷ 0.105 = 3.5714). The value 3.5714 rounded to the nearest integer is 4.

This solves only half the problem. We must also calculate the move-over amount between passes. Here is one way:

$$\text{Move-over amount} = \frac{\text{stock remaining after first pass}}{\text{number of passes} - 1}$$

The first pass will machine to the width of the grooving tool. What remains after this first pass must be used for calculating the move-over amount. If we divide this value by 1 less than the number of passes, an even amount of stock will be removed for each remaining pass, an amount which also takes into consideration the overlap required for each pass.

This reasoning is but one way to handle the problem. Surely there are other ways. Our real point is this: you *must* have a clear picture of how *any* problem will be solved by the parametric program *before* the parametric program can be written. If you do not, your program is doomed to failure.

Keep in mind that the grooving parametric program must also perform properly if the grooving tool is the same width of the groove. In this case, only one pass is to be made, forming the groove to the required width.

With a clear solution in mind, here is a main program which will call the parametric program for the grooving example:

Main program:

```
O0050 (Program number)
(0.125 wide grooving tool)
N005 G50 X _____ Z _____ (Assign program zero)
N010 G00 T0101 M41 (Index to tool station 1, instate offset 1, select low spindle range)
N015 G65 P1003 C.025 T.125 W.25 Z-1. D1.25 B1.5 H.1 F.005
N020 G00 X _____ Z _____ T0100 (Return to tool change position,
cancel offset)
N025 M30 (End of program)
```

Here is a list of the variables used in the call statement and their local variable conversions:

C #3	T #20	W #23	Z #26	D #7
B #2	H #11	F #9		

Parametric program:

```
O1003 (Program number)
#101 = FUP[#23 / [#20 - .02]] (Initialize number of passes)
#102 = #23 - #20 (Initialize stock remaining after first pass)
#104 = 1 (Initialize counter to 1)
#103 = #102 / [#101 - 1] (Initialize incremental move-over amount)
```

```
#105 = #26 (Initialize current Z position for pass)
#106 = #2 + [2 * #11] (Initialize clearance position in X)
G00 X#106 Z[#105] (Move to start position)
IF [#23 GT #20] GOTO 25 (More than one pass)
G01 X[#7] F[#9] (One pass only)
G04 P500 (Pause for 0.5 second)
G00 X[#106] (Rapid out)
GOTO 50 (Skip multiple passes)
N25 IF[#104 GT #101] GOTO 50 (Test if finished)
Z[#105] (Rapid to current Z position for pass)
G01 X[#7] F[#9] (Plunge groove)
G04 P500 (Pause for 0.5 second)
G00 X[#106] (Rapid out of groove)
#105 = #105 + #103 (Step current Z position)
#104 = #104 + 1 (Step counter)
GOTO 25 (Go back to test)
N50 G00 Z[#26 − #3] (Move to left side chamfer)
G01 X[#2] (Feed flush with groove diameter)
X[#2 − [2 * #3]] Z[#26] (Form left chamfer)
G00 X[#106] (Rapid out)
Z[#26 + #23 + #3 − #20] (Rapid to right side chamfer)
G01 X[#2] (Feed flush to groove diameter)
X[#2 − [2 * #3]] Z[#26 + #23 − #20] (Form right chamfer)
G00 X[#106] (Rapid out)
M99 (End of subprogram)
```

Admittedly, it is a rather complicated example. Our intention was not to intimidate you, but rather to show you the kind of programming power you have with this extremely helpful tool. With this verified grooving parametric program stored in your control's memory, machining *any* groove of the given configuration will be as easy as filling in the blanks!

And keep in mind that we are barely scratching the surface of applications that can be aided with parametric programming techniques. To attempt to show all of them would fill a text book by itself. If you maintain your awareness during your CNC career, you will find thousands of possible applications.

CNC-control-related features (system variables)

Parametric programming allows access to many things related to the CNC control. However, these features vary more dramatically between control manufacturers than computer-related features. For this reason, our intention in this text will be only to acquaint you with each feature.

Access to tool offsets.   Most versions of parametric programming allow the programmer to access the current values of tool offsets from within a parametric program. In most cases, the parametric program can also change the value currently stored in each tool offset.

One popular control uses the #2000 series of system variables for this purpose. For example, the command

    #101 = #2001

will set variable #101 to the current value of tool offset 1. On the other hand, the command

    #2001 = #101

will actually set the value of offset 1 to the current value of variable #101.

One application for this feature is milling operations. Instead of using cutter radius compensation commands within a parametric program, most programmers elect to use centerline coordinates to avoid cutter radius compensation–related problems. Yet, the parametric program must know the radius (or diameter) of the tool being used.

One way to do this is to include the tool radius as part of the call statement. Another, more logical, way is to use tool offsets. If cutter compensation is often used, the operator will be in the habit of storing the radius of each milling cutter in a tool offset. In this case, the parametric program can find the tool radius value within the offset table. From then on, the parametric program can use the radius value during the calculation of each end point for motion commands.

Using offsets in this way from within a parametric program is the most common application for tool offset techniques. In most cases, the programmer simply attains the current value of the tool offset, as was the case for the previous tool radius example. However, parametric programming also gives the programmer the ability to write into the tool offsets, though applications for this feature are limited for general-purpose parametric programming.

One application for writing values into the tool offsets is when a probing device is used. Probing can be done, for example, to measure a milled surface. In this application, the probe can touch a milled surface and test its position. If the surface has been milled correctly, the control will continue machining the workpiece. If not, the parametric program can determine what kind of offset adjustment must be made, and can actually change the value of the cutter radius compensation offset used for milling the surface. Milling of the surface is then repeated.

Though this is a simple case of how a probe can be used, you should see how it relates to changing the values of tool offsets.

Using offsets as variables. For complicated applications, there may be times when you run out of variables. Most control manufacturers allow extra variables to be purchased as an option. However, keep in mind that offsets can be used as variables. Of course, you will have to assure that offsets used for other purposes (tool length compensation, cutter radius compensation, etc.) are not affected. Generally speaking, no single program will be using every tool offset. Usually you will have unused tool offsets available. As long as you are careful not to overlap those offsets used by the program, they can be used as variables within the parametric program.

Generating alarms.   An example of alarm generation was given during our discussion of the IF statement. The example given was related to testing variables coming from the call statement for correctness.

As stated, a well-written parametric program should test for *all* variables of the call statement as far as possible. It is hard enough to predict how a parametric program will behave under all conditions of the call statement when the arguments in the call statement have been correctly used. It is next to impossible to predict what the parametric program will do if they are not.

For those variables that are not preset within the parametric program (as shown during the IF statement discussions), we recommend that you test to make sure that they have been included in the call statement. One common mistake a programmer will make is to omit variables from the call statement.

Your parametric program can test and see if each important variable has been included. If not, a mistake has been made by the programmer and an alarm should be generated. Here is the call statement from the grooving call statement being tested within the parametric program in this manner:

    N015 G65 P1003 C.025 T.125 W.25 Z-1. D1.25 B1.5 H.1 F.005

Here is a list of the variables used in the call statement and their local variable conversions.

C #3	T #20	W #23	Z #26	D #7
B #2	H #11	F #9		

Now let's look at the beginning of the parametric program which tests each variable.

Parametric program:

```
O1004 (Program number)
IF [#3 NE #0] GOTO 5
#3000 = 101 (C MISSING FROM CALL STATEMENT)
N5 IF [#20 NE #0] GOTO 6
#3000 = 102 (T MISSING FROM CALL STATEMENT)
N6 IF [#23 NE #0] GOTO 7
#3000 = 103 (W MISSING FROM CALL STATEMENT)
N7 IF [#26 NE #0] GOTO 8
#3000 = 104 (Z MISSING FROM CALL STATEMENT)
N8 IF [#7 NE #0] GOTO 9
```

```
#3000 = 105 (D MISSING FROM CALL STATEMENT)
N9 IF [#2 NE #0] GOTO 10
#3000 = 106 (B MISSING FROM CALL STATEMENT)
N10 IF [#11 NE #0] GOTO 11
#3000 = 107 (H MISSING FROM CALL STATEMENT)
N11 IF [#9 NE #0] GOTO 12
#3000 = 108 (F MISSING FROM CALL STATEMENT)
N12
...
```

Note that, if a variable is left out of the call statement, each alarm generated in the parametric program specifies exactly what is missing. Some programmers feel this is going a little too far. They believe that as long as one general-purpose alarm is generated for missing data, the operator should be able to figure out what is wrong. Here is another example of the beginning to the parametric program given above that is not nearly so specific but is much shorter and easier to write.

Parametric program:

```
O1004 (Program number)
IF [#3 EQ #0] GOTO 98
IF [#20 EQ #0] GOTO 98
IF [#23 EQ #0] GOTO 98
IF [#26 EQ #0] GOTO 98
IF [#7 EQ #0] GOTO 98
IF [#2 EQ #0] GOTO 98
IF [#11 EQ #0] GOTO 98
IF [#9 EQ #0] GOTO 98

...
GOTO 99
N98 #3000 = 101 (DATA MISSING IN CALL STATEMENT)
N99 M99
```

In this case, each IF statement tests for a missing variable from the call statement. If any variable is missing, the same alarm is generated.

Access to machine buttons and switches. Certain versions of parametric programming allow the programmer to take control of several control panel switches like single block, feed-rate override, and feed hold. There are some machining operations that would be negatively affected if these switches are manipulated during machining.

For example, in tapping, if the feed-rate override switch is not at 100 percent or if the feed-hold button is pressed during tapping, the tap will break. Of course, the tapping cycle (G84) automatically takes control of these functions so that they cannot affect the tapping cycle.

However, there are those turning centers which do not have a tapping cycle. For these machines (or whenever the manipulation of these control panel functions is detrimental), the parametric programmer can assure that they do not affect machining.

The method by which these functions are controlled by the parametric program varies dramatically from control to control. You must check your programming manual to find out about this feature.

Access to current modes. Most versions of parametric programming allow the programmer to find current states of the control from within the parametric program. By current state, we mean the current mode of several mode possibilities. For example, the parametric program can determine which motion mode of G00, G01, G02, or G03 the control is currently in.

One good example of when this technique is helpful is related to absolute (G90) versus incremental (G91) mode. Say the programmer wishes the parametric program to work in the incremental (G91) mode. However, at the completion of the parametric program, the programmer wishes to leave the control in whichever state (G90 or G91) it is in when the parametric program is executed.

To accomplish this, the parametric programmer can use a common variable in which to store the current state of the machine. This technique incorporates a system variable. Then, the desired mode (G91) can be instated. At the completion of the parametric program, the system variable can be reinstated using the common variable in which the original mode is stored.

The specific techniques to do this vary from one control to the next. You must check your control's programming manual for more information.

Another similar application is with the inch and metric mode, when the parametric programmer is unsure of which mode the control is in when the parametric program is activated and wishes the control to be left in the same mode at the completion of the parametric program.

Access to current axis position. Most versions of parametric programming allow the programmer to access the current axis position in any axis from within the parametric program. The most popular application for this technique is when a probe of some kind is used.

The probe can be commanded to move until it comes into contact with a surface. When it touches a surface, it sends a signal to the control to immediately stop the axis motion. When the motion stops, the parametric program can access the current axis position which, in essence, tells the parametric program the position at which the probe comes into contact with the surface. What is done with this value depends on the application for the probe.

Timer. Most versions of parametric programming allow the programmer to use the control's clock/timer. In most cases, this feature is used when the parametric program is used as a tool management system. The parametric program can start the timer as each cutting motion begins and stop the timer at the completion of the tool's cutting commands. This lets the parametric program keep track of how long a tool has been cutting. When the tool has cut for its designated length of time, the parametric program can command a tool change.

Generating your own G, M, and T codes. Some versions of parametric programming actually allow the programmer to create new G, M, and T codes. This is helpful for often-used parametric programs.

Some machine-tool builders use this technique for special options they supply to hide the fact that a parametric program is being used to control the feature. To the end user, it simply looks like any other G code.

How this feature is controlled varies from control to control. You must check your control's programming manual to find if this technique is possible and, if so, how it is applied.

Verifying Parametric Programs

Verifying a general-purpose parametric program is much more difficult than verifying a standard CNC program. You must verify that the parametric program behaves properly under *all* possible conditions of the call statement. For example, if a parametric program is written in a way to allow both climb and conventional milling, the programmer must test to assure that both conditions will function properly.

Here is our suggested procedure for verifying parametric programs:

1. Do a machine-lock dry run to make sure that the control can execute the program without generating alarms.

2. With the call statement variables set to the simplest possible condition, dry-run the parametric program to check axis motions.

3. When satisfied that the parametric program is behaving properly with a simple call statement, manipulate the call statement to become progressively more advanced. Do a dry run after *each* call statement variable change to check motions.

4. Run the parametric program without dry run to confirm that cutting motions are where they should be.

5. Set the variables of the call statement for the first workpiece and cautiously run the first workpiece.

Common parametric programming mistakes

It is easier to verify a parametric program when you understand the mistakes you will be most prone to making. Common parametric programming mistakes fall into three distinct categories:

1. *Basic syntax mistakes:* This first-level mistake is the easiest type of mistake to find and correct. The control will usually generate an

alarm, pointing you in the right direction as to how to fix the problem. This problem can result from the programmer's misunderstanding the usage of a parametric programming command. It could also result from typing mistakes when the parametric program is entered.

2. *Simple evaluation mistakes:* This second-level mistake is a little more difficult to find and correct. In most cases the control will not actually generate an alarm, but the parametric program will not behave properly. One example of this kind of mistake is improper use of counters in a loop. In this case, the loop may be executed one too many or one too few times. Another example is referencing the wrong variable in a calculation. With this kind of mistake, it will simply be a matter of finding the basic mistake.

3. *Mistakes in the solution to your problem:* This third-level mistake is the hardest to fix. In fact, once it is determined that this kind of mistake has been made, it is usually better to start over, rewriting the entire parametric program. This mistake occurs when the programmer *thinks* a solution to the problem will work, when in reality, it will not. The best way to guard against this kind of mistake is with good preparation. *Think through* the entire problem before attempting to write the parametric program.

Parametric Program for Machining Forging-Die Block Shanks

This lengthy and elaborate parametric program completely machines a pair of die block shanks with a minimum of input. It uses every one of the techniques presented to this point. You will notice the extensive use of the presetting technique to let the parametric program assume a number of things about the variables coming from the call statements if the programmer does not set them. Alarms are generated if problems exist with the call statement. The technique related to common variables, discussed earlier, is used to let the various parametric programs involved with this system remember variables from one parametric program to another.

There are actually eight total programs that all work together needed in this application. Figure 5.7 is a drawing that shows the application.

Note that only those things that change from one set of die blocks to the next are given as variables. Everything about the workpiece that is not included as a variable is a constant from one workpiece to the next. The width and depth of the dovetail section, the size and positioning of the pockets, and the size of the chamfer on each pocket are among the constants that do not have to be specified in the call statement since they are consistent for *every* die block combination.

Here is the lengthy process used for machining in this parametric program:

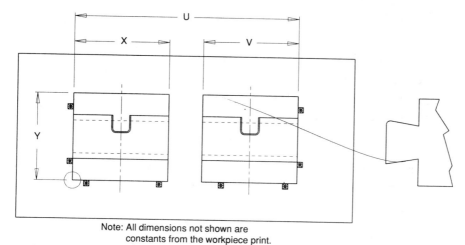

Note: All dimensions not shown are
constants from the workpiece print.

Figure 5.7   Marked-up drawing showing workpiece and variables to be used for forging-die
block shank example parametric program.

1. Finish-mill top surface of dovetail

2. Rough within 0.020 in and finish to depth the front side of both die
   blocks

3. Rough within 0.020 in and finish back side of die blocks

4. Rough and finish front dovetail

5. Rough and finish back dovetail

6. Mill radius of back dovetail

7. Rough-mill pockets

8. Finish-mill pockets

9. Mill chamfers on ends and pockets

Admittedly, this is a very complex use for parametric programming.
It may take you quite some time to truly understand all that is going
on within each program. It is not our intention to intimidate you with
this complex application, but to show you how powerful parametric
programming can be. When you *can* understand what is happening in
each program used in this system, you will have a very good understanding of all parametric programming tools.

Also note that this particular parametric program is written in a
style called *custom macro,* which is a popular version of parametric
programming used by at least three control manufacturers.

Here are the program numbers for the programs used in the system
and a brief description of each one. A lengthy discussion of each program will be given a little later.

O5555 (Main program)

O8001 (Feeds and speeds parametric program)

O8002 (Tools parametric program)

O8003 (Machining parametric program)

O8004 (Subprogram to rough pockets)

O8005 (Subprogram to finish pockets)

O8006 (Subprogram to loop dovetail)

O8007 (Subprogram to loop dovetail)

Here is an example main program that could be used to machine the entire die block shank. Note how short and simple it can be.

Main program:

```
O5555 (Program number)
N005 G54 (Select coordinate system)
N010 G65 P8001 (Set all feeds and speeds)
N015 G65 P8002 (Set all tool station numbers)
N020 G65 P8003 X12. V12. Y14. U28. (Machine workpiece)
N025 M30 (End of program)
```

This is the most basic command to machine the die blocks. There are *many* preset or defaulted variables that are set within the parametric programs (as you will see later).

Though the parametric programs that drive this system are quite complex, notice how simple it is for the person actually programming a pair of die blocks. In as little as 2 minutes, an operator can alter a current main program stored in the control's memory to specify the variables needed to machine the current workpiece. From then on, the control takes over, following the instructions given in the parametric program to machine *any* die block size specified. The actual machining time caused by the parametric program is usually over 3 hours! All generated from less than 5 minutes of programming time. This example truly shows the power of parametric programming!

Here are descriptions of each program used in the system and of each variable within the parametric programs.

O8002—tools parametric program

Variable	Set to	Description
A	1	Station number of 6-in face mill
B	2	Station number of dovetail cutter
C	3	Station number of radius tool
D	4	Station number of chamfer tool
E	5	Station number of 1¼-in rough end
F	6	Station number of ⅞-in finish mill

Note that all variables in this parametric program have been preset to the most commonly used settings. This means that if all stations are as shown above, no variables must be included in the call statement. But say, for example, the operator loads the 6-in face mill in station 10. Then the call statement could be changed to

N015 G65 P1002 A10.

This call statement tells the parametric program that the 6-in face mill is in station 10 and all other tools are as preset.

O8001—feeds and speeds parametric program

Like the tools parametric program, the speeds and feeds parametric program will set all speeds and feeds for the above tools to their most commonly used values. Here is a list of the variables that are preset in O8002.

Variable	Set to	Description
A	170	Rough speed for 6-in face mill
B	12	Rough feed for 6-in face mill
C	200	Finish speed for 6-in face mill
D	12	Finish feed for 6-in face mill
E	326	Speed for dovetail cutter
F	12	Feed for dovetail cutter
H	350	Speed for radius tool
M	4	Feed for radius tool
Q	350	Speed for chamfer tool
R	6	Feed for chamfer tool
S	85	Speed for rough end mill
T	1	Feed for rough end mill
U	100	Speed for finish end mill
V	1	Feed for finish end mill

Though some of these arguments overlap the tools parametric program, note that a technique with common variables will be used to keep track of the desired values.

If the programmer agrees with these feeds and speeds, all of the variables can be left out of the call statement. But if the programmer wishes to change a speed or feed, maybe because of harder material, the desired variable can be included in the call statement. Say that the programmer agrees with all speeds and feeds except the speed for the finish end mill. This call statement will change only that speed:

N015 G65 P8001 U150.

Every variable except the speed for the finish end mill would be as preset. The finish end mill would run at 150 RPM.

O8003—machining parametric program

This is the (lengthy) parametric program that actually machines the part. There are some mandatory variables that must be in the call statement (if they are not, an alarm is generated). There are also many preset variables that can be manipulated if the need arises. Here is a list of all variables available for this parametric program:

Variable	Set to	Description
X	—	Length of left die block
V	—	Length of right die block
Y	—	Width of die blocks
U	—	Distance from left die block to right die block (end to end)
A	-1	This flag tells the parametric program whether to use a right-hand or left-hand 6-in face mill. It is preset to right-hand. If you want to use a left-hand face mill, set A to 1.
B	.005	Amount of move-over for the 6-in face mill between passes (for tool clearance)
C	.200	Clearance for 6-in face mill
D	.250	Depth of cut for 6-in face mill
E	.66	Cutter overlap for 6-in face mill
F	.100	Depth of first dovetail cut
H	.025	Depth of subsequent dovetail passes
M	-1	This flag tells the parametric program whether to climb-mill or conventional-mill with the dovetail cutter. It is set to climb-mill. To conventional-mill, set M to 1.
Q	.125	Chamfer size for ends of dovetail
R	.25	Chamfer size for pockets
S	1	New die block or remachine. This flag tells the parametric program whether to machine the pockets. If S = 1, no pockets will be machined. If S = -1, pockets will be machined.

As you can see, this application allows for many possible changes when the part is run. It shows good planning, before even starting, to write the parametric program. The user determined just exactly what needed to be controlled through the call statement, and then the parametric program was written accordingly.

Now let's look at the programs. You may have to study them cautiously to understand what is going on. Every line of each parametric program is *not* documented. For this reason, we suggest that you break it down into smaller pieces to get a feel for the entire system. When you get to the lengthy machining parametric program, take it one tool at a time. Once you understand what one tool is doing, then go on to the next tool. Based on the previous descriptions given in this chapter, you should be able to figure out what is happening each step of the way.

Main program:

```
O5555 (Program number)
N005 G54 (Select coordinate system)
```

```
N010 G65 P8001 (Set speeds and feeds)
N015 G65 P8002 (Set tools)
N020 G65 P8003 X9.25 Y12.875 U21.5 V9.5 S-1. C.5 (Machine die blocks)
N030 M30 (End of program)
```

Feeds and speeds parametric program:

```
O8001 (Program number)
IF[#1NE#0]GOTO1
#1 = 170 (Speed for 6 in face mill roughing)
N1 IF[#2NE#0]GOTO2
#2 = 12. (Feed for 6 in face mill roughing)
N2 IF[#3NE#0]GOTO3
#3 = 200 (Speed for finish 6 in face mill)
N3 IF[#7NE#0]GOTO4
#7 = 12. (Feed for finish 6 in face mill)
N4 IF[#8NE#0]GOTO5
#8 = 326 (Speed for dovetail cutter)
N5 IF[#9NE#0]GOTO6
#9 = 12. (Feed for dovetail cutter)
N6 IF[#11NE#0]GOTO7
#11 = 350 (Speed for radius tool)
N7 IF[#13NE#0]GOTO8
#13 = 4. (Feed for radius tool)
N8 IF[#17NE#0]GOTO9
#17 = 350 (Speed for chamfer tool)
N9 IF[#18NE#0]GOTO10
#18 = 6. (Feed for chamfer tool)
N10 IF[#19NE#0]GOTO11
#19 = 85 (Speed for rough end mill)
N11 IF[#20NE#0]GOTO12
#20 = 1. (Feed for rough end mill)
N12 IF[#21NE#0]GOTO13
#21 = 100 (Speed for finish end mill)
N13 IF[#22NE#0]GOTO14
#22 = 1. (Feed for finish end mill)
N14 #100 = #1 (Store feeds and speeds in common variables so they are
remembered when machining parametric program is activated)
#100 = #1
#101 = #2
#102 = #3
#103 = #7
#104 = #8
#105 = #9
#106 = #11
#107 = #13
#108 = #17
#109 = #18
#110 = #19
#111 = #20
#112 = #21
#113 = #22
M99
```

Tools parametric program:

```
O8002 (Program number)
IF[#1NE#0]GOTO1
```

```
#1 = 1 (Face mill)
N1 IF[#2NE#0]GOTO2
#2 = 2 (Dovetail cutter)
N2 IF[#3NE#0]GOTO3
#3 = 3 (Radius mill)
N3 IF[#7NE#0]GOTO4
#7 = 4 (Chamfer mill)
N4 IF[#8NE#0]GOTO5
#8 = 5 (Rough end mill)
N5 IF[#9NE#0]GOTO6
#9 = 6 (Finish end mill)
N6 #114 = #1 (Set tool station numbers into common variables so they are
remembered when machining parametric program is executed)
#115 = #2
#116 = #3
#117 = #7
#118 = #8
#119 = #9
M99
```

Machining parametric program:

```
O8003 (Program number)
IF[#1NE#0]GOTO3333
#1 = - 1.
N3333 IF[#24EQ#0]GOTO999 (Test mandatory variables from call statement)
IF[#22EQ#0]GOTO999
IF[#25EQ#0]GOTO999
IF[#21EQ#0]GOTO999
IF[[#21 - #24 - #22]LE0]GOTO998
IF[[#[2000 + #114]]EQ0]GOTO997 (Test all offsets to assure setting)
IF[[#[2000 + #115]]EQ0]GOTO997
IF[[#[2000 + #116]]EQ0]GOTO997
IF[[#[2000 + #117]]EQ0]GOTO997
IF[[#[2000 + #118]]EQ0]GOTO997
IF[[#[2000 + #119]]EQ0]GOTO997
IF[[#[2030 + #114]]EQ0]GOTO997
IF[[#[2030 + #115]]EQ0]GOTO997
IF[[#[2030 + #116]]EQ0]GOTO997
IF[[#[2030 + #117]]EQ0]GOTO997
IF[[#[2030 + #118]]EQ0]GOTO997
IF[[#[2030 + #119]]EQ0]GOTO997
IF[#19NE#0]GOTO1201
#19 = 1.
N1201 T#114
M06
G90 S#102 T#115 F#103
IF[#1EQ[ - 1.]]GOTO26
M04
GOTO33
N26 M03
N33 #144 = #[2000 + 30 + #114] (Tool radius)
(Mill top)
G00 X-[#3 + #144] Y[#25/2 - #144]
G43 H#114 Z0
G01 X[#21 + #3 + #144]
G00 Y[#25/2 - 1. + #144]
G01 X - [#3 + #144]
```

```
G00 Z0.5
(Sides)
#136 = 0
#137 = 0 (Flag for front or back)
IF[#8NE#0]GOTO3
#8 = .66
N3
IF[#2NE#0]GOTO10
#2 = .005
N10 IF[#3NE#0]GOTO15 (Clearance)
#3 = .2
N15 IF[#7NE#0]GOTO16 (Z depth of cut)
#7 = .25
N16 #144 = #[2000 + 30 + #114] (Tool radius)
#143 = [#25/2] − 3.5 (Cut area)
#145 = 1. (Preset to 1 X-Y pass)
#146 = 0 (Preset to no Y shift)
IF[[#8*[#144*2]]GT#143]GOTO20
#145 = FUP[#143/[#*#144*2]] (Number of Y passes)
#146 = #143/#145 (Incremental Y move)
#140 = #143 − #146*#145 − #144 (Current Y pass)
GOTO23
N20 #140 = #143 − #144 (Current Y pass)
N23 IF[#1EQ − 1.]GOTO25
#142 =  − [#3 + #144] (Start X)
#141 = #21 + #3 + #144 (Finish X)
GOTO50
N25 #142 = #21 + #3 + #144 (Start X)
#141 =  − [#3 + #144] (Finish X)
N50 #148 = FUP[1.747/#7] (Number of Z passes)
IF[#136EQ1.]GOTO51
#135 = 1.747/#148 (Current Z depth)
N51 #147 = 0 (Counter for X-Y pass)
IF[#136EQ1.]GOTO52
#139 = 0 (Counter for Z pass)
N52 #138 = #135 (Incremental Z)
IF[#136EQ1.]GOTO501
S#100 F#101
N501 G00 X#142 Y#140
G43 H#114 Z.5
M08
N45 WHILE[#139LT#148]DO1 (Loop Z)
N40 WHILE[#147LT#145]DO2 (Loop X-Y)
G00 Y#140
G00 Z − #135
G01 X#141
G00 Z.5
G00 X#142 Y#140
#147 = #147 + 1 (Step X-Y)
IF[#137EQ0]GOTO34
#140 = #140 − #146 (Step Y position)
GOTO36
N34 #140 = #140 + #146 (Step Y position)
N36 END2 (End X-Y loop)
N30 IF[#137EQ0]GOTO37
#140 = #140 + #145*#146 + #2 (Set Y back for new Z pass)
GOTO38
N37 #140 = #140 − #145*#146 − #2 (Set Y back for new Z pass)
N38 #139 = #139 + 1 (Step Z counter)
```

```
#135 = #135 + #138 (Step Z depth)
#147 = 0 (Reset Y counter)
END1
N35 IF[#136EQ1.]GOTO43
S#102 F#103
#135 = 1.767
#136 = 1.
#139 = #148 − 1.
GOTO23
N43 #136 = 0.
IF[#137EQ1]GOTO41
#1 = #1*[ − 1] (Reverse climb-mill direction for back)
#140 = #25/2 + 3.5 + [#145*#146 + #144] (Set up first Y position for back)
#137 = 1 (Flag for back)
#135 = 1.747/#148
S#100 F#101
GOTO23 (End Z loop)
N41 G91 G28 Z0
M01
(Dovetail cutter)
N2000 T#115
M06
G90 S#104 F#105 T#116 M03
#144 = #[2000 + 30 + #115]
IF[#9NE#0]GOTO101
#9 = .1
N101 IF[#11NE#0]GOTO102
#11 = .025
N102 #140 = .2173 − #9 (Stock after first pass)
#141 = FUP[#140/#11] (Number of passes)
#142 = #140/#141 (Recalculated cut depth)
#146 = #25/2 − 3.5 + #9 − #144 (First pass front)
#147 = #25/2 + 3.5 − #9 + #144 (First pass back)
IF[#13NE#0]GOTO105
#13 = − 1.
N105 IF[#13EQ − 1.]GOTO110
#136 = − [#3 + #144]
#137 = [#21 + #3 + #144]
GOTO111
N110 #136 = [#21 + #3 + #144]
#137 = − [#3 + #144]
N111 G00X#136Y#146 (First cut)
G43 H#115 Z.5
G01 Z − 1.767 F30. M08
G01 X#137 F#105
G00 Z.5
#146 = #146 + #142
#138 = 0 (Counter for loop)
M98 P8006
N120 G00 X#137 Y#147
Z − 1.767
G01 X#136
G00 Z.5
#147 = #147 − #142
#138 = 0
M98 P8007
N130 G91 G28 Z0 M19
M01
```

```
N3000 T#116
M06
(Radius mill)
G90 S#106 F#107 M03
IF[#19EQ1.]GOTO1205
T#118
GOTO1206
N1205 T#117
N1206 #144 = #[2000 + 30 + #116]
G00 X[#21 + #3 + #144 + .5] Y[#25/2 + 3.5 + #144]
G43 H#116 Z0
M08
G01 X − [#144 + #3 + .5]
G00 Z.75
M09
G91 G28 Z0 M19
M01
IF[#19EQ1.]GOTO1202
N4000 T#118
M06
(Rough end mill for pocket)
G90 M03 S#110 F#111 T#119
#144 = #[2000 + 30 + #118]
G00 X[#24/2] Y[#25/2 + 3.5 + #3/2 + #144]
G43 H#118 Z.5
M08
M98 P8004
G90 Z.5
G00 X[#21 − #24/2] Y[#25/2 + 3.5 + #3/2 + #144]
M98 P8004
M09
G91 G28 Z0 M19
M01
N5000 T#119
M06
(Finish end mill for pocket)
G90 S#112 F#113 M03 T#117
#144 = #[2000 + 30 + #119]
G00 X[#24/2] Y[#25/2 + 3.5 + #3/2 + #144]
G43 H#119 Z.5
M08
M98 P8005
G90 Z.5
G00 X[#21-#24/2] Y[#25/2 + 3.5 + #3/2 + #144]
M98 P8005
G90 Z.5
M09
G91 G28 Z0 M19
N1202 M01
N6000 T#117
M06
(Chamfer tool)
G90 S#108 F#109 M03 T#114
#144 = #[2000 + 30 + #117]
IF[#17NE#0]GOTO300
#17 = .125
N300 IF[#18NE#0]GOTO301
#18 = .25
```

N301 G00X[#17-#144] Y[#25/2 + 3.5 + #3/2 + #144]
G00 G43 H#117Z − .25
M08
G01 Y[#25/2 − 3.5 − #3/2 − #144]
G00 Z.5
G00 X[#24 − #17 + #144]
Z − .25
G01 Y[#25/2 + 3.5 + #3/2 + #144]
G00 Z.75
X[#21 − #22 + #17 − #144]
Z − .25
G01 Y[#25/2 − 3.5 − #3/2 − #144]
G00 Z.75
X[#21 − #17 + #144]
Z − .25
G01 Y[#25/2 + 3.5 + #3/2 + #144]
G00 Z.75
IF[#19EQ1.]GOTO1203
X[#21 − #24/2 + .875 + .25 − #144]
Z − .25
G01 Y[#25/2 + 3.5 − 2.5 + #144]
X[#21 − #24/2 − .875 − .25 + #144]
Y[#25/2 + 3.5 + #3/2 + #144]
G00 Z.75
X[#24/2 + .875 + .25 − #144]
Z − .25
G01 Y[#25/2 + 3.5 − 2.5 + #144]
X[#24/2 − .875 − .25 + #144]
Y[#25/2 + 3.5 + #3/2 + #144]
G00 Z.75
N1203 M09
G91 G28 X0 Y0 Z0 M19
GOTO1000
N997 #3000 = 103 (Offset data missing)
N998 #3000 = 102 (X + V too great)
N999 #3000 = 101 (Input data missing)
N1000 M99

Subprogram for roughing pockets

O8004 (Program number)
G00 G91 X[.875 − #144 − .03]
Z − 1.38
G90 G01 Y[#25/2 + 3.5 − 2.22 + #144]
G91 X − [1.75 − 2*#144 − .06]
G90 Y[#25/2 + 3.5 + #3/2 + #144]
G00 Z.5
G91 X[.875 − #144 − .03]
G90
G00 G91 X[.875 − #144 − .03]
Z − 2.067
G01 Z − .2
G90 Y[#25/2 + 3.5 − 2.22 + #144]
G91 X − [1.75 − 2.*#144 − .06]
G90 Y[#25/2 + 3.5 + #3/2 + #144]
G00 Z.5
M99

Subprogram for finishing pockets

```
O8005 (Program number)
G00 G91 Z-2.067
G01 Z - .2
G90 Y[#25/2 + 3.5 - 2.25 + .03 + #144]
G91 G00 Z.2
G90 Y[#25/2 + 3.5 + #3/2 + #144]
G91 X[.875 - #144]
G01 Z - .2
G90 Y[#25/2 + 3.5 - 2.25 + #144]
G91 G01 X - [1.75 - #144*2]
G90 Y[#25/2 + 3.5 + #3/2 + #144]
G00 G91 X[1.75 - 2*#144]
G90 G01 Y[#25/2 + 3.5 - 2.25 + #144]
G91 X - [1.75 - #144*2]
G90 Y[#25/2 + 3.5 + #3/2 + #144]
G00 Z.5
M99
```

Subprograms for looping dovetail

You may be questioning why we needed these two looping programs for
the dovetail. Since this parametric program is extremely long and since
these loops occur toward the end of the parametric program, the execution time is dramatically reduced by creating a separate program for
these loops. When the CNC control processes IF statements and GOTO
statements, a statement label (N word) must be searched. To do this, the
control returns to the *beginning of the current program* and begins the
search. This means that if the parametric program is extremely long, as
this one is, the GOTO statement will take as much as 3 to 5 seconds just
to find the statement label. With these two short looping parametric programs, the execution time is almost instantaneous:

```
O8006 (Program number)
N115 IF[#138GE#141]GOTO120
G00 X#136 Y#146
Z - 1.767
G01 X#137
G00 Z.5
#146 = #146 + #142
#138 = #138 + 1
GOTO115
N120 M99

O8007 (Program number)
N125 IF[#138GE#141]GOTO130
G00 X#137 Y#147
Z - 1.767
G01 X#136
G00 Z.5
#147 = #147 - #142
#138 = #138 + 1
GOTO125
N130 M99
```

As stated, this is a very complicated example application. It includes at least a little of every technique shown in this chapter. Also, some rather elaborate techniques are used, especially during the face milling, roughing prior to the dovetail cutter, and the dovetail operation. Notice how few program commands are needed in these areas because of the looping techniques used. Also note that the same series of commands used to rough one side of the die shank are also used to rough the other.

Minimizing CNC
Control Execution Time

The importance of the cycle time required to machine a workpiece will vary from one company to the next. Of course, all companies would like to machine each workpiece as quickly as possible, but the extent to which each company will go to optimize programs varies widely.

Largely, the single most important factor which determines how far a company will go to minimize cycle time is related to the quantity of workpieces to be produced. The larger the quantity of workpieces to be machined, the more important it will be to keep the machining cycle as short as possible.

As production quantities grow, even seemingly small changes in cycle time will have a great effect on how long it will take to machine the total quantity of workpieces. And of course, cost is directly related to time in this regard. Most shops price their work on the machine's hourly rate. The faster they can get the job finished, the more profit they can make.

Here is an example that should stress the relationship between cycle time and production quantity. Say, for example, 25 workpieces (of the same configuration) must be machined on a CNC machining center. Say the cycle time for this particular job comes out to precisely 3 minutes. In this case, the total machining time (not including workpiece loading time) is 75 minutes, or 1 hour and 15 minutes.

In this case, an improvement that would lower the machining time will not have much effect on the overall time it takes to machine the total number of workpieces in this production run. In fact, it is quite probable that any attempt to improve cycle time (while the job is being run) will actually *increase* the time required to machine the workpieces.

On the other hand, say the company has to run 10,000 of these same workpieces. At 3 minutes per workpiece, the total time to machine the workpieces this time is 30,000 minutes, or 500 hours. If the shop is working 8-hour days, this production run would require over 2 months to complete, especially when you consider that part-loading time has not been included in our calculation.

This time, any improvement that can be made will have a dramatic impact on the length of time it takes to machine the entire production run. For example, if cycle time per workpiece could somehow be reduced by only 15 seconds, the overall time it would take to produce these 10,000 workpieces would come down by about 42 hours (almost 6 days at 8 hours a day)!

Keep in mind that most companies that turn out high production quantities will normally do so over and over again. The same workpiece will eventually have to be produced again in the future (in similar quantities). For this reason, it will be well worth the time needed to implement an improvement (optimize the program), even as production is being run.

There are many factors that contribute to a minimized cycle time. The most important of these factors are related to process, tooling, and cutting conditions. However, since each company sets its own standards by which these basic factors are judged, we cannot address them in this text.

However, we can and will address those factors of which the programmer has direct control within a program. Though these factors have a lesser effect on cycle time than machining-practice-related factors, they can have a significant effect on maximizing the productivity of your CNC equipment.

General Cycle-Time Reduction Techniques

We will start by looking at the general things a programmer can do in any program to reduce cycle time. Then, we will look at techniques that reduce cycle time specifically for machining centers, and, finally, for turning centers. In all cases, we will assume that production quantities are very high, meaning even very small reductions in cycle time will have an impact on the profitability of the job.

Minimizing internal control execution time

If you understand how the CNC control processes CNC programs, many times you can avoid less efficient techniques. We will begin looking at general techniques to reduce cycle time that are related to specific programming features.

Subprogramming techniques. As you know, subprogramming keeps the programmer from having to include redundant information in the program. When subprogramming techniques are applied, the repeated commands need only be entered one time. This minimizes the number of commands required and makes it easy to repeat the commands as many times as necessary. In fact, one command calling the subprogram can execute it as many times as required.

However, there is a cycle-time compromise that occurs when you use subprogramming techniques. When the control reads the command

N065 M98 P1000

it is being told to execute the program named O1000. Before the control can execute the program named O1000, it must *find* it. This searching does not occur instantaneously.

For newer (32-bit) controls, this searching is close to instantaneous. But for older controls, it could take as much as 0.500 second for the control to find a subprogram. While this short time may not seem like much, if subprogramming techniques are used heavily within the program, searching time can add up fast.

To completely avoid subprogram searching time, subprogramming techniques cannot be used. However, if you know how the control searches for subprograms, you can keep searching time to the bare minimum.

One way to minimize subprogram searching time is to keep only those programs in the control's memory that are related to the current job. This way, the control does not have to scan through unrelated programs to find the one being searched.

Also, most CNC controls scan for subprograms in numerical order, meaning that if you name a subprogram with a small number, the control can find it faster. For example, if there are currently 20 programs in the control's memory, numbered 1 through 20, the control will be able to find program 1 in a shorter time than it would take to find program 20.

Admittedly, this difference in scanning time is minute. But in these days, when 1 or 2 seconds of cycle time can mean the difference between profit or loss on a job, knowing how a CNC control scans subprograms may make a big difference in how your company fares when machining high-production work.

Parametric programming techniques.   In Chap. 5, we gave a lengthy description of parametric programming. You now know the various features of parametric programming as well as how it can be applied.

Because the typical parametric program makes a great many calculations, and since branching techniques requiring searching (like the IF statement and GOTO statement) are heavily used, most programmers agree that high production (highly optimized programs) and parametric programming do not mix.

For the most part, we tend to agree with this statement. However, the new 32-bit controls can search and make calculations almost instantaneously, meaning you may not notice a difference in cycle times between a parametric program and a longhand CNC program. Also, there are techniques possible with parametric programming that keep nonproductive time to a minimum. We gave one example in Chap. 5, related to making each motion calculation under the influence of an optional block skip (/) code. By using this technique, calculations need take place only for the first workpiece. From then on, the optional block skip switch can be turned on, letting the control skip the calculations until the power is turned off.

Admittedly, there are many applications where the above technique is not feasible. But do not be too quick to give up on parametric programming. Many CNC control manufacturers offer an optional feature (at extra cost) that is used to convert parametric programs into simple CNC programs. (One control manufacturer calls this feature *NC data output.*) With this feature, the programmer sets the variables in the call statement as usual, but instead of activating the cycle in the normal manner, makes a command that tells the control to convert the parametric program to a normal CNC program. During this process (which takes only a few seconds), the control creates an entire program including a command for literally everything done by the parametric program. Once converted, this CNC program can be used to run production and will execute as quickly as any program written in a longhand manner.

Without the ability to convert parametric programs into CNC programs, parametric programming does not do well with high production. Generally speaking, parametric programming techniques are most helpful when setup or programming time must be kept to a minimum. But the compromise is longer cycle time.

Canned cycles and other special features.   Certain older CNC controls will execute a series of longhand motion commands (commanded by G00, G01, G02, and G03) faster than they will execute the same series of motions commanded by a canned cycle. Just as subprogramming and parametric programming techniques take time while the control makes calculations, so do certain canned cycles (this is especially true with some turning-center CNC controls which offer very powerful rough-turning and rough-boring cycles).

With newer controls (especially 32-bit controls) you may see no noticeable difference in execution time. However, there will usually have to be a compromise between ease of programming and control execution time.

General programming format techniques to reduce execution time

In all cases, the format you use to write your programs will have an impact on cycle time. Knowing how the control will follow your commands will help you optimize your format.

Admittedly, the format we have been using throughout this text (for both machining centers and turning centers) is not very efficient. We have chosen these formats to illustrate our points only because they are safe and easy to understand. But from an efficiency standpoint, they are not very good. At the completion of this section, you will know why.

Include *all* M codes in motion commands. Though CNC controls vary with regard to how M codes are handled, they share one characteristic: they will wait until the function of the M code is completed *before* continuing to the next command. For example, look at the following series of commands.

```
...
N010 S4000 M03 (Turn spindle on CW at 4000 RPM)
N015 G00 X5. Y5. (Move to position in X and Y)
...
```

In line N010, almost all CNC controls will wait until the spindle is running at 4000 RPM *before* they execute line N020. Depending on the size of the machine and the weight of the tool in the spindle, it could take as much as 5 to 15 seconds for the spindle to reach this programmed RPM. Here is a better way to format this portion of the program.

```
...
N010 G00 X5. Y5. S4000 M03 (Move to X-Y position and turn the spindle on CW
at 4000 RPM)
...
```

If the spindle start (M03) is included with the motion, at least the machine will be moving to the X and Y position as the spindle revs up. It is quite possible that the spindle will reach its programmed RPM *before* the X-Y end point is reached. This, of course, would directly reduce the program's cycle time by the amount of time it takes for the spindle to reach its programmed RPM.

At first glance, this may seem like a trivial savings. But when you multiply the number of times the spindle is started in the program by the number of workpieces to be machined, you will see that this savings can add up fast.

This is but one time when including an M code in a motion command reduces program execution time. Keep in mind that many M codes are nothing more than programmable on/off switches. Here is a list of common M codes that are used as switches. Note that there may be more on your particular CNC machine.

M03 Spindle on CW

M04 Spindle on CW

M05 Spindle off

M07 Mist coolant on

M08 Flood coolant on

M09 Coolant off

M13 Indexer command

With all of these programmable switches, cycle time can be reduced by including them with a motion command. Whenever one is executed, the control will send a signal telling the function to activate. The control will *wait* until a confirmation signal comes back to the control assuring that the function is completed.

Keep the program's starting position as close to the workpiece as possible. Current CNC controls are quite flexible about the location at which the program begins and ends. If your control does not have restrictions in this regard (some older controls require that the program start and end at the machine's reference position), by all means, keep the starting position as close to the workpiece as possible. This will minimize the distance the machine must travel in order to reach the workpiece and, therefore, the cycle time.

If there are multiple tools in the program, keep the tool change position close to the workpiece as well. While some machines (especially machining centers) require that at least one axis be positioned to the machine's reference position before a tool change is allowed, many do not.

To gain an idea of how much time can be saved by keeping the starting position close to the workpiece, let's look at an example. Say, for example, the machine has a rapid positioning rate of 400 inches per minute (a very common rapid rate for today's CNC machine tools). To travel a distance of 20 in will take about 3 seconds. Cycle time will add up if the program commands the machine to move great distances for the purpose of tool changing.

Command approach and return in all axes. This is another example of how our given format (for machining centers) is not very efficient. In every machining-center example program given in this text, the approach was made in X-Y before the Z axis moves to the work surface.

```
...
N010 G00 X5. Y5. (Move in X-Y)
N015 G43 H01 Z.1 (Move just above work surface in Z)
...
```

For the purpose of our examples, this allowed us to separate each command and make it more understandable. Also, some operators feel this technique is safer. However, when it comes to cycle time, it is not very efficient to approach in this manner. This example command shows how a three-axis approach can be made:

```
...
N015 G00 G43 H01 X5. Y5. Z.1 (Approach workpiece in all axes)
...
```

Note that most machining-center controls allow the words in this command to be in any order.

Make the tool take the shortest series of motions. Before writing your program, consider how you will make the motions in your program. Throughout your motion commands, be sure there are no wasted motions. For example, if machining a rectangular pattern of holes, make sure your program always makes the shorter of the two axis movements first, minimizing the travel distance for the tool.

Along these same lines, if a subsequent tool is going to continue machining the hole pattern (drill and tap, for example), be sure to reverse the order of hole machining. For example, say you have a line of 20 holes along the X axis to center-drill and drill that are equally spaced on 1-in centers. In this case the machine will traverse 20 in in X while the holes are center-drilled. After changing tools, be sure to machine the holes in the reverse order. If you start back on the first hole, a wasted 20-in movement will occur.

While much of what has just been presented is little more than common sense, you would be surprised at the number of so-called expert programmers who ignore these simple techniques.

Reduce the rapid approach amount. A common approach distance throughout the industry is 0.100 in. For most applications, this is a very acceptable and safe distance. However, if you must reduce the cycle time to the bare minimum, this approach distance can be reduced (to 0.050 or 0.025 in) for previously machined surfaces. Note that by decreasing this approach distance, you are increasing the possible danger. If an offset is set in a negative direction by more than your resulting approach distance, you could be in for real problems.

For this reason, many programmers feel that the small benefit of slightly reduced cycle time is not worth taking the chance of having a mishap.

Cycle-Time Reduction Techniques for Machining Centers

Here are two suggestions that will help you keep cycle time down on machining centers. Both are easy to understand and incorporate. Both have been used for every example program shown in this text.

Get the next tool ready as each tool begins machining

Most current CNC machining centers use a double-arm–style tool changer with which the tool in the spindle is exchanged with a tool in the tool magazine. The magazine position at which a tool is positioned prior to being placed in the spindle is called the *waiting* or *ready position*. The magazine is told to rotate to this position by a T word. If, for example, the word T22 is commanded, the magazine will rotate until station 22 is in the waiting position.

If more than one tool is used in the program, the programmer should include the tool station command for the *next tool* close to the beginning of each tool in the program. This will get the tool magazine rotating while the tool in the spindle goes to work on the workpiece. In most cases, the next tool station of the magazine will be reached before the spindle tool is finished. Every machining-center example program given in this text that required more than one tool used this technique.

Note that not using this technique is very inefficient indeed. If the tool magazine must wait to start rotating until the tool in the spindle is finished, a great deal of cycle time can be wasted. The tool magazines on most machining centers rotate very slowly. In some cases, it can take 1 minute or more for the next tool station to come into position. If the previous tool is currently machining the workpiece when the T word is executed, no cycle time is lost.

Orient the spindle on each tool's return to the tool change position

CNC machining centers that incorporate a double-arm automatic tool changer system rely on keyways in the tool holder to align with keys in the double arm during the tool change. The key and keyway must be angularly aligned before a tool change can occur. The spindle's angular location at which the key and keyway are aligned is called the *orient position*. During an M06 tool change command, if the key and keyway are not aligned, the M06 will cause the spindle to rotate to its orient position.

The M06 will work just fine, but time will be wasted while the spindle rotates to its orient position. This can take from 0.5 to 3.5 seconds, depending on the machine-tool builder. While this may not sound like much, it will add up quickly when you consider the number of tool changes a machining center will make during its use.

An M19 also causes the spindle to rotate to its orient position. The M19 command can be included in *every tool's* return to the tool change position. If this is done, the spindle will be rotating to its orient position on the Z-axis return to the tool change position. When it arrives at the tool change position, it is likely that the spindle orient will be completed and the tool change can occur immediately, saving from 0.5 to 3.5 seconds per tool change.

Cycle-Time Reduction Techniques for Turning Centers

Here are two techniques that can be used with turning center programs to minimize cycle time. Though most were not used as part of the format shown throughout this text, if applied, they can greatly reduce machining time.

Understanding constant surface speed's influence on cycle time

Constant surface speed (G96) is a very helpful programming tool. For single-point machining operations (like turning, boring, and grooving), it allows the programmer to specify speed in surface feet per minute or meters per minute, depending on the measurement system. Once constant surface speed mode is specified, the control will constantly and automatically calculate the correct RPM throughout the tool's motions.

Constant surface speed gives three distinct advantages: programming is easier, the workpiece finish will be better, and tools will last longer. However, if no consideration is given to how constant surface speed affects cycle time, it can also be a time-wasting feature.

All turning centers take time to accelerate and decelerate the spindle. The size and power of the machine as well as the weight of the chuck and workpiece determine how long it takes for this acceleration and deceleration to occur. For a 20-horsepower machine with an 8-in-diameter chuck, it is not uncommon for the turning center to take as much as 12 to 20 seconds to accelerate from zero to 3500 RPM. The same amount of time will be required to decelerate from 3500 RPM to zero. Knowing this, let's look at an example showing how constant surface speed can be wasteful of cycle time.

Say, for example, the machine described above has a maximum turning diameter of 10 in. Say this is the machine's reference position in X and that your program starts from and changes tools at this 10-in-diameter reference point. Say the current workpiece you are machining is 1 in in diameter. The machine's rapid rate is 400 inches per minute.

As shown much earlier in this text, RPM is calculated with this formula:

$$RPM = 3.82 \times SFM \div \text{current diameter}$$

With this example, if a constant surface speed of 600 SFM is instated at the tool change position (10 in in diameter), the spindle will be turned at a relatively slow 229 RPM (3.82 × 600 SFM ÷ 10). When the tool is positioned (at rapid) to the 1-in workpiece diameter, the spindle will rev up to 2292 RPM. In this case, it is quite likely that the axis motion will occur much faster than the spindle acceleration. The motion will occur in less than 1 second. The spindle acceleration will take much longer, depending on the machine. In this case, the machine will sit idle, waiting for the spindle to reach its commanded RPM.

When the tool returns for a tool change, the reverse will occur. The spindle will slow down to 229 RPM on the motion back for the tool change. Again, the motion will occur much faster than the spindle deceleration. And again the machine will sit idle while the spindle slows down.

If this sequence is allowed to occur for every tool, it is likely that a great deal of cycle time will be wasted while the spindle speeds up and slows down. This is not to mention wasted electricity and the excess wear on the machine.

There is a way to format your programs that will still allow the benefits of constant surface speed but remove the unwanted spindle RPM changes, and in turn, reduce cycle time, reduce spindle wear, and save electricity. If you switch to the RPM mode (G97) whenever the machine is told to return to its tool change position and specify a speed (in RPM) for the *next tool's* starting speed, you will rid the program of unwanted spindle-speed changes.

This requires a little more work on the programmer's part. The programmer must make RPM calculations (using the formula given a little earlier) to determine each tool's starting RPM. Here is an example program that uses this technique. Pay particular attention to how the spindle speed commands are given.

Program:

```
O0050 (Program number)
(Rough turning tool)
N005 G50 X _____ Z _____ (Assign program zero)
N010 G00 T0101 M41 (Index to station 1, instate offset 1, select low spindle range)
N015 G00 G96 X4. Z.1 S400 M03 (Rapid to position, turn spindle on CW at 400 SFM)
N020 M08 (Coolant on)
N025 G71 P030 Q085 U.040 W.005 D.200 F.015
N030 G00 X.8
N035 G01 Z0
N040 X1. Z-.1
N045 Z-2.
N050 X1.6
N055 X2. Z-2.2
N060 Z-4.
N065 X2.6
N070 G03 X3. Z-4.2 R.2
N075 G01 Z-6.
N080 X3.4
N085 X4. Z-7.
N090 G00 G97 S573 X _____ Z _____ T0100 (Keep spindle at first RPM for next tool on the return to tool change position)
N095 M01
(Finish-turning tool)
N100 G50 X _____ Z _____ (Assign program zero)
N105 G00 T0202 M42 (Index to station 2, instate offset 2, select high spindle range)
N110 G97 S573 M03 (Keep spindle at 573 RPM)
N115 G00 X4. Z.1
N118 G96 S600 (Select constant surface speed mode. Note that no RPM change will occur here)
N120 G70 P030 Q085 F.007
N125 G00 X _____ Z _____ T0200 M05 (Return to tool change position, cancel offset, stop spindle on the way back)
N130 M30
```

Though this program involves only two tools, it should nicely stress the point being made here. These techniques can simply be repeated for each extra tool in the program.

In line N015 the spindle is started during the tool's first approach to the workpiece. There is little that can be done about this first time the spindle accelerates to its machining RPM. The spindle must be started at one time or another. At least the spindle will accelerate during the tool's approach, meaning that some cycle time will be saved as compared to the format given in other turning-center examples in this text.

At the completion of tool 1, in line N090, the tool is sent back to its tool change position. During this motion, notice that the RPM mode (G97) is selected and that an RPM is included. This RPM is the starting RPM for the *next* tool in the program. The next tool is to run at 600 SFM and its starting diameter is 4 in; 600 × 3.84 ÷ 4 = 573 RPM. During this movement in line N090, the spindle will maintain this RPM instead of slowing down.

In line N110, this spindle command is repeated for the sake of the program's format. If this program must be run from the beginning of the second tool, the spindle will come on in the normal manner.

After the second tool approaches the workpiece, the SFM mode is selected with the proper speed in line N118. This command will cause absolutely no change in spindle RPM, since 573 is the RPM generated at 600 SFM and a 4-in diameter. Generally speaking, all this command is doing is switching the spindle mode to SFM.

From this point on, tool 2 will use constant surface speed in its normal manner. As stated, this technique can be repeated for every tool in the program to keep the spindle speed in RPM from changing.

At the end of the last tool in the program (tool 2 in our case) in line N125, when the tool is sent back to the tool change position, the spindle is stopped (with M05). This will make the spindle begin its deceleration during this lengthy movement.

Instate the tool offset on the tool's approach

This technique was mentioned in Chap. 2. At that time, we explained that this technique made for a cleaner program. It also minimizes cycle time.

Consider what happens in these two commands:

```
...
N050 G00 T0101
N055 X3. Z.1
...
```

In line N050, the turret indexes and offset 1 is instated. With most CNC controls, the instating of offset 1 will cause the X and Z axes to move by the amount stored in the offset. The motion in line N055 will bring the tool up to the workpiece.

The motion that occurs when the offset is instated takes time. Also, two movements will occur when the tool approaches the workpiece. It is wiser to instate the offset on the tool's approach to the workpiece, as shown in this series of commands:

```
...
N050 T0100
N055 G00 X3. Z.1 T0101
...
```

This time, line N050 simply indexes the turret. No offset is instated (yet). In line N055, as the tool approaches the workpiece, offset 1 is instated. The control will actually recalculate the end point on the basis of the values stored in the offset. In essence, the control combines the movement command with the installation of the offset, requiring only one motion.

Index

ABOUT THE AUTHOR

Mike Lynch is president of CNC Concepts, Inc., a supplier
of training materials and computer software to users of
computer numerical control equipment. He also presents
CNC training seminars conducted by the Society of
Manufacturing Engineers. Previously, Mr. Lynch was NC
operations manager for K.G.K. International Corporation,
and prior to that, held various technical positions with
Cincinnati Milacron, Rockwell International, and G.T.E.
Automatic Electric. He writes a monthly column, "CNC
Tech Talk," for *Modern Machine Shop* magazine, and is the
author of *Computer Numerical Control for Machining*, also
published by McGraw-Hill.